READING

skills for Kindergarten

by Katy Pike

Welcome to the Reading Eggs Workbook for Kindergarten!

I know how much you care about giving your child a great start in reading, because I had the EXACT same feeling, too.

I remember life before **Reading Eggs**. Like you, I was determined to give my four kids the BEST start in life, and that meant helping them learn to read.

The problem was, reading is complicated. There are so many skills they need to learn. From phonemic awareness, phonics, sight words, and vocabulary to comprehension and fluency; it's hard to know where to start. And most children need lots of time and a whole lot of repetition to get all these skills in place. If you're busy, this can get very challenging very quickly.

We knew there had to be an easier way. So I used my 25 years of experience in educational publishing, along with the most SOLID scientific research on reading instruction and child motivation, to create the online **Reading Eggs** program.

This reading program completely transformed the way millions of children around the world learned to read. 10 MILLION children to be exact (and counting)!

I witnessed the magic of **Reading Eggs** with my own children. Laughter replaced the tantrums, excitement replaced the tears, and the best part was they were ACTUALLY learning to read.

Reading Eggs works because it's built on the five pillars for reading success. The program is used in thousands of schools because it's so effective. And kids love it. And you will too as you watch your child make real progress in the most important skill they need for future academic success.

Yours sincerely *Katy Pike*

By the same team that brought you **Mathseeds**

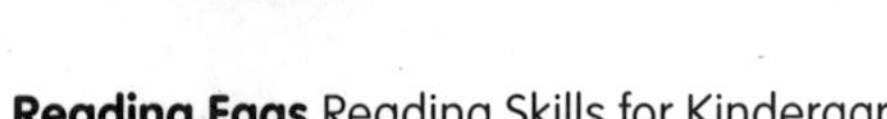

Reading Eggs Reading Skills for Kindergarten

www.readingeggs.com

ISBN: 978-1-74215-341-4

Reprinted 2020

Distributed by:
Blake eLearning
37 West 26th Street
Suite 201. New York, NY 10010

Written by Katy Pike
Publisher: Katy Pike
Editors: Amy Russo and Amanda Santamaria
Design and layout by Modern Art Production Group
Printed by 1010 Printing International LTD

CONTENTS

THE FIVE PILLARS OF READING SUCCESS

Reading Eggs is built on the five components for reading success: phonological and phonemic awareness, phonics, vocabulary, fluency, and comprehension. These proven strategies support learners to achieve reading success.

Phonological and phonemic awareness

Phonological and phonemic awareness are skills we use to hear and play with the individual sounds (phonemes) in words. Skills include being able to break a word into syllables, hear the sounds that make up a word, recognize words that rhyme, and use alliteration. Poems, songs, tongue twisters, and rhymes are good ways to build these skills.

Phonics

Phonics is the relationship between letters and sounds—the correspondence between the sounds in words (phonemes) and the spelling patterns (graphemes) that represent them. Help children develop phonics skills by talking about letters and sounds. For example, *'Cat starts with /c/. The letter c makes the sound /c/ in cat.* Point out letters in words and stories. These skills help learners decode words for reading and encode sounds for writing and spelling.

Vocabulary

Vocabulary is the number of words a child knows and plays an enormous role in the reading process. Build vocabulary by reading books together every day. Discuss new and interesting words and explain what they mean.

Fluency

Fluency is the ability to read a text with accuracy, speed, and expression. One of the best ways to develop fluency is to model good reading when you read aloud. And best of all, reading to your child is proven to be the most important thing you can do to foster a lifelong love of reading.

Comprehension

Comprehension is reading with understanding. A good way to build comprehension skills is to talk about books as you read them together. Ask Who, What, Where, and How questions to discuss what the characters did, what happened and where the story is set.

To find more free tips, printables and ideas, check out the **Reading Eggs** blog at **blog.readingeggs.com**

Reading Eggs Reading Eggs is the fun learn-to-read program that is highly effective, motivating and easy to integrate into your daily routine.

HOW TO USE THIS BOOK

This book covers the first 60 lessons of the **Reading Eggs** program for Kindergarten. The program is built on the five pillars of reading success: phonemic awareness, phonics, vocabulary, fluency and comprehension.

The year Planner on pages vi-ix provides an overview of the lesson focus in an easy-to follow, lesson-by-lesson format. If you are using this book alongside the online lessons, we suggest completing the online lesson first before working through the matching workbooks pages.

Lessons

- Each lesson has 4 pages to reinforce learning.

Lesson Review

- At the end of each 4-page lesson, the yellow review panel helps track achievement.

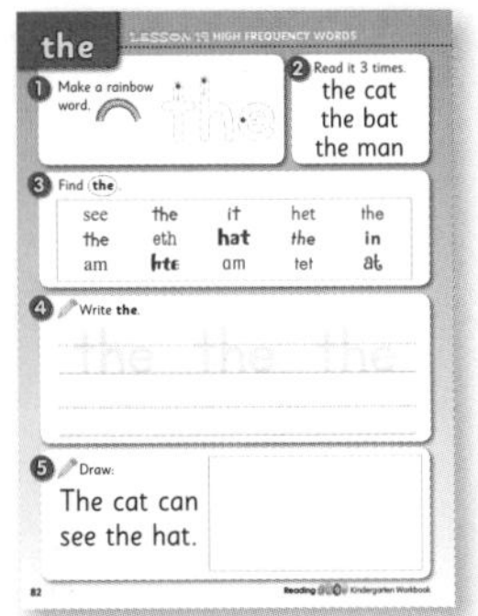

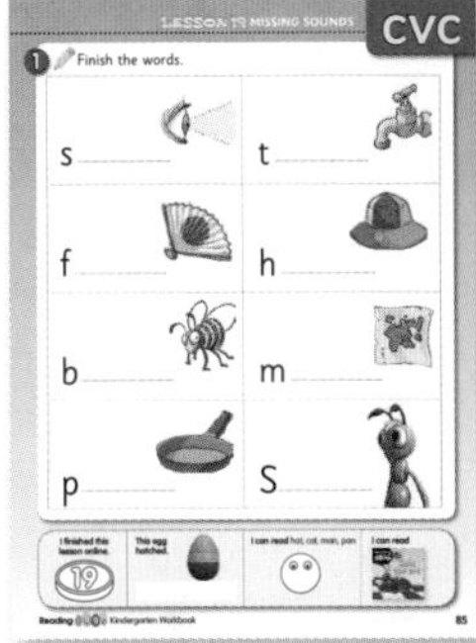

Color when lesson is complete.

I finished this lesson online.
20

This egg hatched.

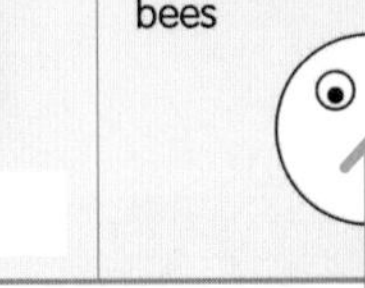

I can read cats, hats, bats, bees

I can read
Can you see?

This is the book title read online.

At the end of each online lesson a critter hatches. Write its name here.

Have your learner draw a mouth on the face for each lesson. Are they happy with their learning?

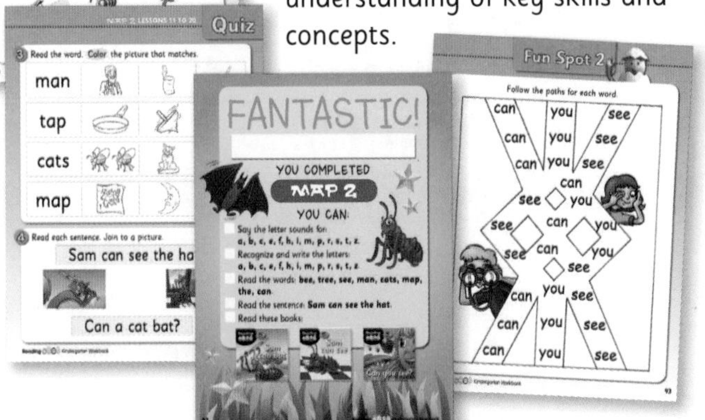

Quizzes

- Quizzes test knowledge from the previous five lessons and are followed by a reward certificate.
- Certificates include a checklist to celebrate achievement. These check your learner's understanding of key skills and concepts.

Online Lessons

For a program that is proven to boost reading skills, use this workbook alongside the Reading eggs lessons at **www.readingeggs.com**. The online reading lessons provide a fun and comprehensive program that motivate children to keep learning. Children enjoy the animated lessons, songs and games. By following each online lesson with the matching four lesson pages in this book, children put into practice their new reading skills as well as building essential writing skills.

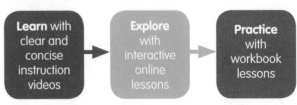

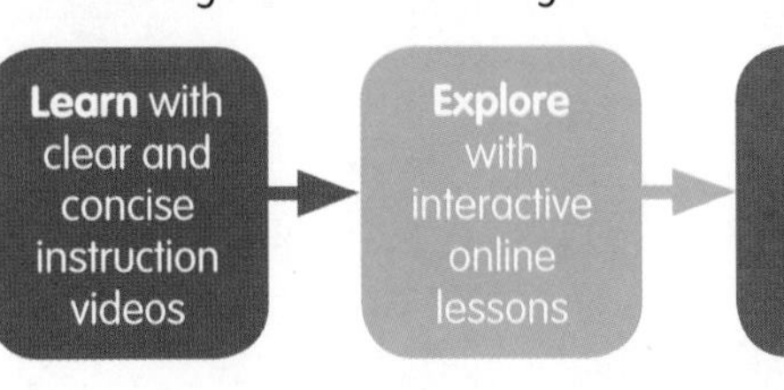

Learn with clear and concise instruction videos
Explore with interactive online lessons
Practice with workbook lessons

YEAR PLANNER

Map 1

Lesson	Lesson Focus	Book Pages	Phonic letters and sounds	Phonically decodable words	High-frequency sight words	Skills
1	the letter **m**	4–7	m			• Find the sound m. • Find words that begin with m. • Recognize and write m and M.
2	the letter **s**	8–11	s			• Find the sound s. • Find words that begin with s. • Recognize and write s and S.
3	words **I** and **am**, and the letter **i**	12–15	a, m, am, i	Sam	I, am	• Find the words I and am. • Use the rime am to build words. • Recognize and write i and I. • Read and write the words I and am.
4	the letter **t**	16–19	t			• Find the sound t. • Find words that begin with t. • Recognize the letters t and T.
5	the word **and** sound **at**	20–23	a, t, at	bat, cat, fat, pat, rat, sat, mat, hat	at, a, I, am	• Find the sound a. • Recognize the rime at and the word at. • Find words that contain the rime at.
6	the letter **b**	24–27	b	bat		• Find the sound b. • Find words that begin with b. • Recognize and write b and B.
7	the letter **c**	28–31	c	cat		• Find the sound f. • Recognize and write f and F. • Blend onsets and the rime at to make words.
8	the letter **f**	32–35	f, at	cat, bat, fat, mat, sat		• Find the sound f. • Recognize and write f and F. • Blend onsets and the rime at to make words.
9	the word **a**	36–39	a, m, t, at, am	am, Sam, cat, bat, fat, mat	I, a, am	• Recognize and write the letter a. • Read the words a, I and am in sentences. • Read and find words using the rime at.
10	Review	40–43	a, b, c, f, i m, s, t, am, at	am, Sam, at, bat, cat, fat, mat, sat	I, am, at, a	• Review the sounds a, b, c, f, i, m, s and t. • Revise word families at and am. • Review the words I, am, a.
Map 1 Quiz	Revision	44–45	a, b, c, f, i m, s, t, am, at	am, Sam, at, bat, cat, fat, mat, sat	I, am, at, a	• Say the letter sounds m, s, t, b, c, f. • Recognize and write the letters: m, s, t, b, c, f, i, a. • Read the words: cat, Sam, bat, I, am. • Read the sentence: I am a cat. • Read a book.

Map 2

Lesson	Lesson Focus	Book Pages	Phonic letters and sounds	Phonically decodable words	High-frequency sight words	Skills
11	the letter **n**	50–53	n	cat, sat, bat	I	• Find the sound n. • Find words that contain n. • Recognize and write n and N.
12	the letter **p**	54–57	p, am	pat	am	• Find the sound p. • Find words that contain p. • Recognize and write p and P.
13	the sound **ap**	58–61	a, p, ap	Sam, pats, cat, bat, fat, sat, zap, map, cap, tap, nap, rap, lap, gap	I, am, a	• Find the rime ap. • Find words that contain ap. • Blend onset and rime to make a word.
14	the letter **h**	62–65	h	hat, ham		• Find the sound h. • Find words that contain h. • Recognize and write h and H.
15	the letter **r**	66–69	r	rat, ram, rap		• Find the sound r. • Find words that contain r. • Recognize and write r and R.
16	the sound **an**	70–73	a, n, an	ran, fan, can, van, pan, ant, Sam, bat, cat, rat	I, am, a, an, can, man	• Find the sound an. • Find words that contain an. • write an words.
17	the letter **z**	74–77	z	zap		• Find the sound z. • Find words that contain z. • Recognize and write z and Z.
18	the letter **e**, the sound **ee**	78–81	e, ee	bee, tree, see, seed, weed, Zee, three, tee	see	• Find the sound ee. • Find words that contain ee. • Recognize and write e and E.
19	the words **see** and **the**	82–85	s, ee	Sam, can, see, man, fan, pan, tap, cap, hat, bat, cat, sat, rat, mat, fat, zap, map	see, the, I, can, man, at, am	• Find the sight words see and the. • Read and use the words see and the. • Review word families at, an, ap, am, ee.
20	Review	86–89	n, p, h, r, z, e, ap, an, ee	see, can, hat, man, bee, bat, Sam	see, the, can, man, you, I	• Review the sounds n, p, h, r, e, z, at, ap, an and ee. • Revise the words see, the and can. • Find and read the word you.
Map 2 Quiz		90–91				• Say the letter sounds for: a, b, c, e, f, h, i, m, p, r, s, t, z. • Recognize and write the letters: a, b, c, e, f, h, i, m, p, r, s, t, z. • Read the words: bee, tree, see, man, cats, map, the, can. • Read the sentence: Sam can see the hat.

Map 3

Lesson	Lesson Focus	Book Pages	Phonic letters and sounds	Phonically decodable words	High-frequency sight words	Skills
21	the letter **v**	96–99	v	van	see, the	• Find the sound v. • Find words that contain v. • Recognize and write v and V.
22	**and**	100–103		see, ant, band, rat, hat, sand, hand, land, amt, bee, bat, cat, Sam	and, see, the	• Find the rime and. • Find words that contain and. • Read and write the word and.
23	the letter **d**	104–107	d	Dan, dad	you	• Find the sound d. • Find words that contain d. • Recognize and write d and D.
24	the words **in** and **had**	108–111		rat, cat, hat, sat, fat, map	in, had, I, can, see, the, a	• Find the words in and had. • Read the words in and had. • Revise other sight words.
25	the letter **j**	112–115	j	jam	see, you, the, can	• Find the sound j. • Find words that contain j. • Recognize and write j and J.
26	the sound **ad**	116–119	ad	dad, bad, had, pad, mad, sad, cats, rats, bees, ants	had, I, can, see	• Find the rime ad. • Find words that contain ad. • Recognize and write ad words.
27	the letter **o**	120–123	o	on		• Find the sound o. • Find words that contain o. • Recognize and write o and O.
28	the word **is**	124–127		bee, ant, bad, sad, cap, bat	is, good, a, has, see, the, can, bad, an, I, am	• Find the word is. • Read and write the word is. • Recognize the words good and bad.
29	the word **on**	128–131	on	zap, mat, sat, bee, ant	on, the, and, is, a, see, can, you, had, an	• Find the word on. • Read and write the word on. • Revise word families.
30	the letter **q**	132–135	q	queen	I, am, a, an, at, can, see, the, you, and, in, had, is, on, good, bad	• Revise known letters, sounds and sight words. • Find the sound q. • Read and write q and Q.
Map 3 Quiz	Review	136–137				• Say the letter sounds for: a, b, c, d, e, f, h, j, m, o, p, r, s, t, v, z. • Recognize and write the letters: a, b, c, d, e, f, h, j, m, o, p, r, s, t, v, z. • Read the words: and, hand, sand, band, bed, had, is, in, on. • Read the sentence: Zee the bee is on the mat.

Map 4

Lesson	Lesson Focus	Book Pages	Phonic letters and sounds	Phonically decodable words	High-frequency sight words	Skills
31	the letter **g**	142–145	g	pig, bag	had, see, the, bad, on, is, good	• Find the sound g. • Find words that contain g. • Recognize and write g and G.
32	the letter **l**	146–149	l	lap, lad		• Find the sound l. • Find words that contain l. • Recognize and write l and L.
33	the words **he** and **she**	150–153		cat, sat, tap, can, jam, van, man, Dan, zap, mat, fat, bee, see	he, she, on, had, the, can, see, is, you, and, in, a, I	• Find the words he and she. • Read and write the words he and she.
34	the letter **k**	154–157	k			• Find the sound k. • Find words that contain k. • Recognize and write k and K.
35	the words **as** and **has**	158–161		cat, bat, mat, hat, can, map, rat, man, fan, ham	as, has, is, it, on, a, the, on	• Find the words as and has. • Read and write the words as and has.
36	the letter **y**	162–165	y	yoyo	had, has, can, is, she, he	• Find the sound y. • Find words that contain y. • Recognize and write y and Y.
37	the words **yes** and **you**	166–169		hat, cat, ant, man, van, map, has, and, bat, Dan, can, fat, rat, bad, see, bee	yes, you, has, a, and, it, as, I, am, an, in, he, see, the, can	• Find the words yes and you. • Read and write the words yes and you.
38	the letter **x**	170–173	x	box, fox, wax, mix, six	yes, see	• Find the sound x. • Find words that contain x. • Recognize and write x and X.
39	the letter **w**	174–177	w	web, win,wig		• Find the sound w. • Find words that contain w. • Recognize and write w and W.
40	Review	178–181	am, at, an, ap, ad	van, sad, dam, zap, hat, man, gap, ran, jam, bat, pad, ham, ram, cat, can, see, hid, in, tin, sits, tin, fin	he, she, as, has, yes, you, man, the, can, see, in, and, a	• Revise short word families a. • Recognize and write new word families using /i/. • Revise known letters and sight words.
Map 4 Quiz		182–183				• Read and write the alphabet. • Read these words: yes, you, fish, she. • Read lots of new sentences.

Map 5

Lesson	Lesson Focus	Book Pages	Phonic letters and sounds	Phonically decodable words	High-frequency sight words	Skills
41	the letter **u**	188–191	u	fun, sun, run		• Find the sound u. • Recognize and write u and U. • Identify reading rules.
42	the alphabet	192–195	Alphabet	cat, mat, rat, ham, map, tap, hat, gap, zap, sat, bat, van, fan, can, man, ran, tan, pan, lap, cap, nap, jam, Sam, ant, fun, sun, fox, box, pun, fin, bee	words, it, the, see, you, yes, a	• Say every sound and letter of the alphabet. • Find the word 'words'.
43	the sound **id**	196–199	id	hid, lid, kid, Sid, did, bin, rid, hit, bat	has, a, the, can, see, I, am, yes, it, in, he	• The id word family. • Read and write words using id.
44	the sounds **ix** and **in**	200–203	ix	six, fix, mix, tin, win, pin, fin, din, bin	in, him, I, can, see, you, yes, a	• The ix and in word families. • Read and write words using ix and in.
45	the sound **it**	204–207	it	hit, sit, bit, fit, spin, lit, pit, wit	it, can, you, on, I, we, and	• The it word family. • Read and write words using it. • Read the word it.
46	the sound **ig**	208–211	ig	big, wig, dig, fig, gig, pig, rig	like, said, I, it, my, the, has	• The ig word family. • Read and write words using ig. • Read and write the words said and like.
47	the word **this**	212–215		wag, bin, kid, pig, big, wig, fig	this, is, yes, the, it, can, he	• Find the word this. • Read and write sentences using this.
48	the sound **ip**	216–219	ip	lip, zip, pip, rip, dip, hip, nip, sip, tip, wip	little, black, blue, big	• Read and write words using ip. • Recognize the words big and little. • Find some color words.
49	the sound **ill**	220–223	ill	hill, will, sill, pill, bill, kill, till, mill, dill, fill, gill, jill		• The ill word family. • Read and write words using ill.
50	the sound **ing**	224–227	ing	king, ring, sing, wing	bird, two, cannot, has, the, can, this, and	• Read and write words using ing. • Revise /i/ word families. • Recognize the sight words has, two, and cannot.
Map 5 Quiz						• Read and write CVC words. • Read these words: little, sing, said, this. • Read lots of sentences.

Map 6

Lesson	Lesson Focus	Book Pages	Phonic letters and sounds	Phonically decodable words	High-frequency sight words	Skills
51	the word **go**	234–237		six	go, by, you, can, see, the	• Find the words go and by. • Read and write the words go and by.
52	the sound **ot**	238–241	ot	cot, dot, hot, pot, lot, got, jot, rot, not	look, got	• The ot word family. • Read and write the word look.
53	the sound **og**	242–245	og	dog, log, fog, cog, bog, hog, jog, rock, sock, shop	of, this, got, lots, the, had, to, go, at, and	• The og word family. • Read and write words using og.
54	the sound **op**	246–249	op	cop, hop, mop, pop, top, shop, stop	play, got, can, the, we, all, in	• The op word family. • Read and write words using op.
55	the sound **o**	250–253	o	lots, dog, hog, log, fog, jog, cog, bog, pop, mop, hop, top, sock, cot, put, dot, hot, not, nod	got, he, lots, of, the, on	• Revise short o word family. • Read and write words using the short o sound.
56	the word **are**	254–257		not	are, happy, said, not, this, you, yes, like, no, to	• Find the words are, not, and said. • Read the words are, not, and said. • Recognize words for red, yellow, and green.
57	the words **his** and **her**	258–261		dog	his, her, we, said, like, it, she, this, is, the, he, all	• Find the words his, her, and we. • Use the words his, her, and we in sentences. • Read and write words within a theme.
58	the sound **ock**	262–265	od, ock, ox	fox, cod, rod, nod, god, pod, dock, lock, clock, boxes, sock, rock		• Word families: od, ock, and ox. • Read and write words using od, ock, and ox.
59	the sound **od**, **y** at the end	266–269	ox, y at the end	puppy, muddy, bossy, messy, silly, sorry, pod, rod, cod, fox, box, rocks, socks, pot, cot, hot, dot, rot, got	very	• The od and ot word families. • Recognize the sight word very. • Read and write words with y at the end.
60	Review	270–273	ock, ot, og, od, op, ox	clock, dock, rocksock, lock, pod, rod, cod, dog, cog, joh, hog, log, fog, dot, cot, hot, pot, rot, lot, top, mop, hop, pop, fox, box		• Review short o word families – ot, og, od, op, ock, ox. • Read and write words using short o rimes.
Map 6 Quiz		274–275				• Read and write short vowel word families. • Read these words: frog, clock, shop, said, his, hers. • Read lots of new sentences.

HOW DO THESE LESSONS BUILD READING SUCCESS?

Every page in this book is carefully structured to improve your child's reading and writing skills. These powerful learning activities are based on the five pillars for reading success: phonological and phonemic awareness, phonics, fluency, vocabulary, and comprehension.

Letters, sounds, and phonemic awareness

These pages focus on letter sounds and listening skills. Children say the focus sound and then name each picture. Listen for the focus sound in the words. Color the matching pictures. Listening skills are an important part of learning to read.

High frequency sight words

100 words make up 50% of the text young children read, so learning these words is important for reading success. For the rainbow words activity, children should use different colored pencils to trace the word many times. This repeated tracing makes the words look great and helps kids build the muscle memory they need to write these important words.

Phonics

To read, children need to learn that words are made up of sounds. Sound out each letter from beginning to end. Sound out each letter and then blend them together.

Handwriting, letter formation, and writing skills

Writing letters actively builds reading skills. Correct letter formation helps children recognize the letter and write more clearly. The red dots show children where they need to begin.

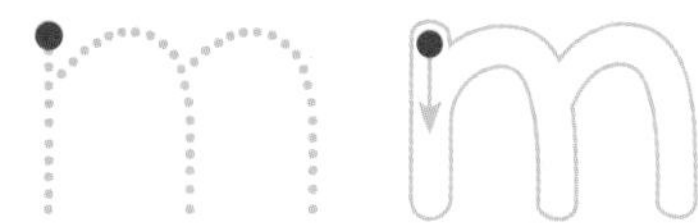

Comprehension

As children's reading ability improves, comprehension skills become more important. The comprehension pages build reading comprehension skills at the same time as providing essential reading practice.

Read, then answer the questions.

The van

I can see the van.
The cat is in the van.
The cat had a nap in the van.

These features help young learners focus on what they need to do

 Trace, write, or draw your answer.

 Draw a loop around the correct answer.

 Color the correct answer.

 Draw a cross to complete the activity.

ALPHABET CHART

Dogfin

Eggyphant

Frogfish

Jelly Jag

Kangako

Lemon Lizard

Pinkipoo

Queenie Quail

Red Rabbit

Village Van

Wheely Whale

Xpanda

Zebstar

Warm up fun

1 Follow Jet Set's trails. Start at the dot.

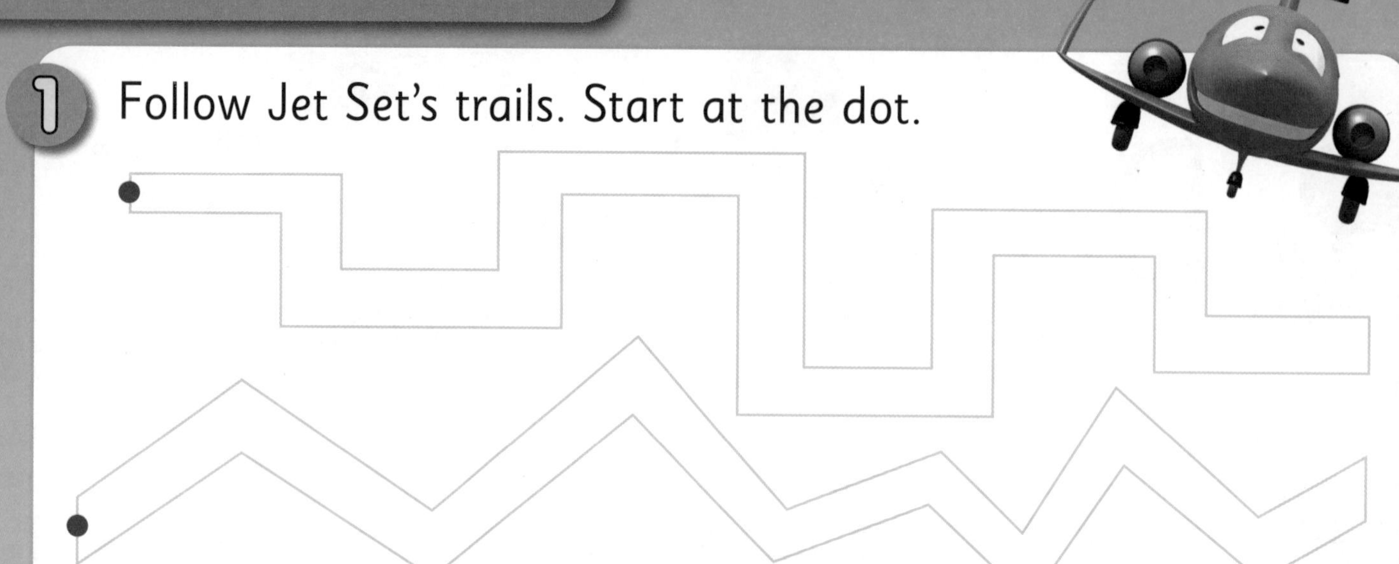

2 Swim through Wheely Whale's waves.

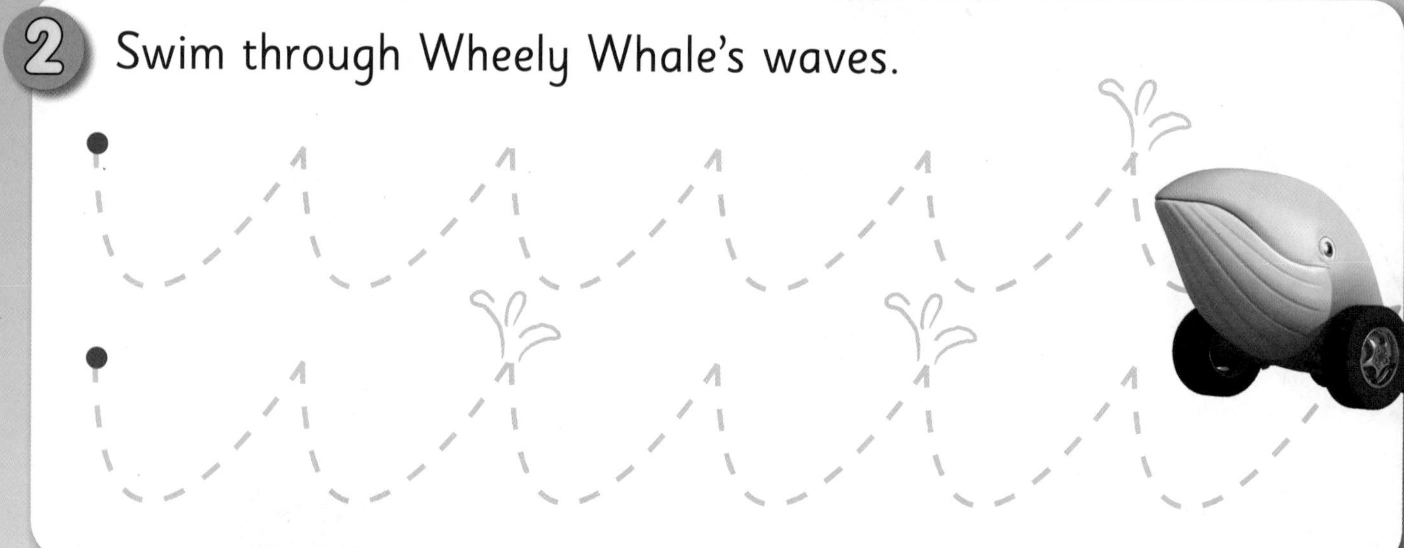

3 Follow Sunny Snail's trails.

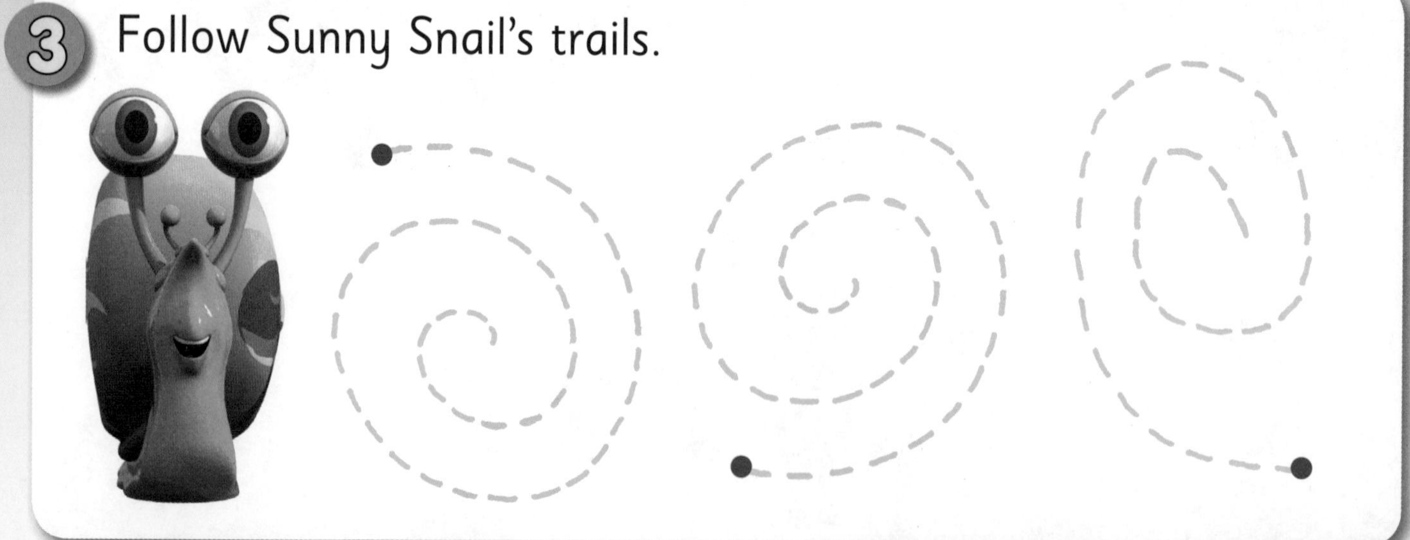

4 Slither with Jake Snake.

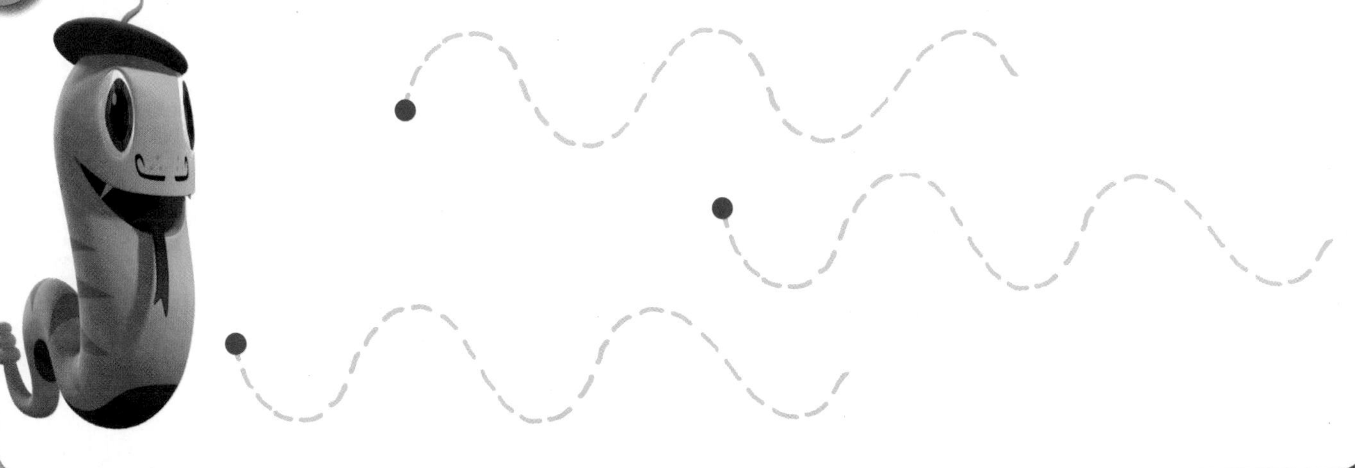

5 Fly with Flutter Bye Bye.

6 Hop along with Frogfish.

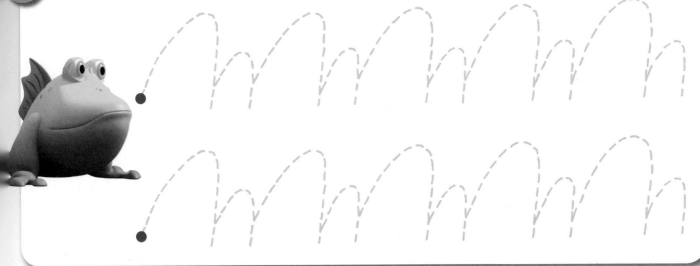

Hello, I'm Marshmallow Mouse.

1 Color things that begin with **m**.

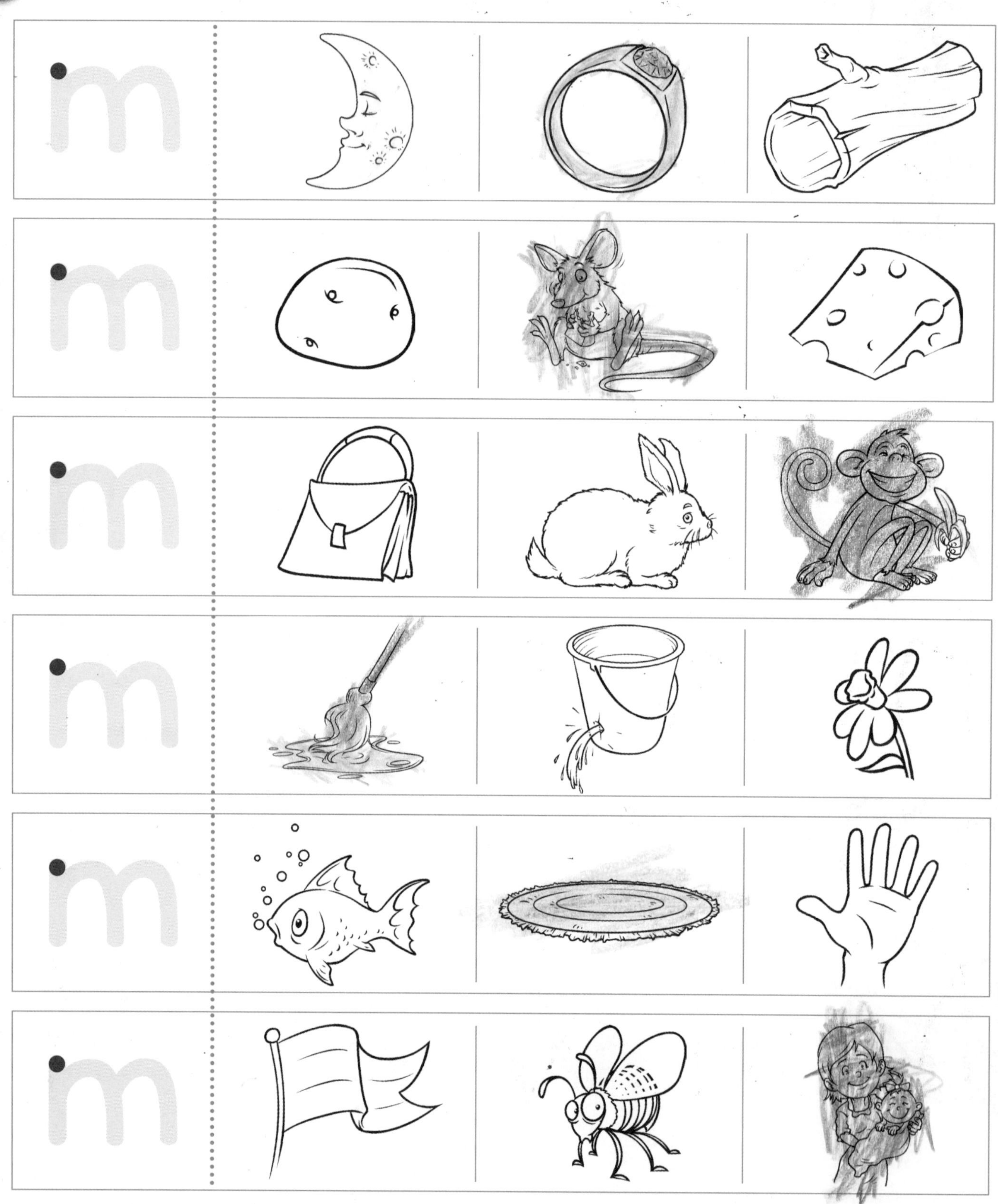

Mm

1 Hop.

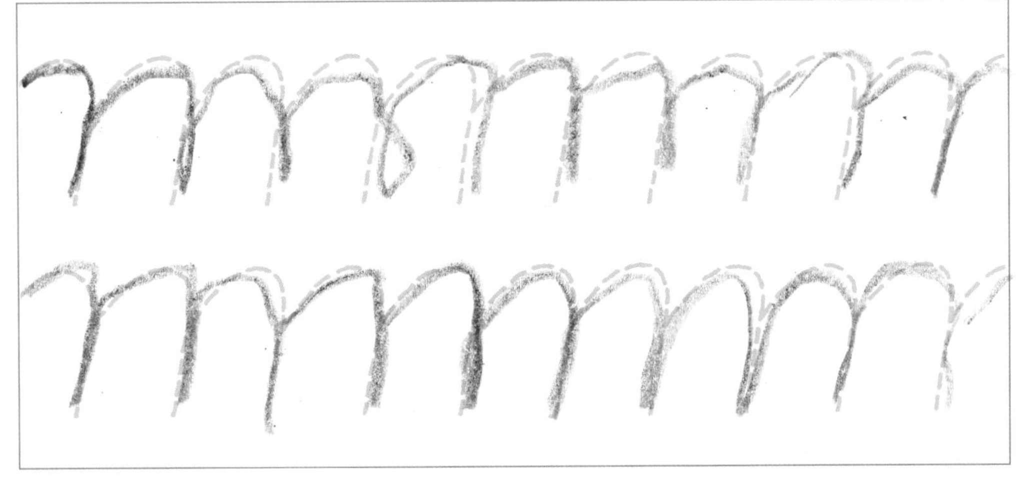

2 Trace.

3 Trace and write.

Circle your best letter.

1 Add **m**. Say the word.

 m an	 m ouse
 m onkey	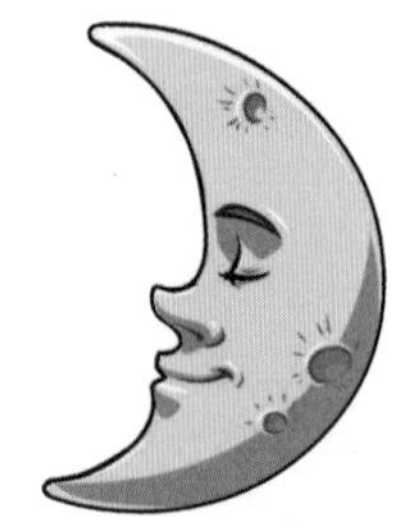 m oon
 m ap	 m ilk
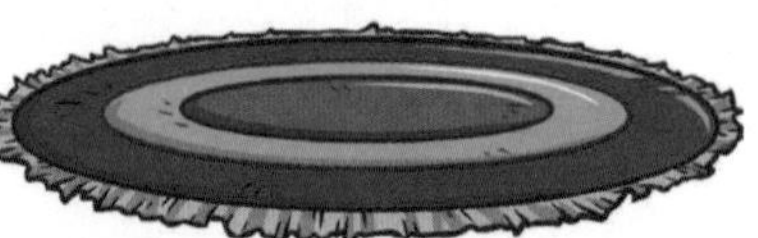 m at	 m op

2 Draw a mask.

1 Color the things that begin with **m**.

2 Circle every **M**.

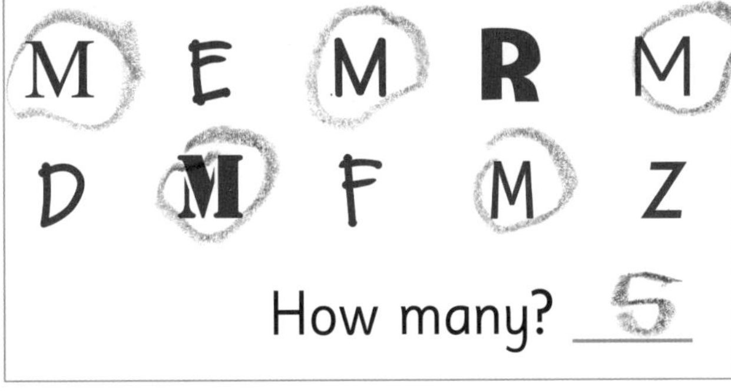

Circle every **m**.

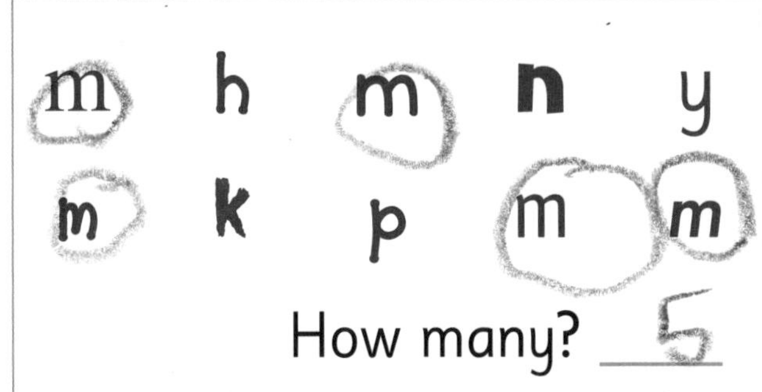

3 Write the letter **m**.

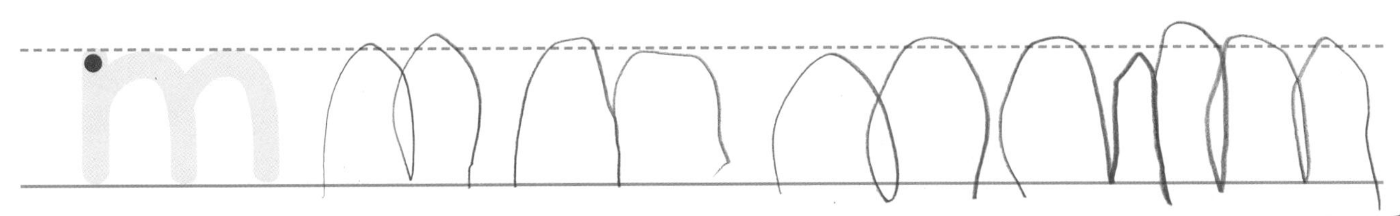

I finished this lesson online.	This egg hatched.	I know the letter sound: Mm	I can read

Say hello to Sunny Snail!

1 Color things that begin with **s**.

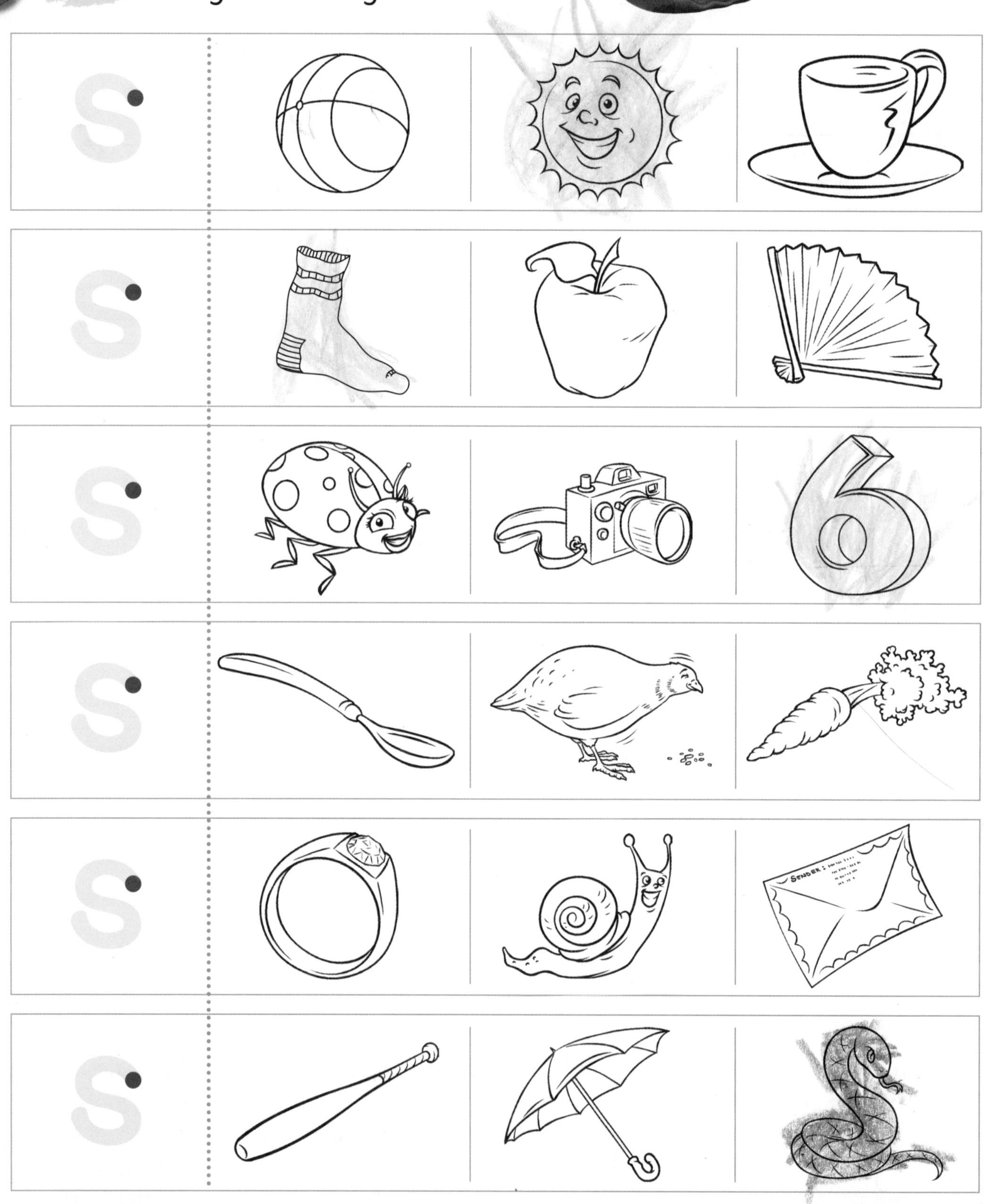

Ss

1 Follow Sunny Snail's trails.

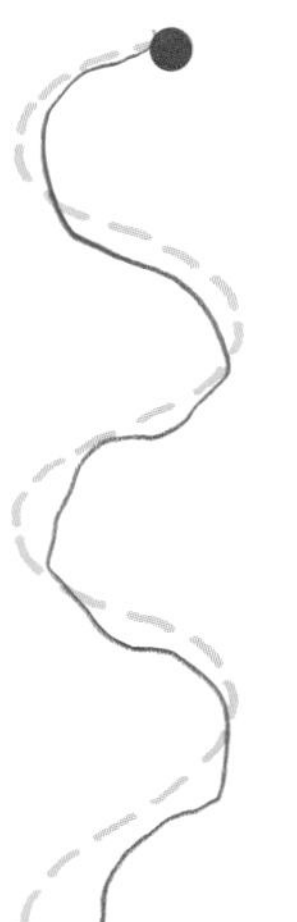

2 Trace.

3 Trace and write.

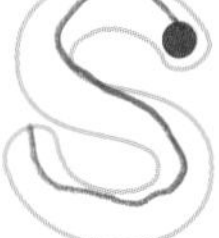
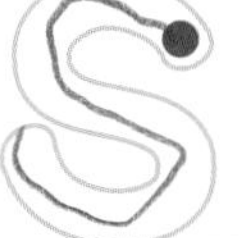

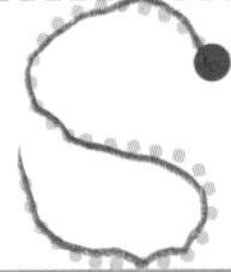
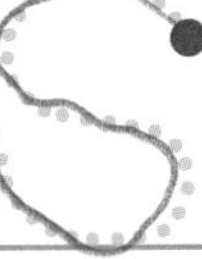
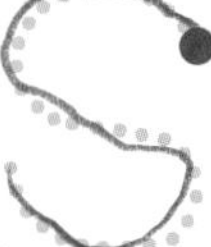
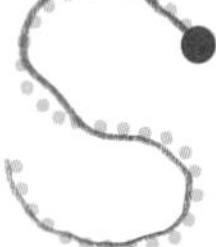
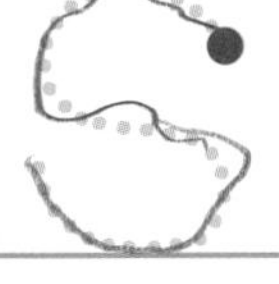

Circle your best letter.

1 Add **s**. Say the word.

 s un	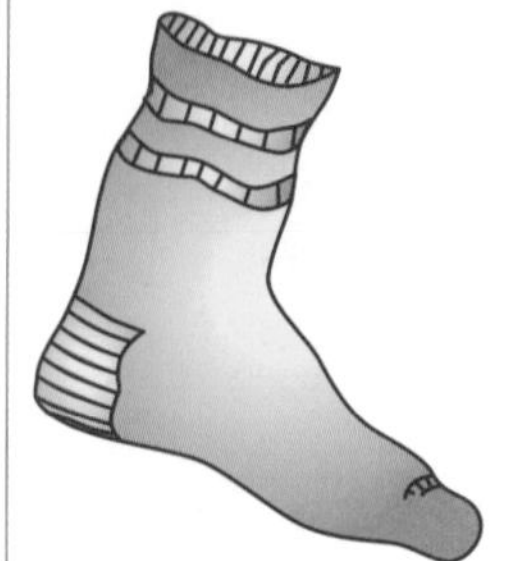 ___ock
 ___ix	 ___andwich
 ___nake	 ___nail
 ___tar	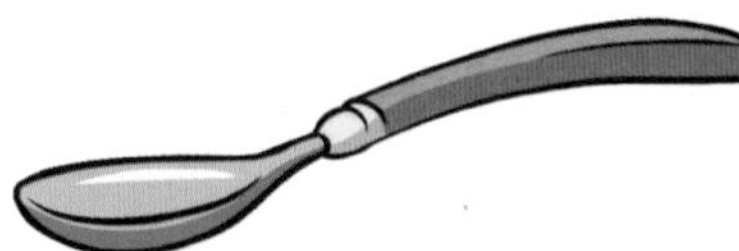 ___poon

2 Draw six socks.

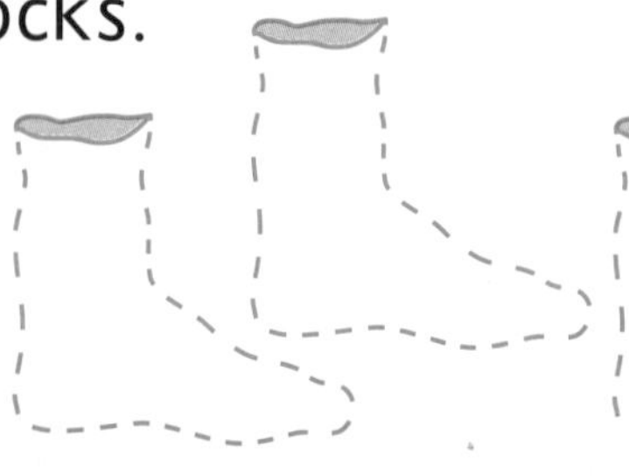
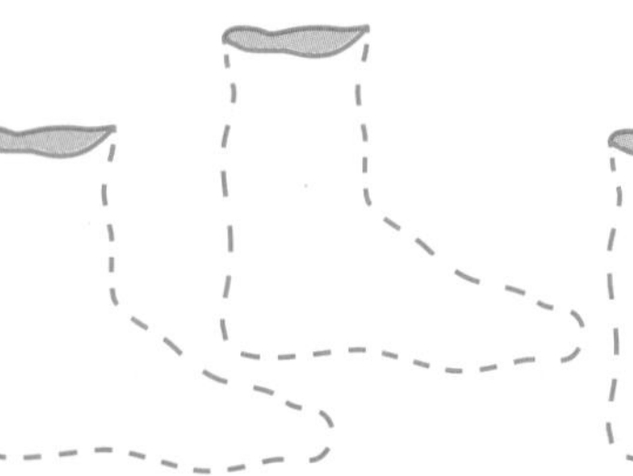
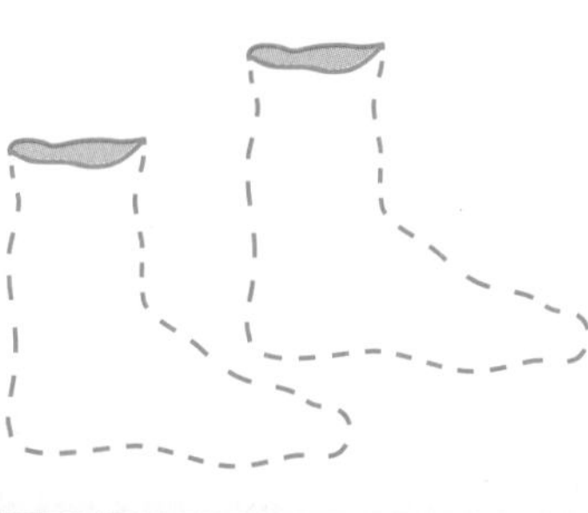

1 Color the things that begin with **s**.

2 Circle every **S**.

S C t C S
T S G S U

How many? ____

Circle every **s**.

s s d c s
a r b s y

How many? ____

3 Write the letter **s**.

s

I finished this lesson online.

This egg hatched.

I know the letter sound: Ss

I can read

I is for Insillysect

1 Color things that begin with **i**.

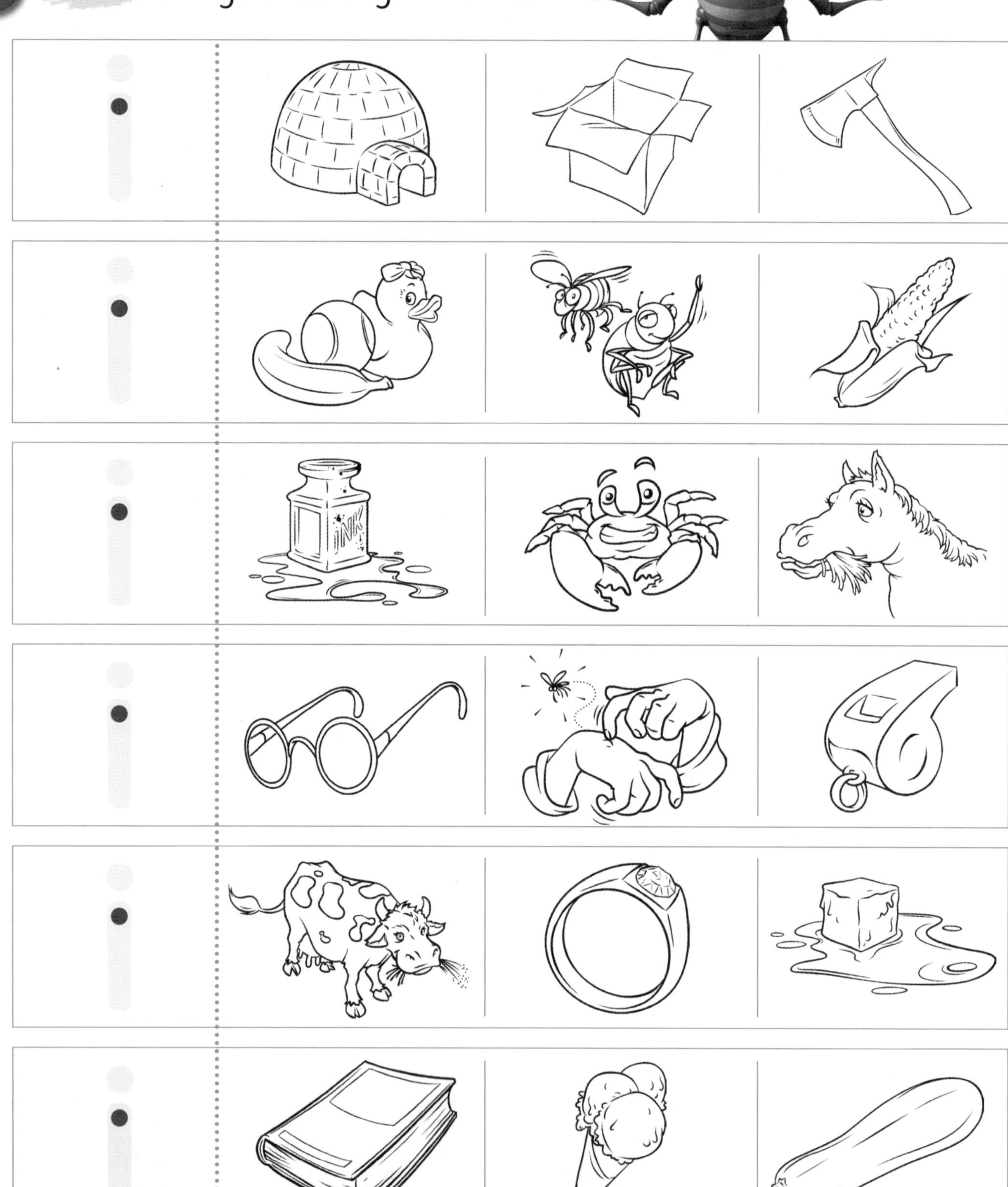

1 Trace and write.

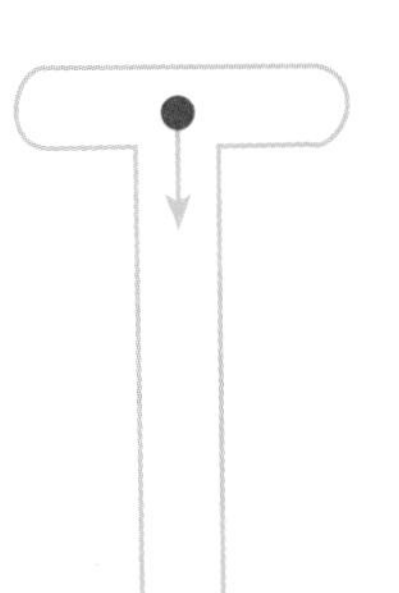

Icy igloo

2 Circle every **I**.

I	N	I	L	I
l	T	F	I	V

How many? ____

Circle every **i**.

i	t	h	i	i
e	i	k	l	i

How many? ____

3 Trace and write.

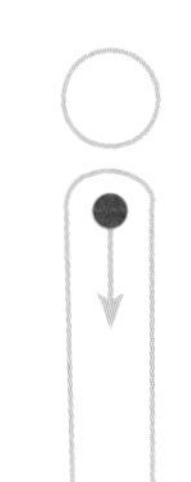

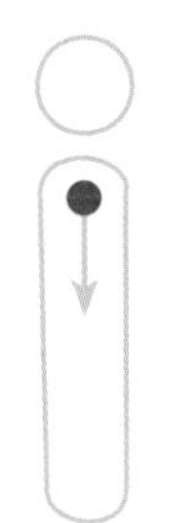

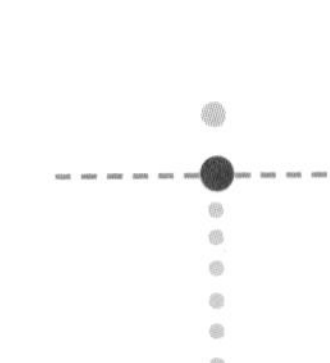

Circle your best letter.

1 Add **i**. Say the word.

 ___nk	 ___nsects
 ___tch	 ___nternet
 ___ce	 ___ce-cream

2 Draw more insects on the icy igloo.

Insects on an icy igloo.

Ii

1 Make rainbow words. 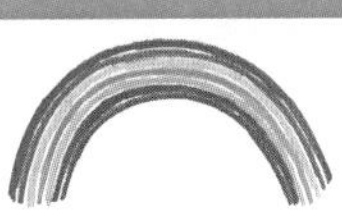

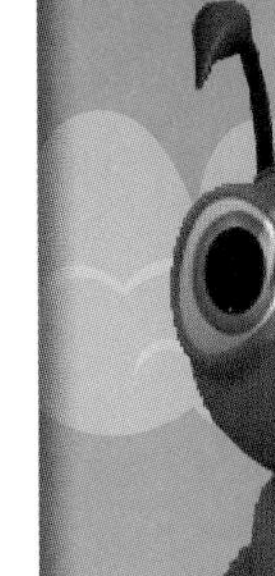

I am

2 Find **am**.

tam	am	a	me	in
am	Sam	at	on	am
am	om	am	to	is

3 Write **am**.

am am am

4 How old are you?

I am

I finished this lesson online.	This egg hatched.	I know the letter sound: I i, the word am	I can read

1 Color things that begin with **t**.

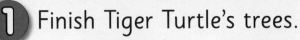

1 Finish Tiger Turtle's trees.

Tiger Turtle is terrific!

2 Trace.

1

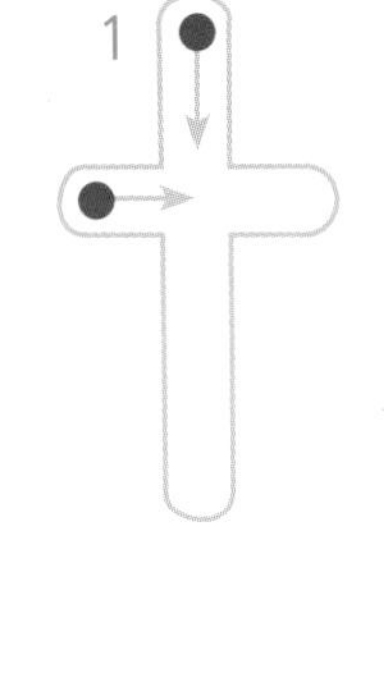
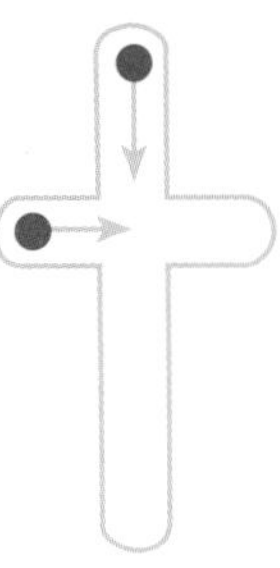
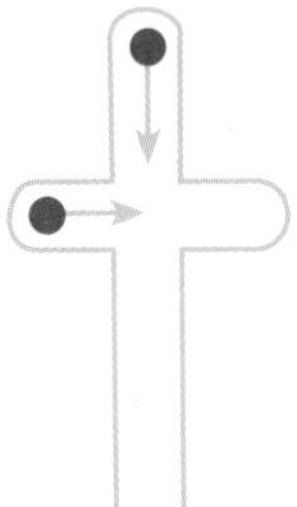
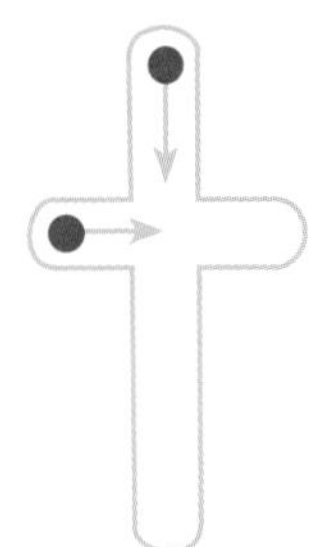
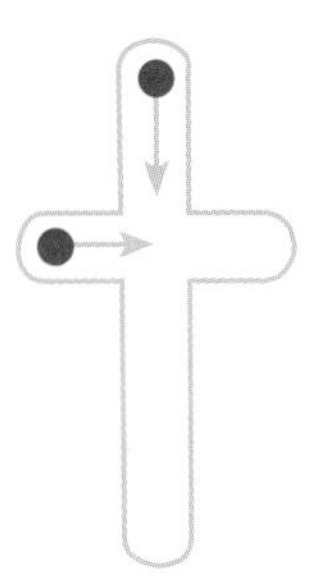

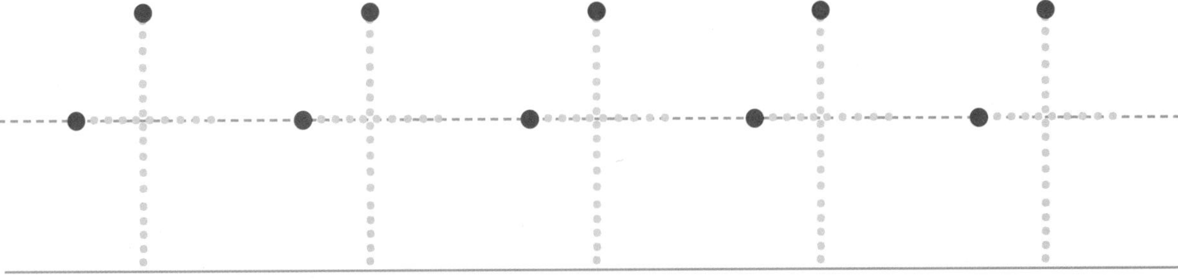

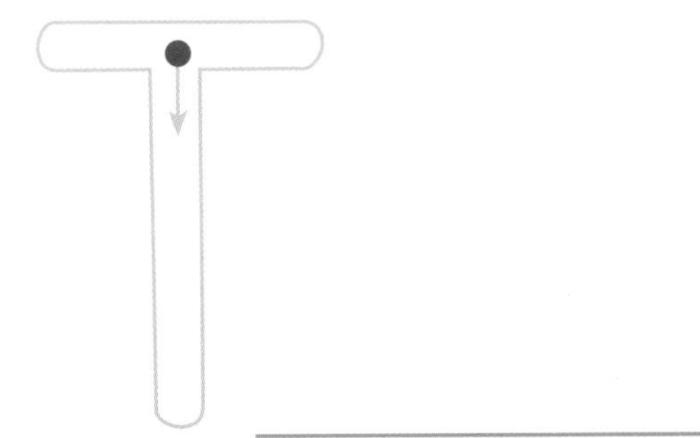
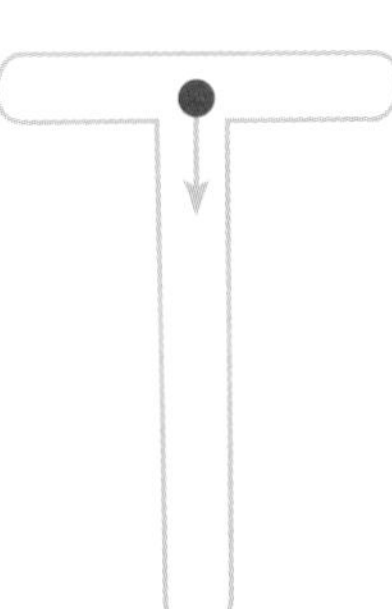

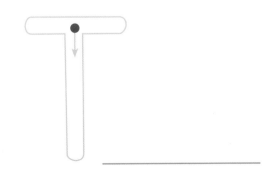

Circle your best letter.

Ten tiny toes.

1  Add **t**. Say the word.

 ___iger	 ___urtle
 ___ent	 ___ree
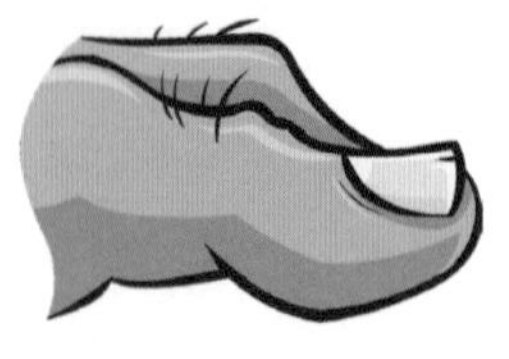 ___oes	 ___eddy
 ___op	 ___ap

2 Draw some teeth.

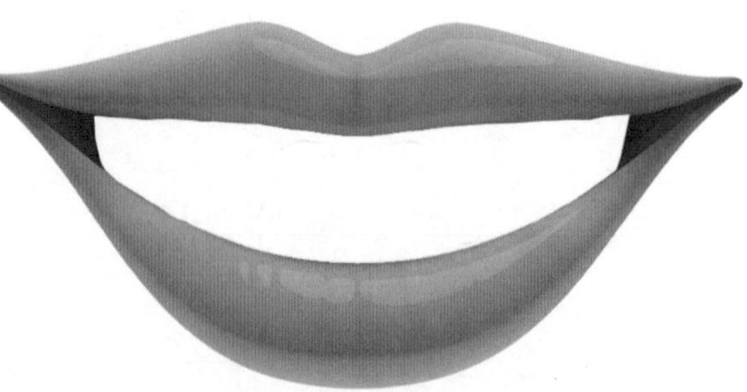

1 Trace. Join to a picture that begins with that sound.

2 Circle the beginning sound. Write the letter.

t m s

i m s

I finished this lesson online.

This egg hatched.

I know the letter sound: Tt

I can read

A is for Appley Ant.

1 Color things that begin with **a**.

a			
a			
a			
a			AMBULANCE

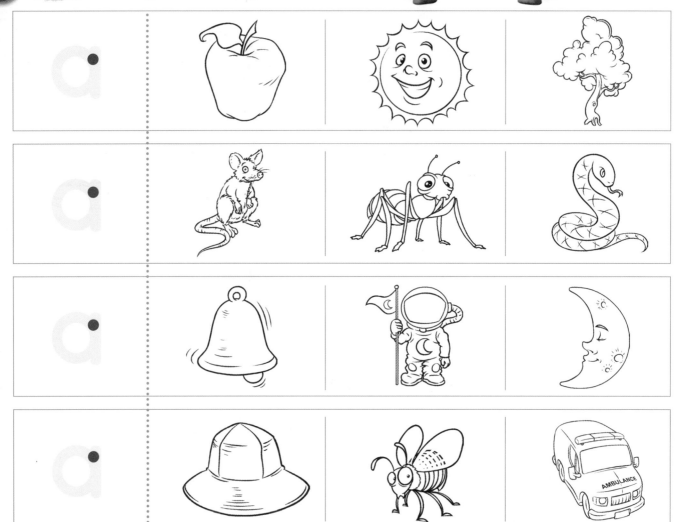

2 Match to a picture.

sat cat mat bat

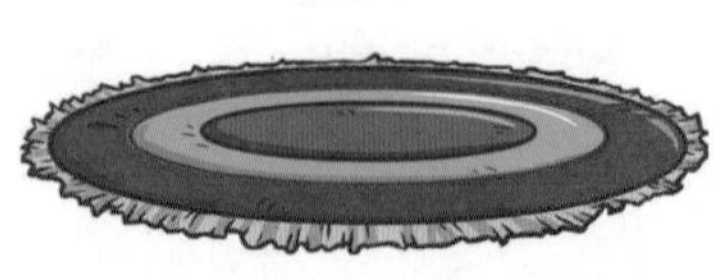

Aa

1 Trace.

2 Draw the spiral.
Start at the apple.

3 Trace.

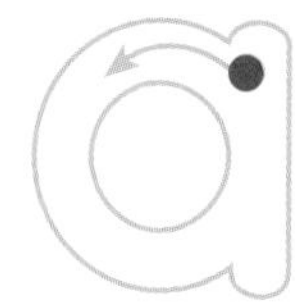 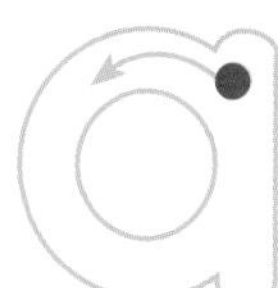  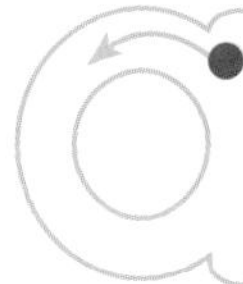 

 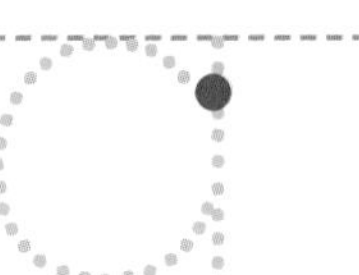 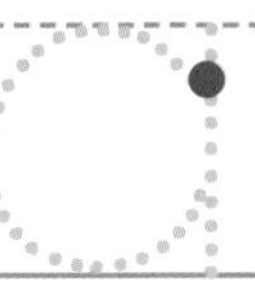 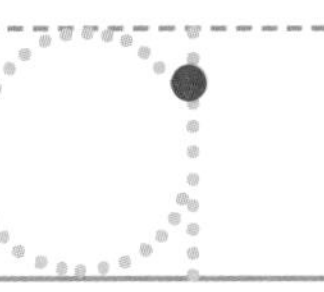 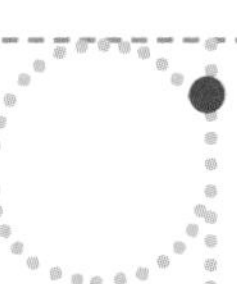

 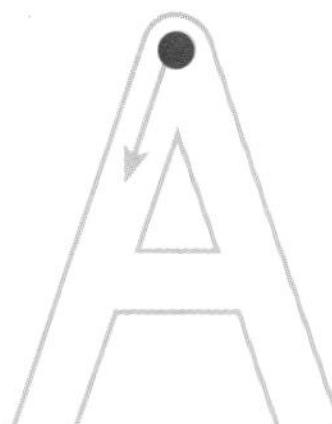

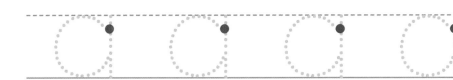

Circle your best letter.

1 Trace.

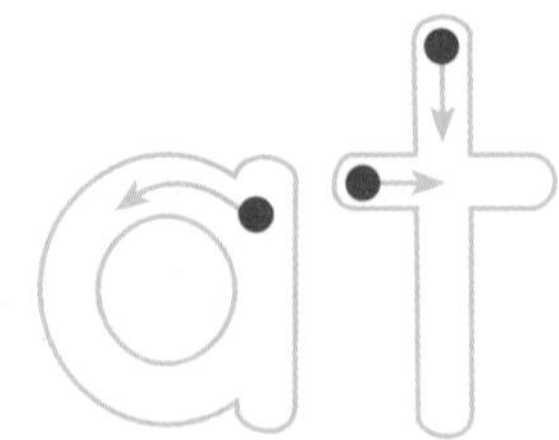

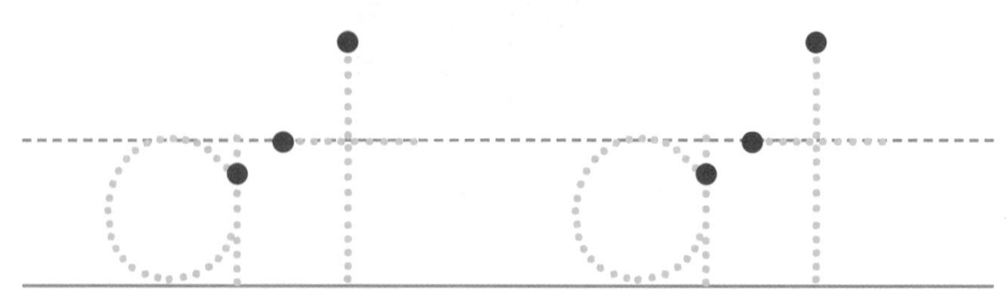

2 Find **at**.

am	at	am	at	oth
at	in	ant	*it*	**at**
in	**to**	at	om	at

3 Write **at**.

at at at at

4 Draw a cat.

1 Trace and write.

2 Circle every **A**.

A B A E S
T A N A A

How many? ____

Circle every **a**.

a c n a g
c a o a a

How many? ____

3 Add **a** and then say the word.

____pple

____nt

4 Join the word to the picture.

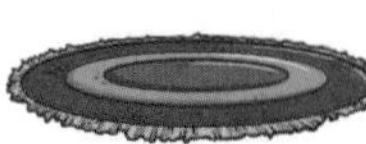
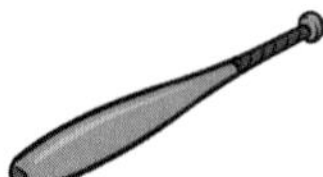
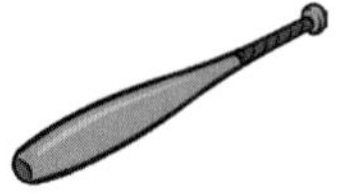

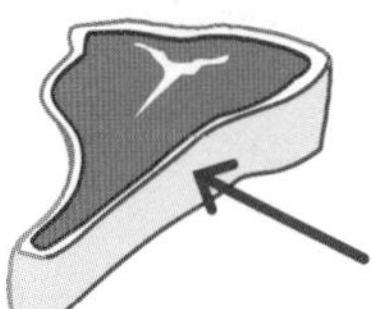

sat	fat	mat	bat

I finished this lesson online.	This egg hatched.	**I know** the letter sound: Aa, the word: at	**I can read**

Buzz, buzz! I'm Bee Bee Bear.

1 Color the bubbles that begin with **b**.

2 Match each letter to a picture.

1 Draw a ball next to each bat.

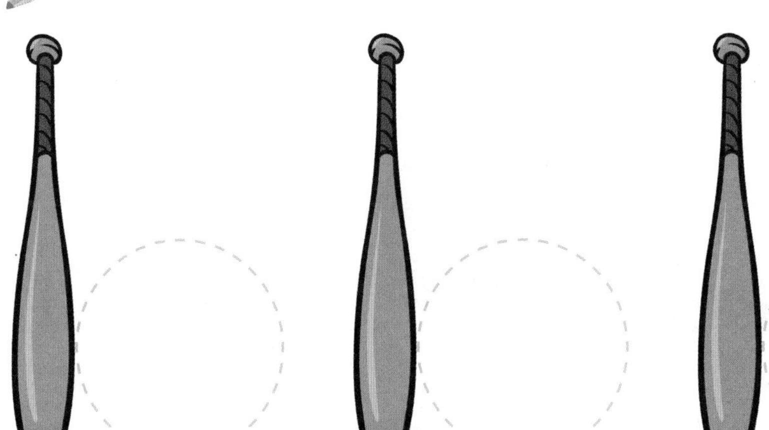

2 Trace and write.

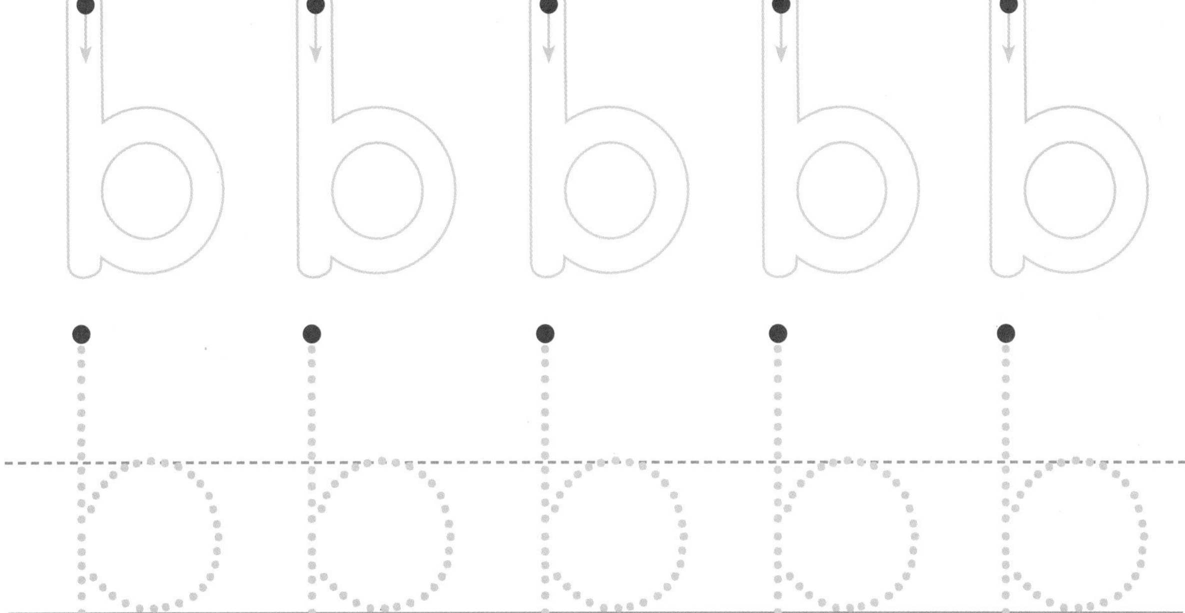

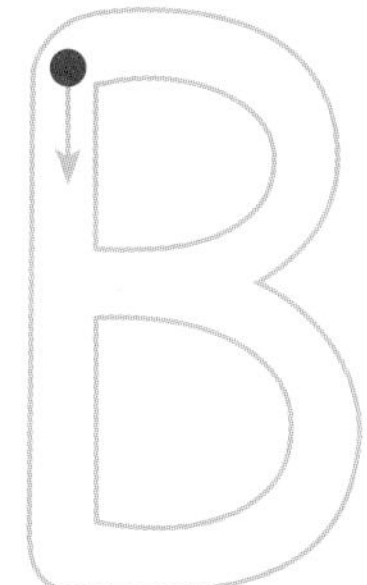

Circle your best letter.

1 Add **b**. Say the word.

 b ee	 ____ear
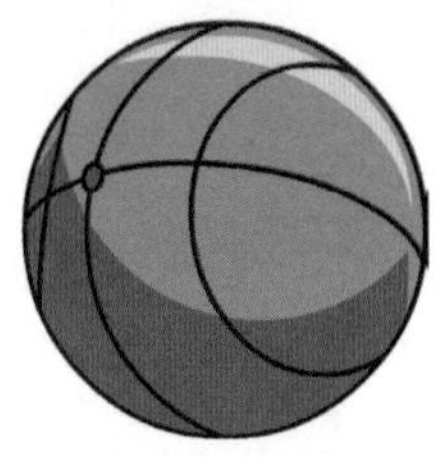 ____all	 ____ook
 ____ag	 ____ath
 ____ell	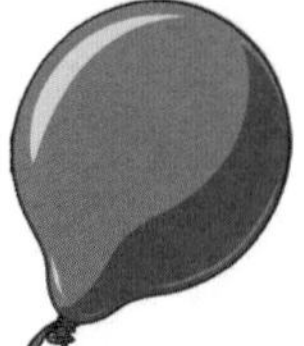 ____alloon

2 Circle every **B**.

B A P B C
B A O R B

How many? ____

Circle every **b**.

b b d p b
a b e b g

How many? ____

Bb

1 Trace and write.

2 Trace the letter. Join to a picture that begins with that sound.

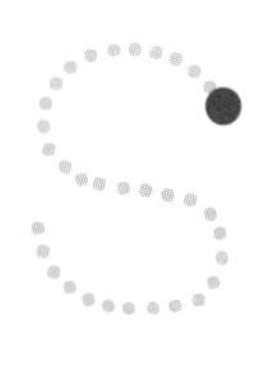
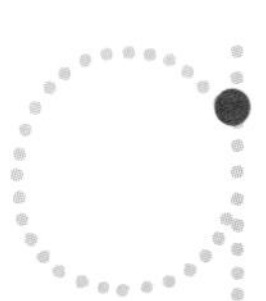

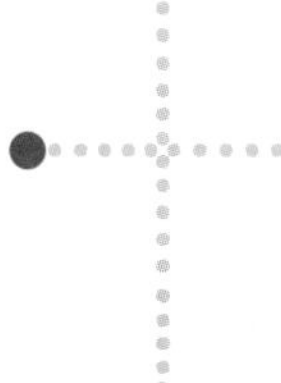

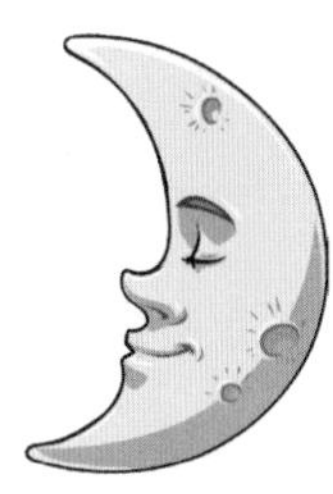

3 Circle the beginning sound. Write the letter.

 ______	 ______
s i t	t b m

I finished this lesson online.	This egg hatched.	I know the letter sound: Bb	I can read

1 Color the pictures that begin with **c**.

2 Match each letter to a picture.

1 Complete the cats.

Catty Cake is cute!

2 Trace and write.

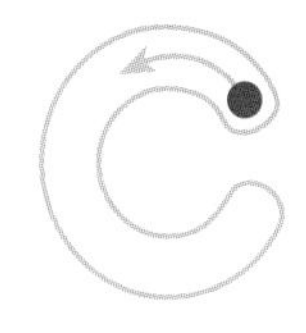
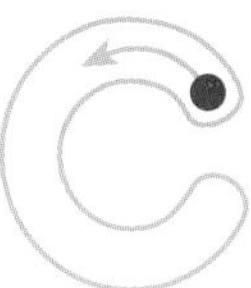
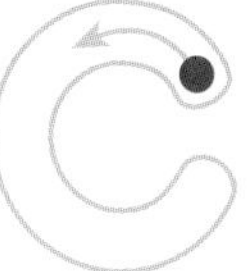
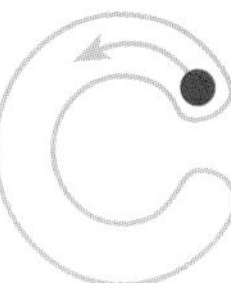
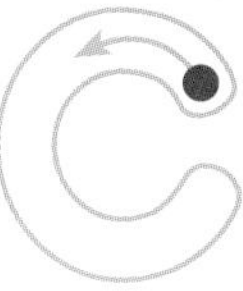

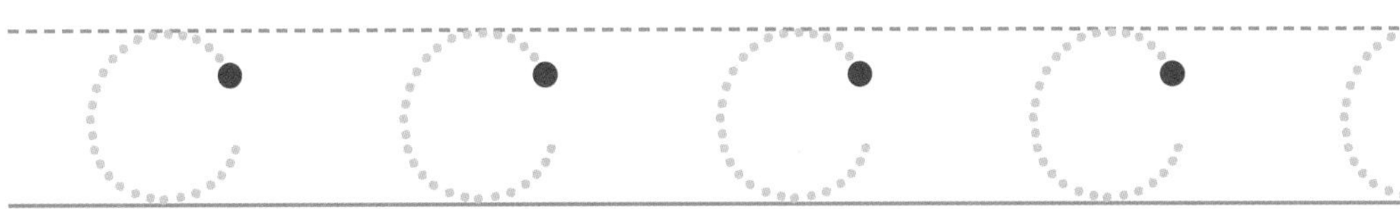

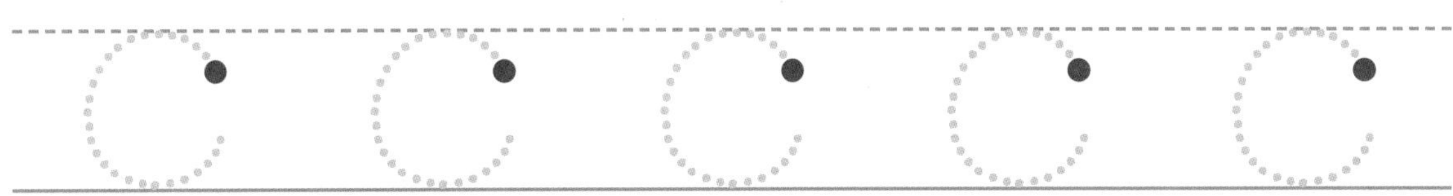

Circle your best letter.

Cc

1 Add **c**. Say the word.

	c___at		___amel
	___oat		___arrot
	___up		___ow
	___ake		___orn

2 Circle every **C**.

C	C	C	A	C
B	O	C	D	G

How many? ___

Circle every **c**.

c	a	o	c	c
b	c	c	a	c

How many? ___

1 Circle the beginning sound.

b m c	m c b	t a i	c b a

a c b	i m t	c t b	t m s

i t b	m b a	t i a	a b c

2 Write the word **cat**.

I finished this lesson online. 	This egg hatched. 	**I know** the letter sound: Cc 	**I can read** 

I am Frogfish!
I have fins.

1 Color things that begin with **f**.

f			
f	5	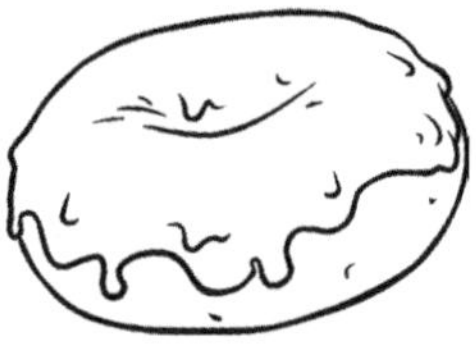	
f	6		

2 Match each letter to a picture.

1 Finish the flowers.

2 Trace.

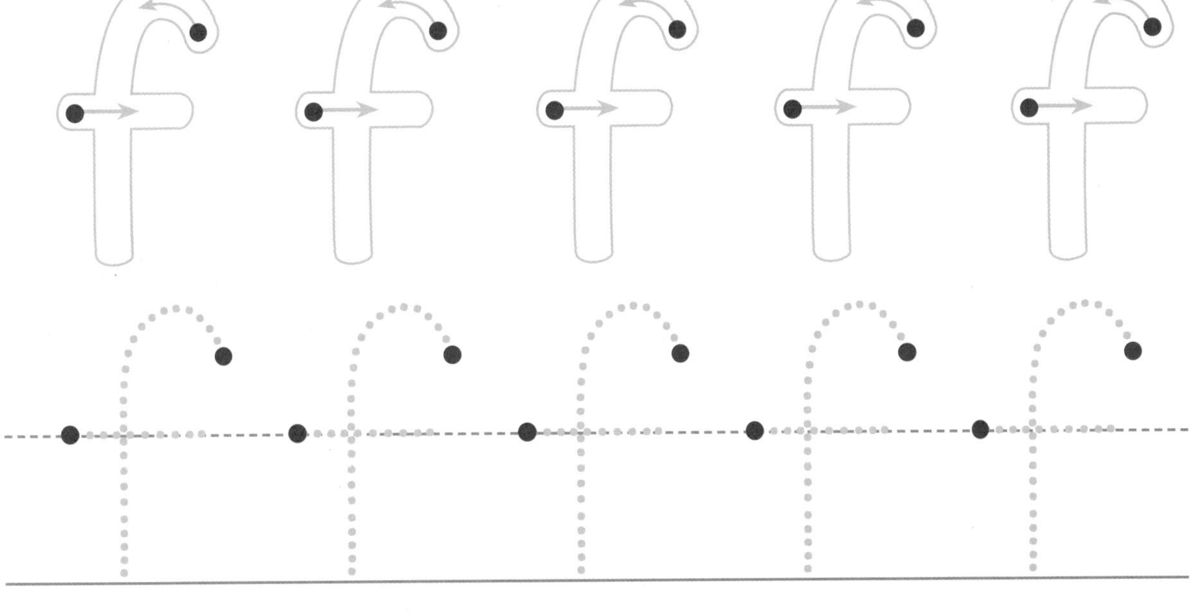

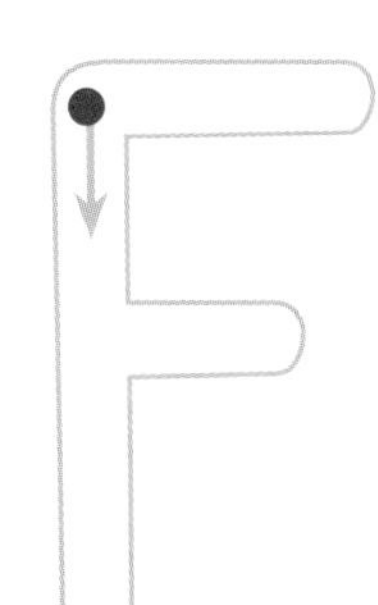

Circle your best letter.

five flowers

1 Add **f**. Say the word.

 f rog	 ____ ish
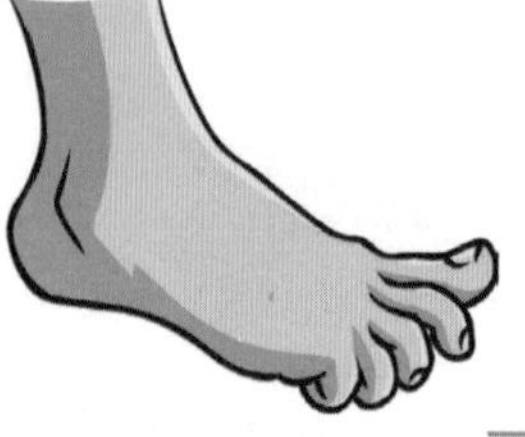 ____ oot	 ____ ly
 ____ lag	 ____ ive
 ____ inger	 ____ ootball

2 Circle every **F**.

F	F	F	F	Z
B	F	C	A	F

How many? ____

Circle every **f**.

f	i	f	f	f
f	j	l	t	f

How many? ____

1 Write the beginning sound.

_ a t

_ a t

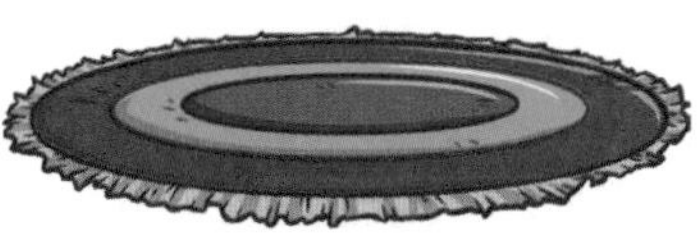

_ a t

_ a t

_ a t

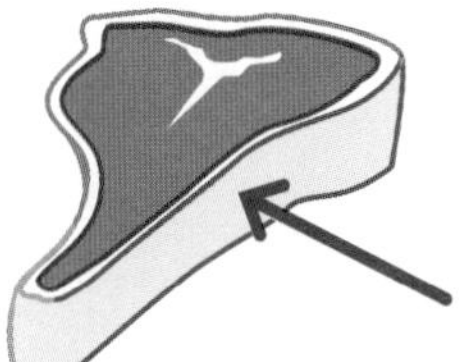

_ a t

2 Complete the word.

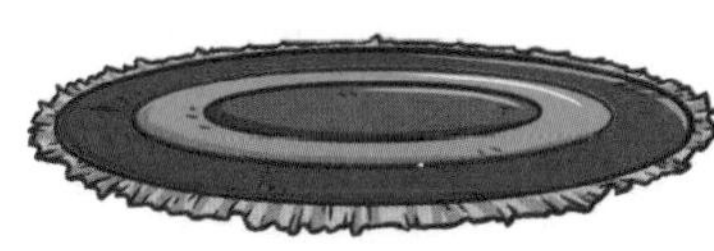

_ a _

_ a _

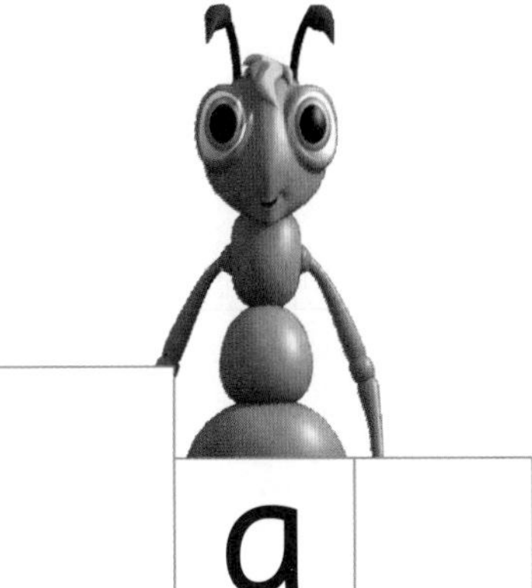

_ a _

I finished this lesson online.	This egg hatched.	I know the letter sound: Ff	I can read

1 Circle the thing in each row that begins with **a**.

Color them.

a			
a			
a			
a			
a			AMBULANCE
a			

1 Complete.

Read	Write	Color
cat		
bat		
Sam		
mat		
fat		

CHALLENGE

How many fruits can you name?
4 Good! 8 Great!! 12 Excellent!!!

1 Complete each sentence with a word from the box.

cat bat Sam

I am a

________________.

I am a

________________.

I am

________________.

I am a fat

________________.

I am

1 Write each word.

I am a

I am a

2 Complete each sentence with one of the words.

I am ________ cat.

I ________ a bat.

________ am a fat cat.

I ________ Sam.

I finished this lesson online.

This egg hatched.

I can read I am a

I can read

1 Trace and color.

a b

c f

i m

s t

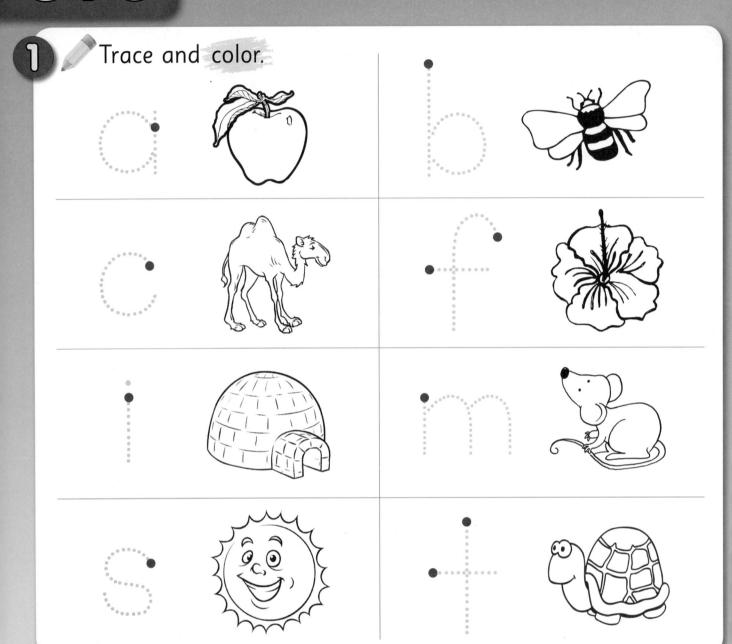

2 Label each picture. Write the word.

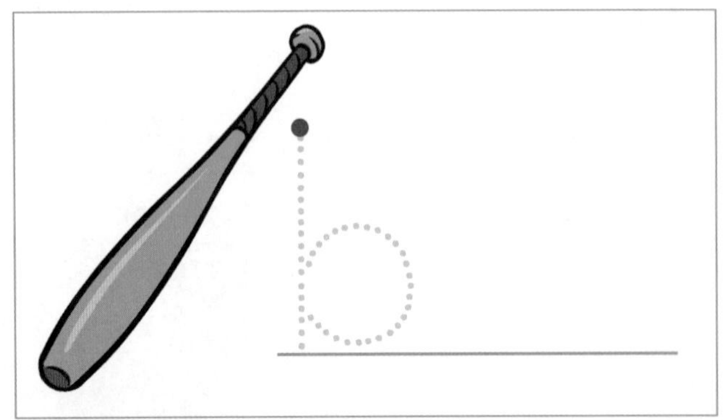

1 Match each picture to its beginning sound.

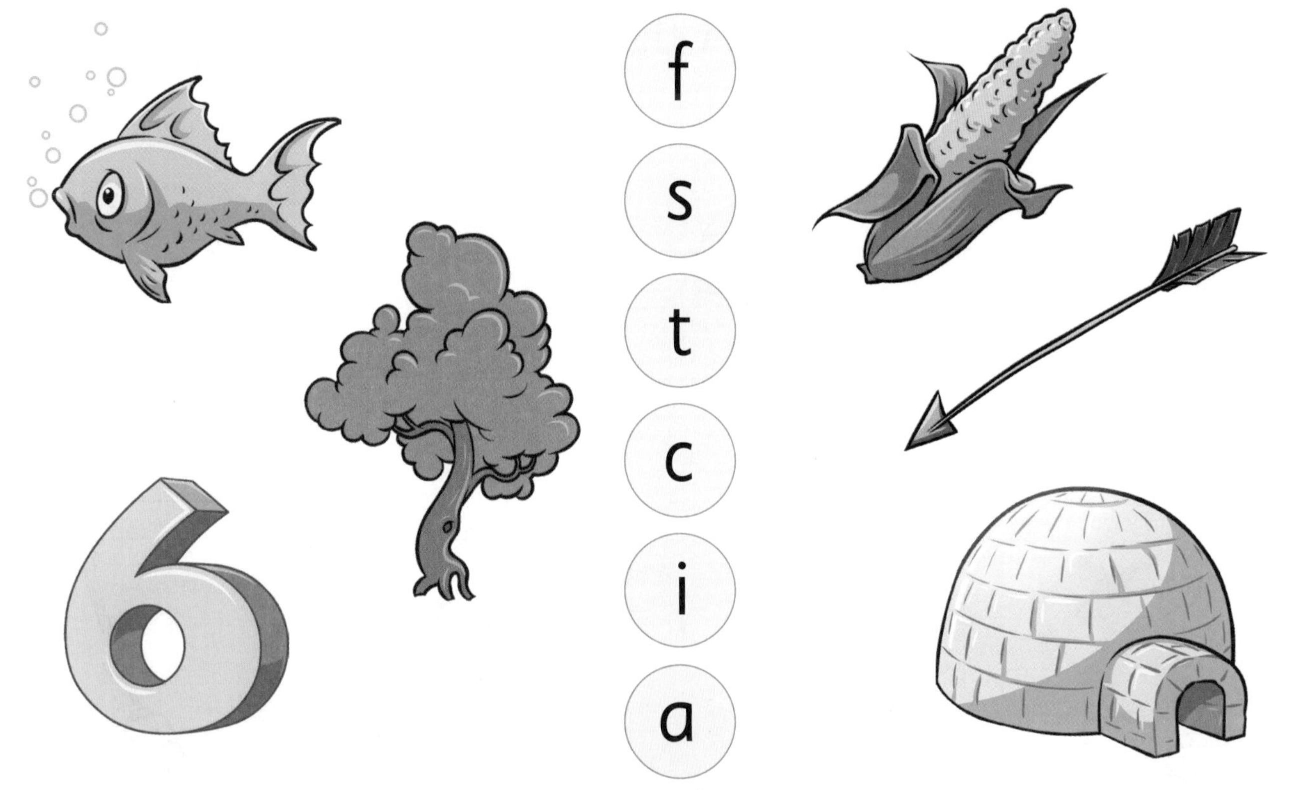

2 What sound does the word begin with? Write the letter.

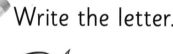

1 Circle the sound you hear at the **end** of the word?

s t	t s	m t	m s

s t	t s	m t	m t

2 Complete the word.

ca____

I am Sa____ .

1 Circle the bubbles that begin with **b**.

2 Color the pictures that rhyme.

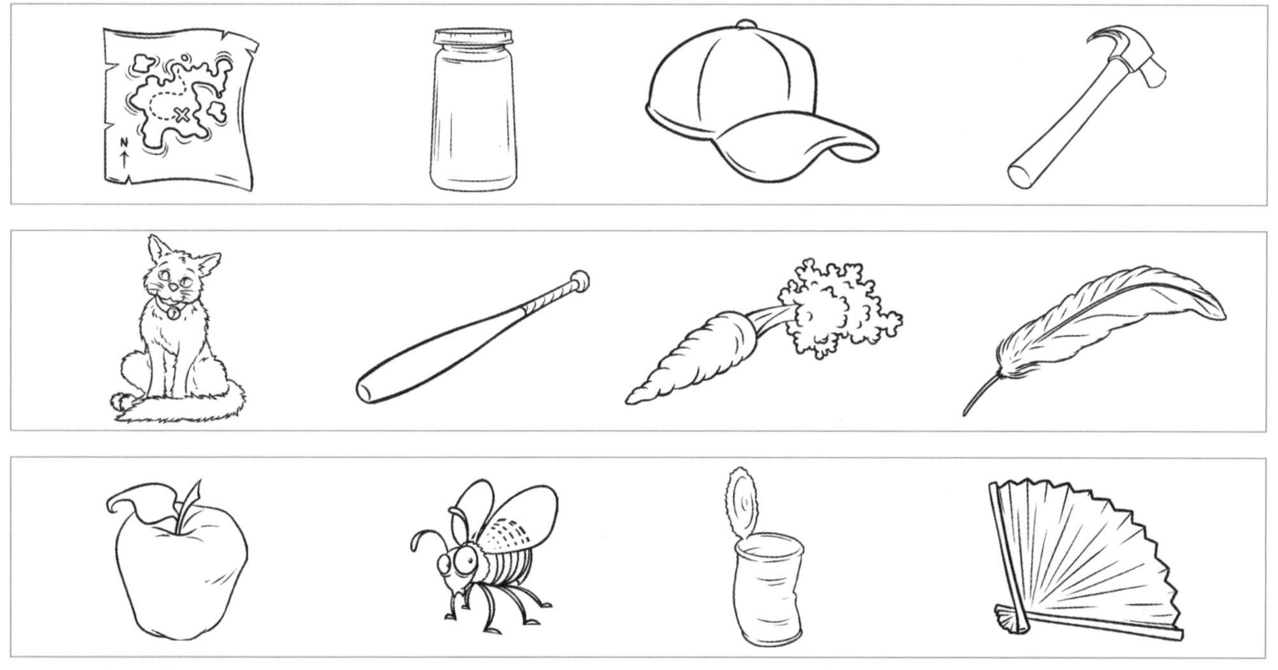

I finished this lesson online.	**This egg hatched.**	**I can read** cat, mat, sat, bat, Sam	**I can read**

Quiz

MAP 1 LESSONS 1 TO 10

1 Write the letter. Color the pictures that begin with the letter.

m				
s				
t				
b				
c				
f				
i				

2 Read the word. Color the picture that matches.

cat			
Sam			
bat	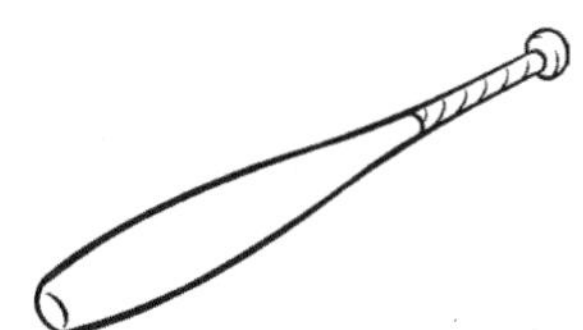		

3 Read each sentence. Join to a picture.

I am a cat.

I am a bat.

I am a fat cat.

YAY!
YOU COMPLETED
MAP 1
YOU CAN:
Say the letter sounds for: **m, s, t, b, c, f**.
Recognize and write the letters: **m, s, t, b, c, f, i, a**.
Read the words: **cat, Sam, bat, I, am**.
Read the sentence: **I am a cat**.
Read a book.

Fun Spot 1

1 Complete the dot-to-dots.

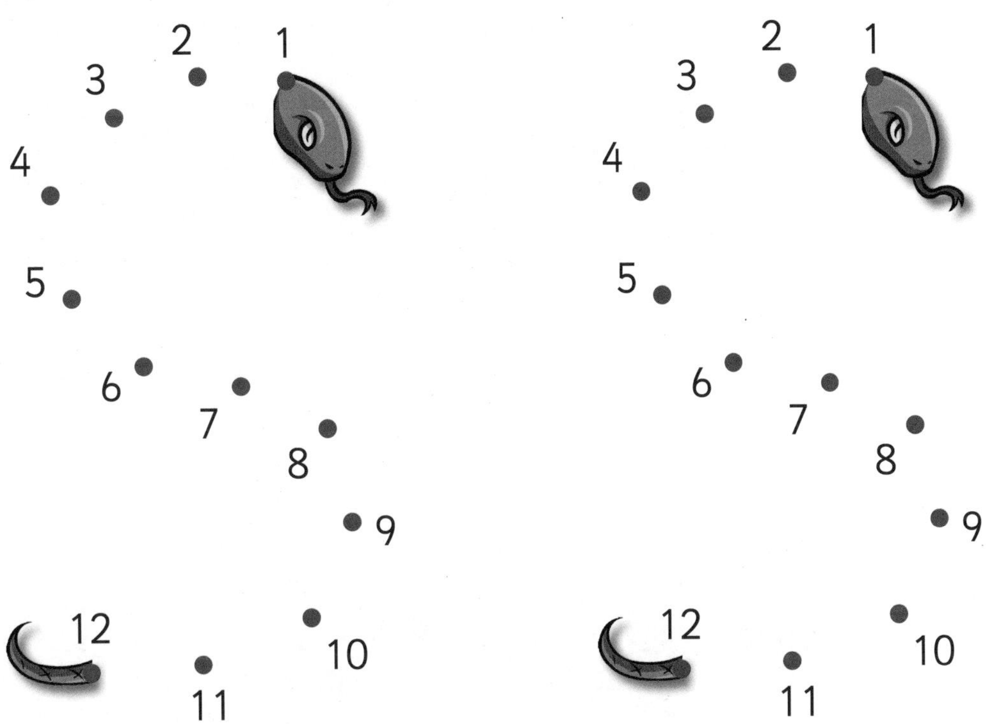

2 Color every **m**.

m	m	m	m	m	m	m	j
m	t	i	m	z	x	m	k
m	s	u	m	b	g	m	h
m	q	o	m	f	c	m	n
m	r	p	m	n	a	m	d
m	w	n	m	r	w	m	v

Find the hidden pictures

Find each drawing in the picture.

Dd
dinosaur
dice
dog
duck
doll

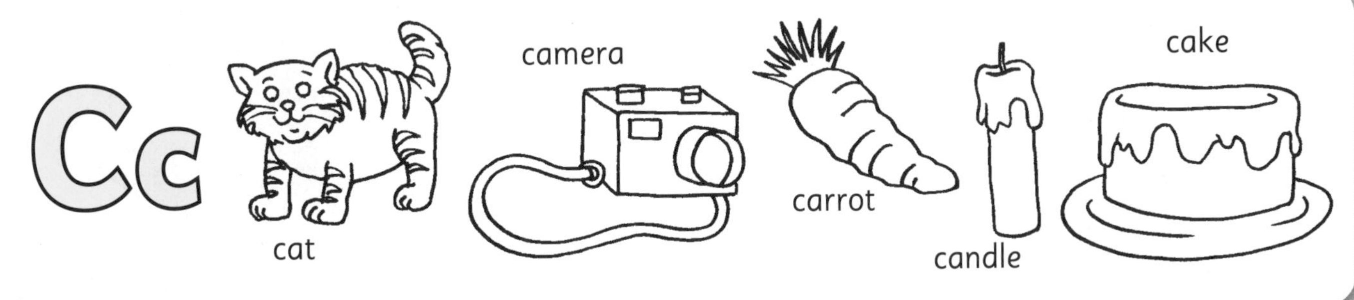
Cc
cat
camera
carrot
candle
cake

N is for Nutty Newt.

1 Color things that begin with **n**.

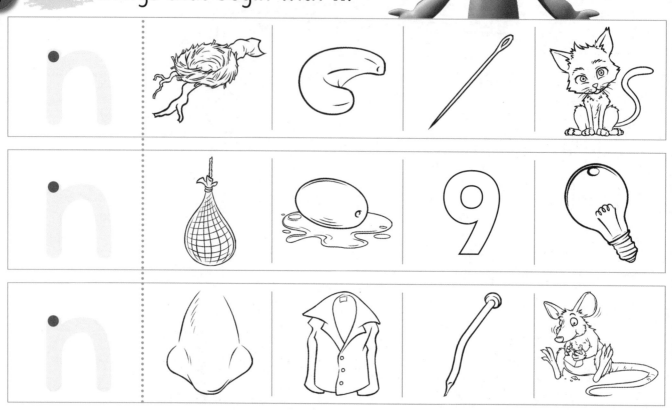

2 Match each letter to a picture.

1 Add **n**. Read the word.

2 Circle every **N**.

N	N	N	Z	T
H	M	J	N	N

How many? ____

Circle every **n**.

n	n	h	n	n
a	n	m	o	r

How many? ____

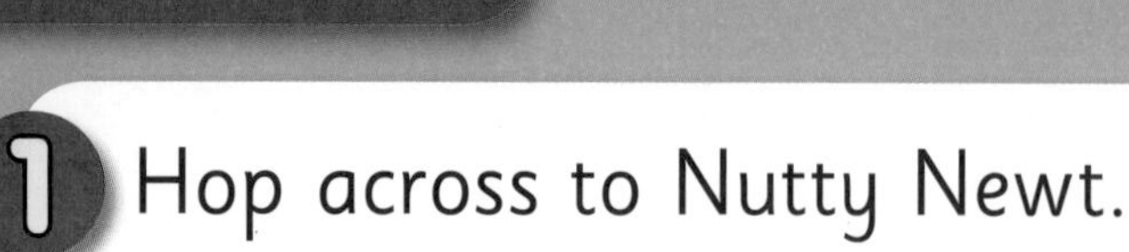

1 Hop across to Nutty Newt.

2 Trace and write.

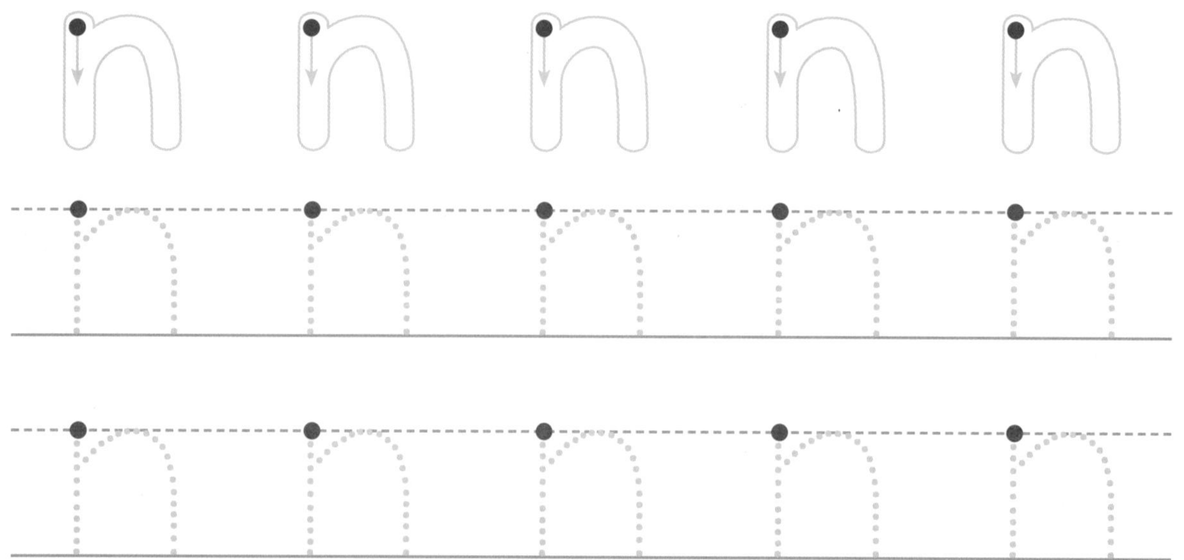

3 Trace over the horse's door.

4 Trace and write.

1 Finish the sentences.

I am a

I am a

2 Circle the beginning sound.

n c	i t	c s	b n

f m	s m	a n	f b

I finished this lesson online.	This egg hatched.	I know the letter sound: Nn	I can read

Peek a boo!
I'm Pinkipoo.

1 Color the pictures that start with **p**.

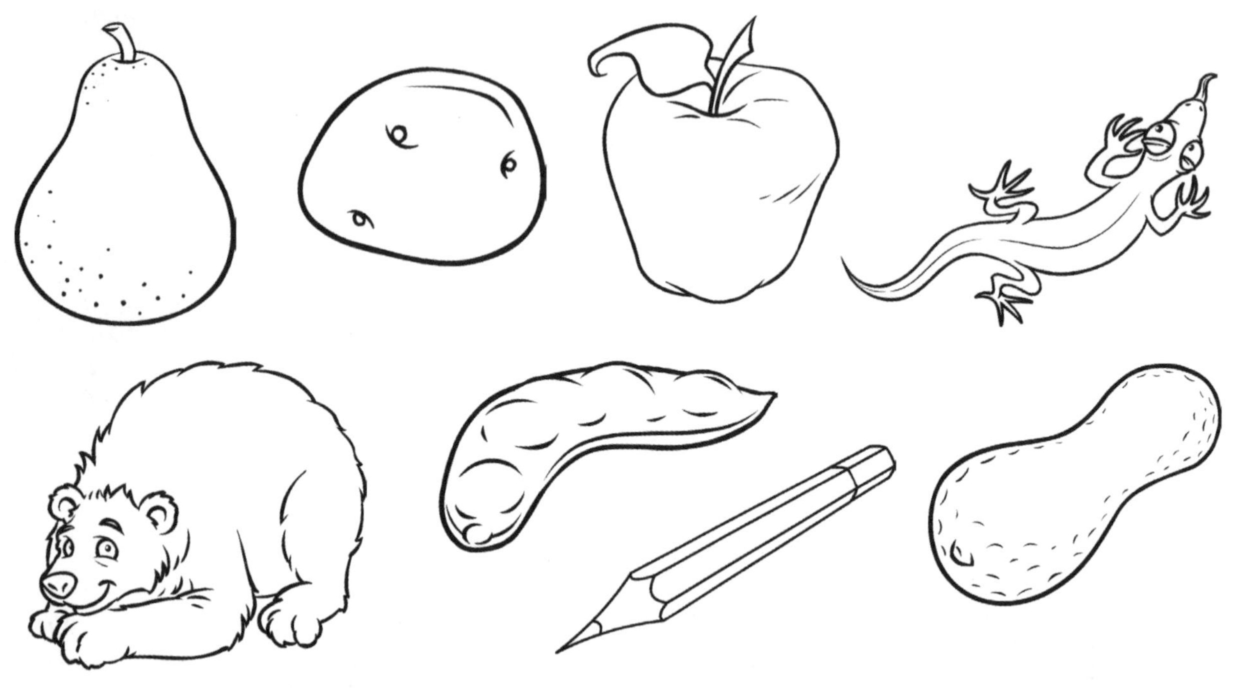

2 Match each letter to a picture.

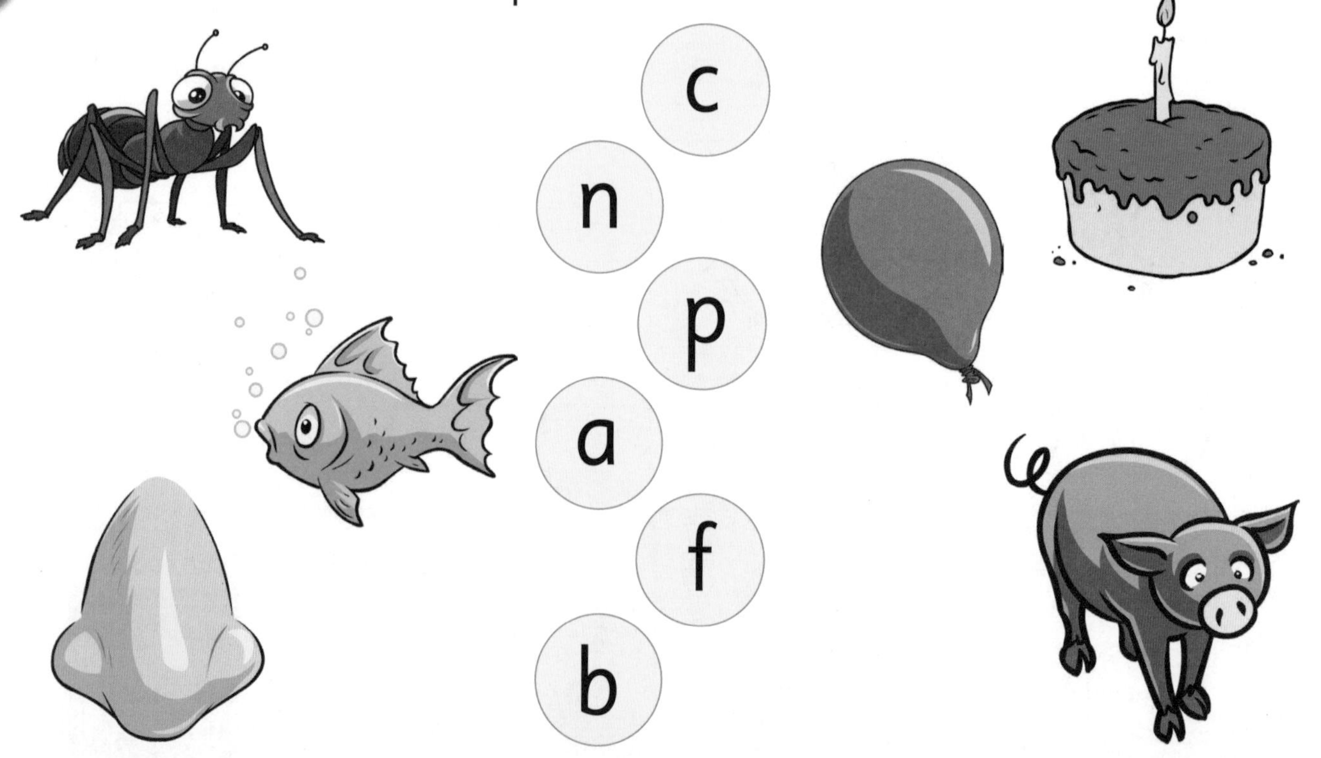

1 Trace and write.

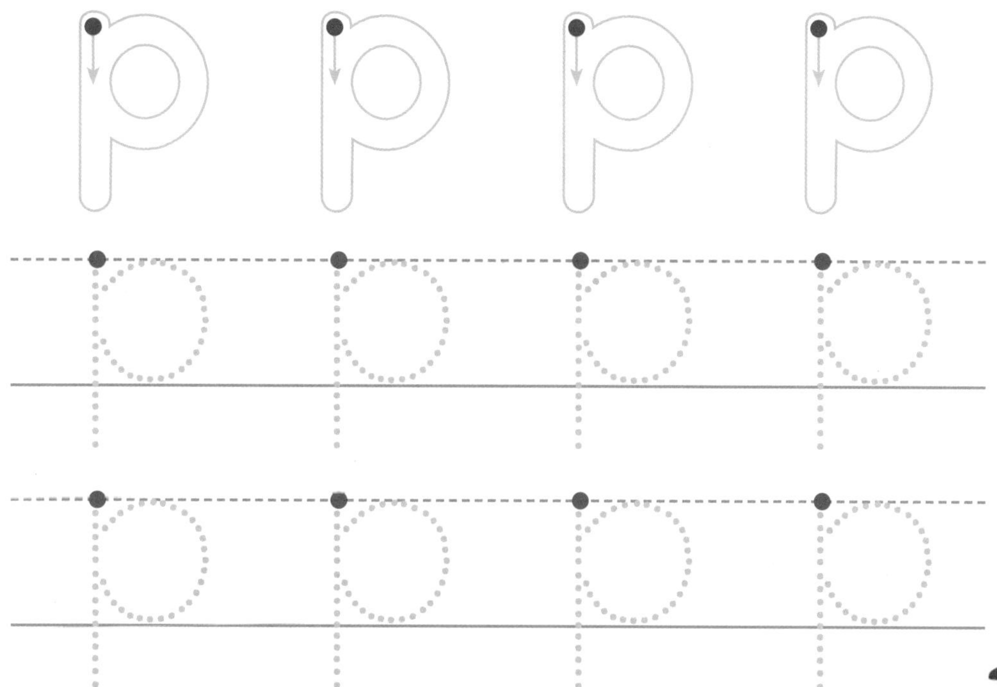

2 Complete each pair of scissors.

3 Trace and write.

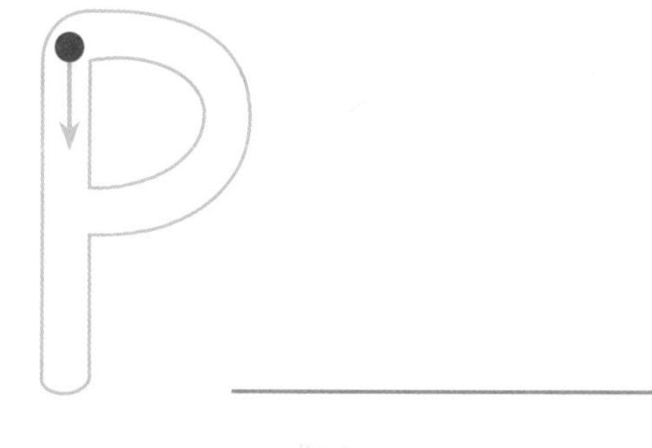

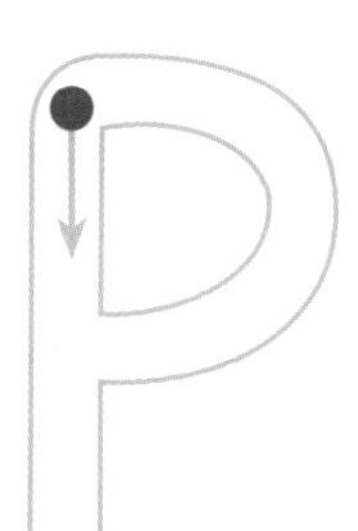

Circle your best letter.

1 Add **p**. Say the word.

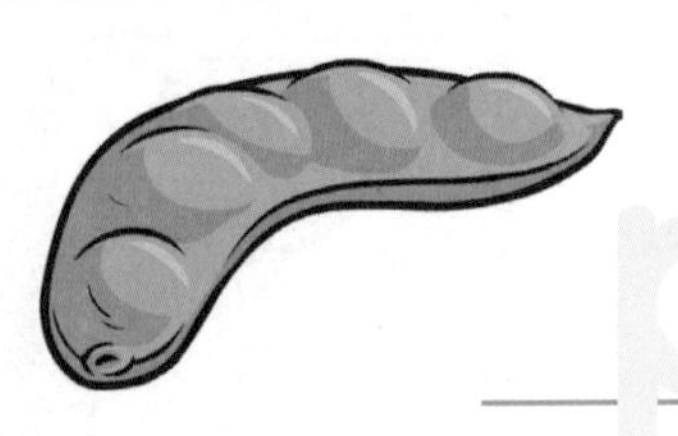 p eas	 ___ en
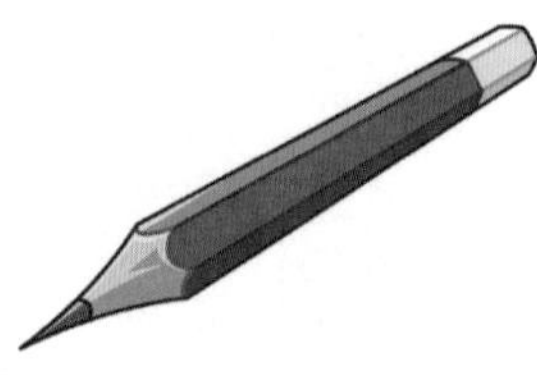 ___ encil	 ___ enguin
ca ___ 	cu ___ 
mo ___ 	ma ___ 

2 Circle every **P**. / Circle every **p**.

P	D 	P	P 	B
P	B 	P 	D 	P 

How many? ___

p	p 	p 	b 	g
j	b 	p 	a 	p 

How many? ___

1 Circle the letter each picture **starts** with.

p c	n m	c n	n p

c b	p g	m p	n m

2 Color the pictures that **end** with **p**.

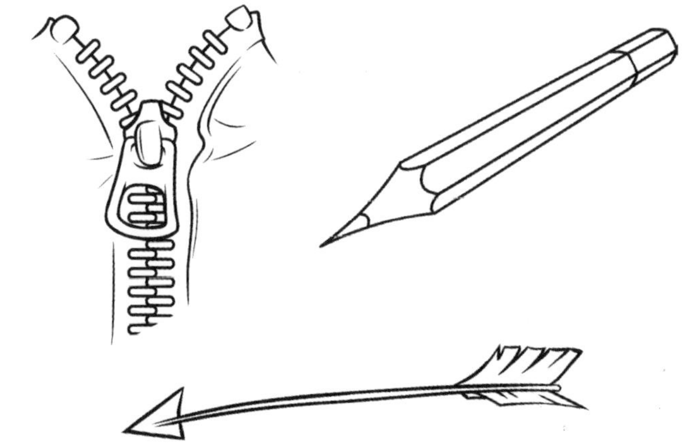
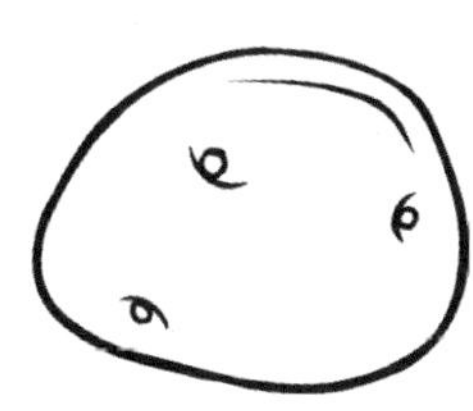

I finished this lesson online. 	**This egg hatched.** 	**I know** the letter sound: Pp 	**I can read** 

1 Read the word. Color the picture that matches.

cap			
map			
tap			
nap			

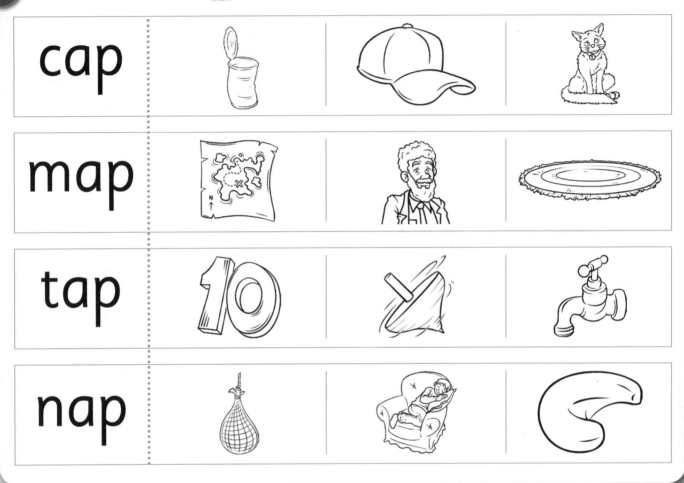

2 Finish the **ap** words.

1 Match each word to a picture.

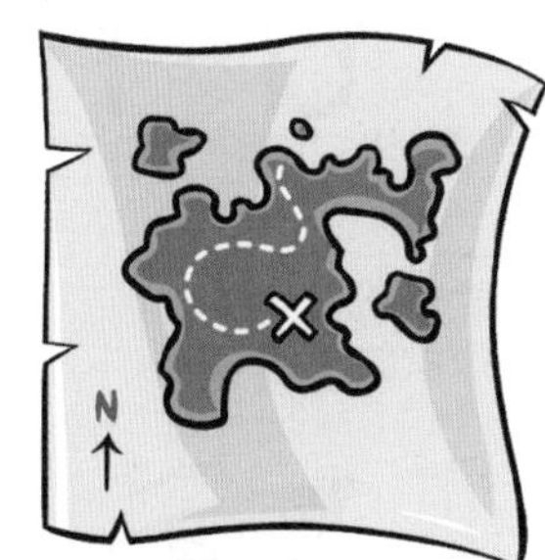

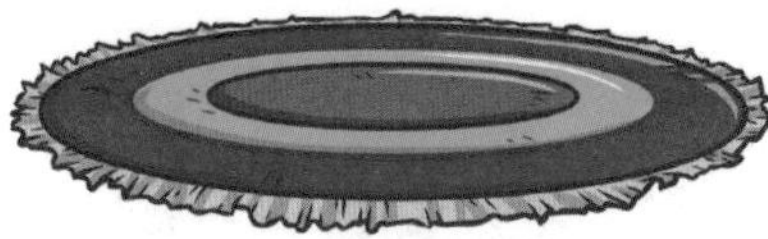

ant

bee

cap

bat

mat

tap

map

sat

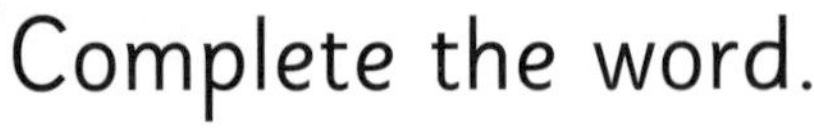

1 Complete the word.

a t

a n

a p

a n

a n

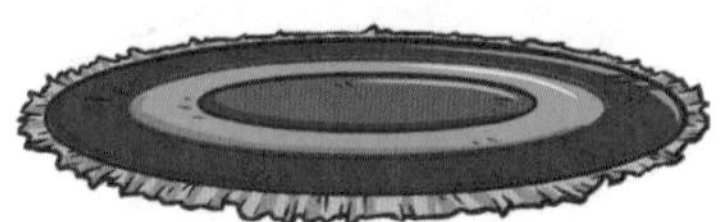

a t

a t

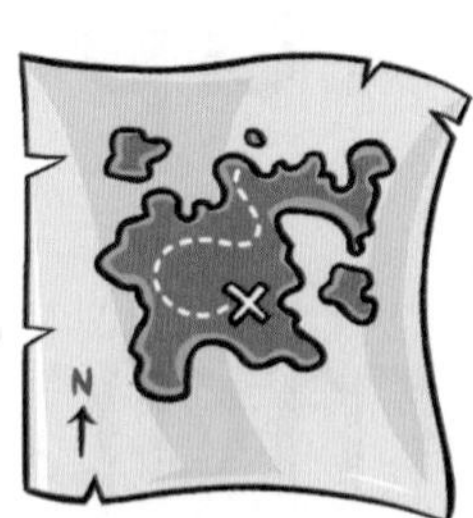

a p

a p

1 Complete each sentence with a word from the box.

has a am cat

Sam pats a ________ .

I ________ a bat.

Sam pats ______ fat cat.

Sam ________ a rat.

I finished this lesson online.	This egg hatched.	I can read cap, map, tap	I can read

Hello, I'm Horse Hee Heepo.

1 Circle the jigsaw parts that begin with **h**.

2 Circle the things in each row that begin with **h**. Color them.

Hh

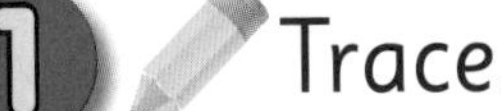

1 Trace.

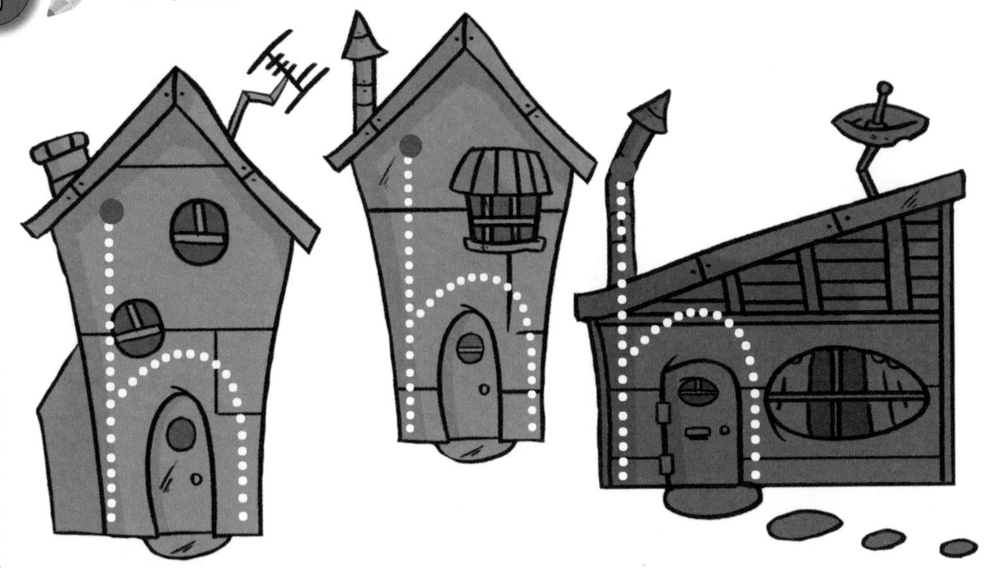

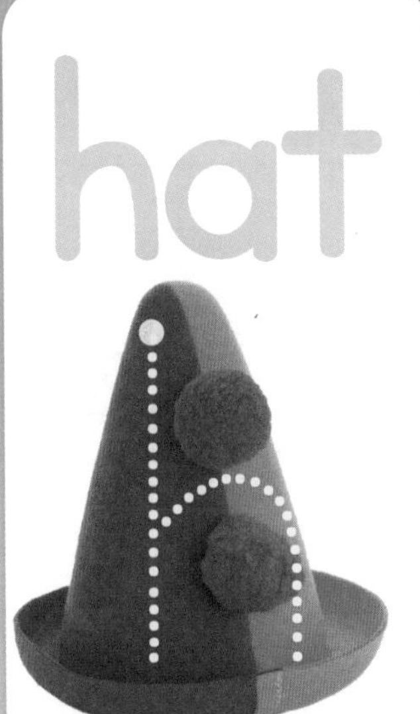
hat

2 Trace and write.

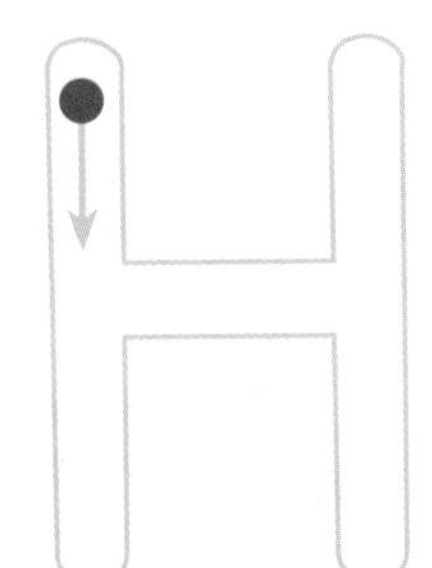
Circle your best letter.

1 Add **h**. Say the word.

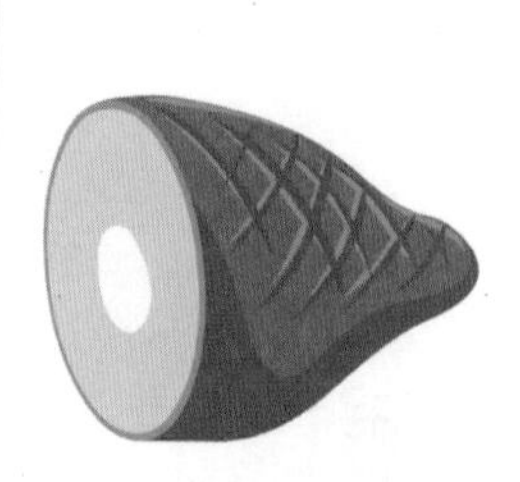 h____ am	 ____ en
 ____ at	 ____ ippo
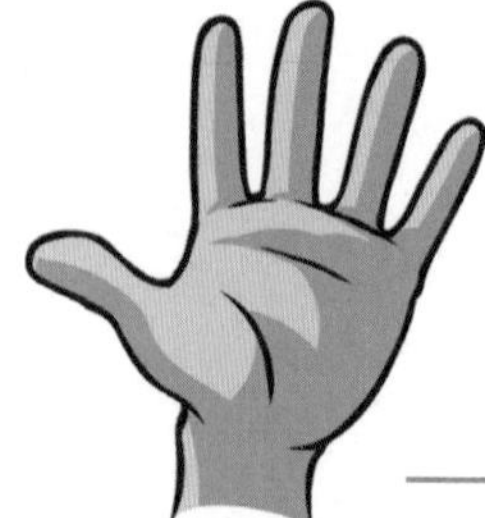 ____ and	 ____ ook
 ____ ut	 ____ orse

2 Draw hats on heads.

1 Match each letter to a picture.

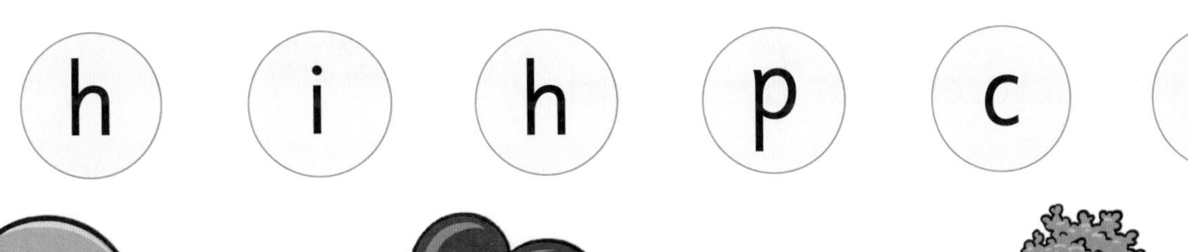

2 Circle every **H**. Circle every **h**.

H	H	H	N	T
I	J	H	H	H

How many? ____

h	m	h	t	h
h	n	o	h	y

How many? ____

3 Trace and write.

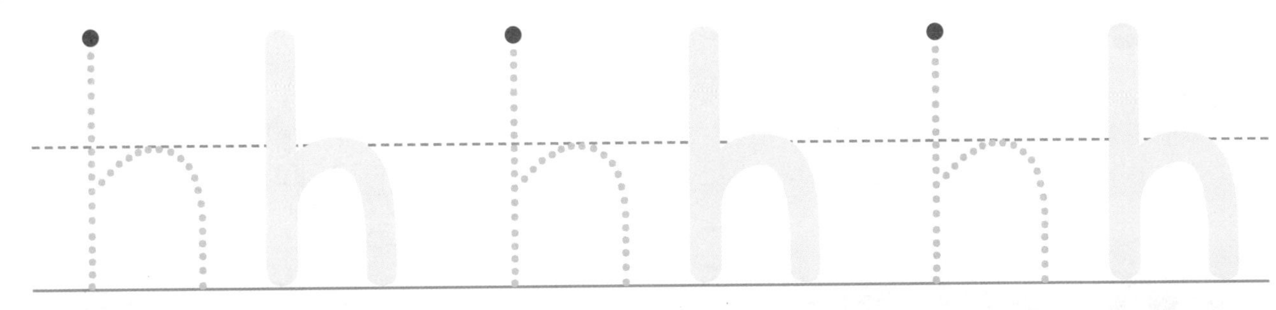

I finished this lesson online.	This egg hatched.	**I know** the letter sound: Hh	**I can read**

R is for Red Rabbit

1. Color the pictures that begin with **r**.

2. Match each letter to a picture.

Rr

1 Run over to the **r** food.

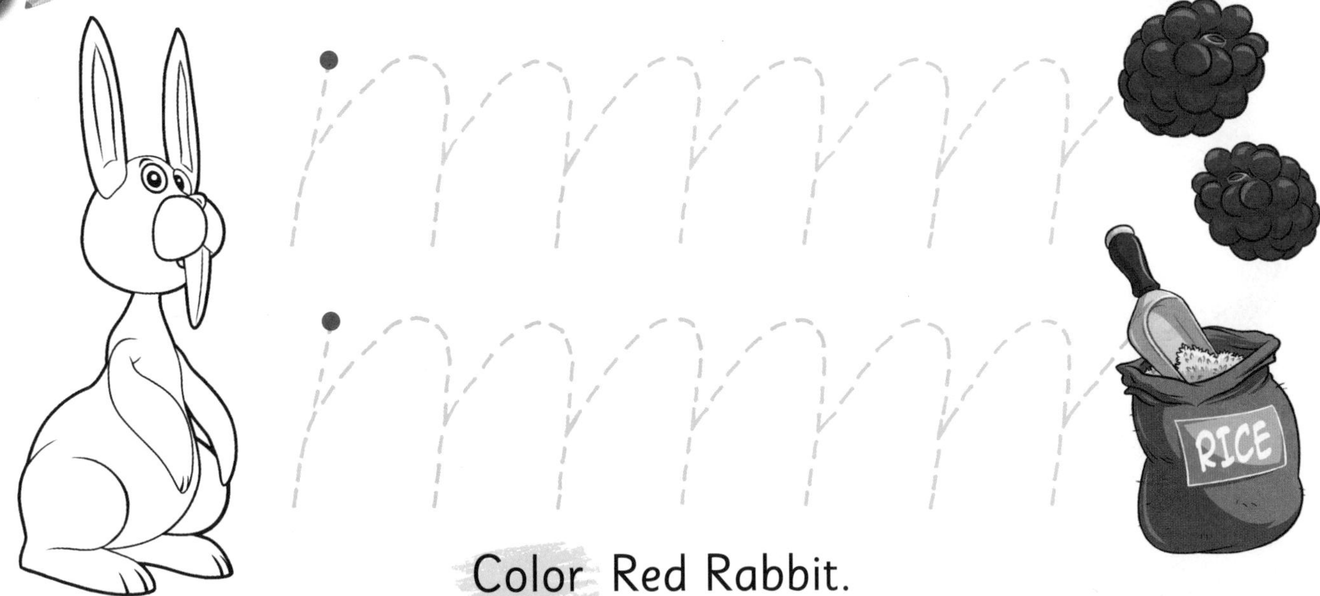

Color Red Rabbit.

2 Trace and write.

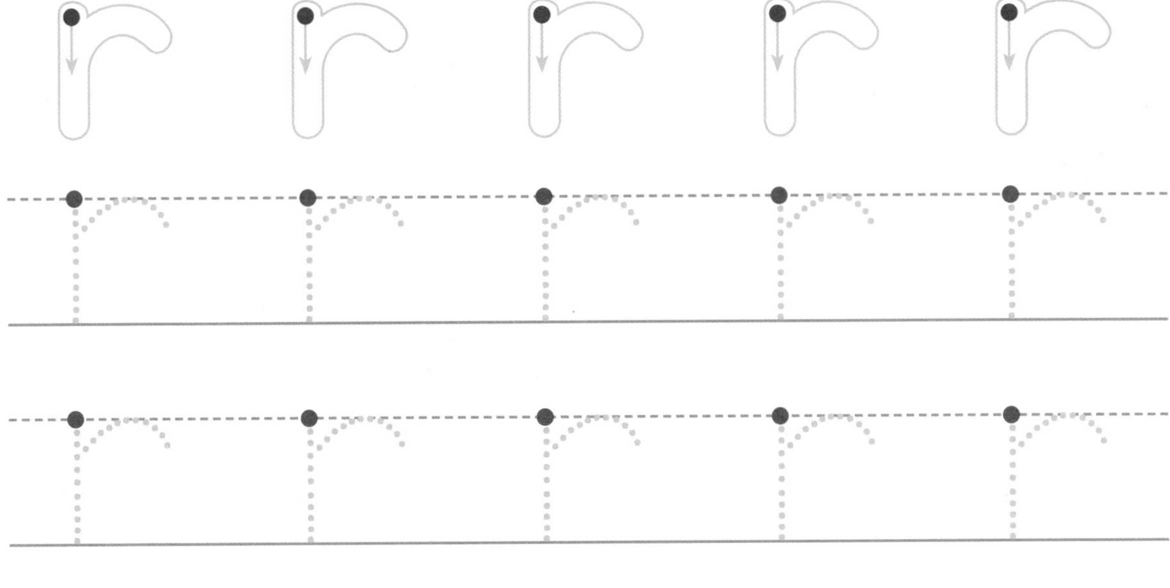

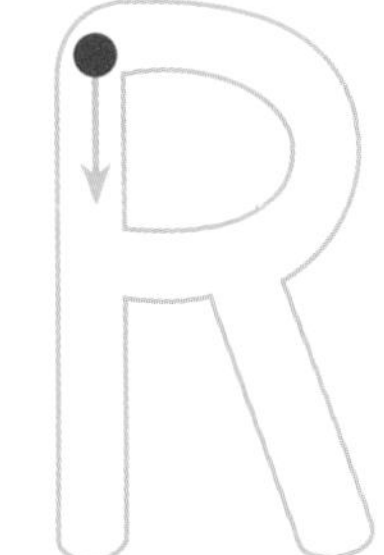

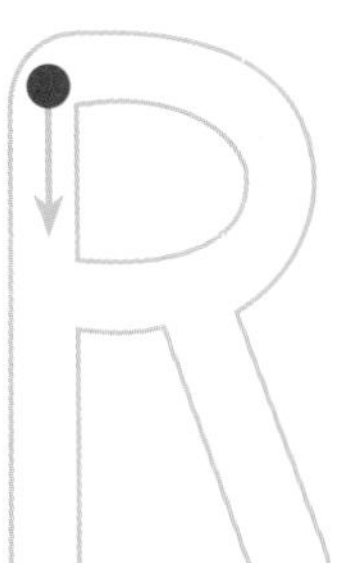

Circle your best letter.

1 Add **r**. Say the word.

 r ing	 ___obot
 ___abbit	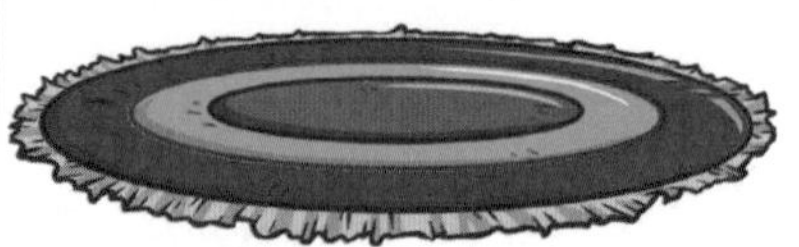 ___ug
 ___ose	 ___at
 ___ake	 ___ope

2 Draw a rainbow.

Rr

1 Trace and write.

2 Circle every R.

R	P	A	B	R
T	R	R	I	A

How many? ____

Circle every r.

r	r	r	g	m
t	i	n	r	r

How many? ____

3 Circle the beginning sound.

r s	p r	t r	r f

I finished this lesson online.	This egg hatched.	I know the letter sound: Rr	I can read

can

1 Make a rainbow word.

2 Read it 3 times.

Sam can bat.

3 Find **can**.

can	at	can	can	ath
cat	in	can	cit	can
an	to	cat	can	atc

4 Write **can**.

can can can

5 Complete the sentence.

A man can

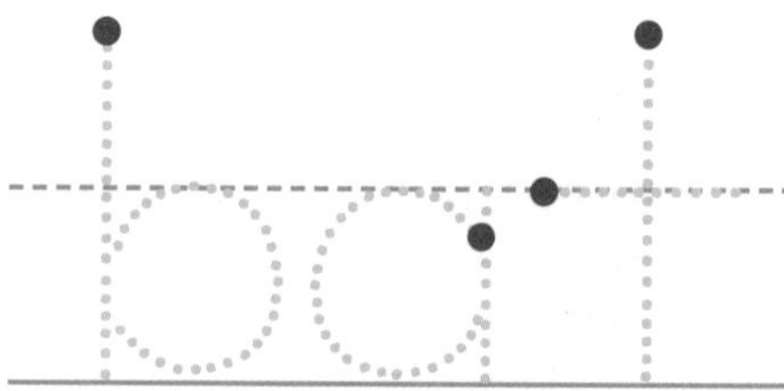

1 Complete.

Read	Write	Color
can		
pan		
ran		
man		
fan		

CHALLENGE

How many colors can you name?
4 Good! 8 Great!! 10 Excellent!!!

1 Color the rhyming words.

2 Write the word.

1 Circle the **beginning** sound.

		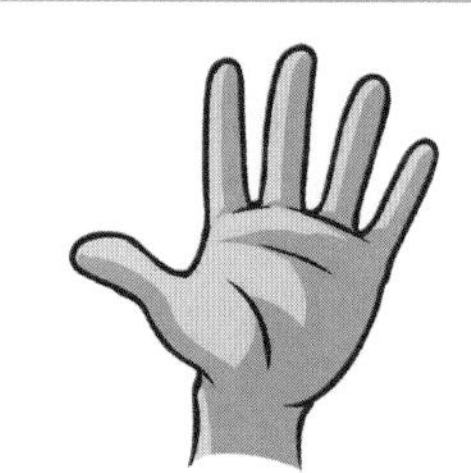	
t m	s r	h b	t f

a p	b r	v s	p c

2 Finish the **an** words.

 ____an	 ____an
 ____an	 ____an

I finished this lesson online. 	**This egg hatched.** 	**I can read** man, cat, bat, rat 	**I can read** 

Zz

Say hello to Zebstar.

1 Color the pictures that start with **z**.

1 Trace Happy Nap's snores.

2 Trace and write.

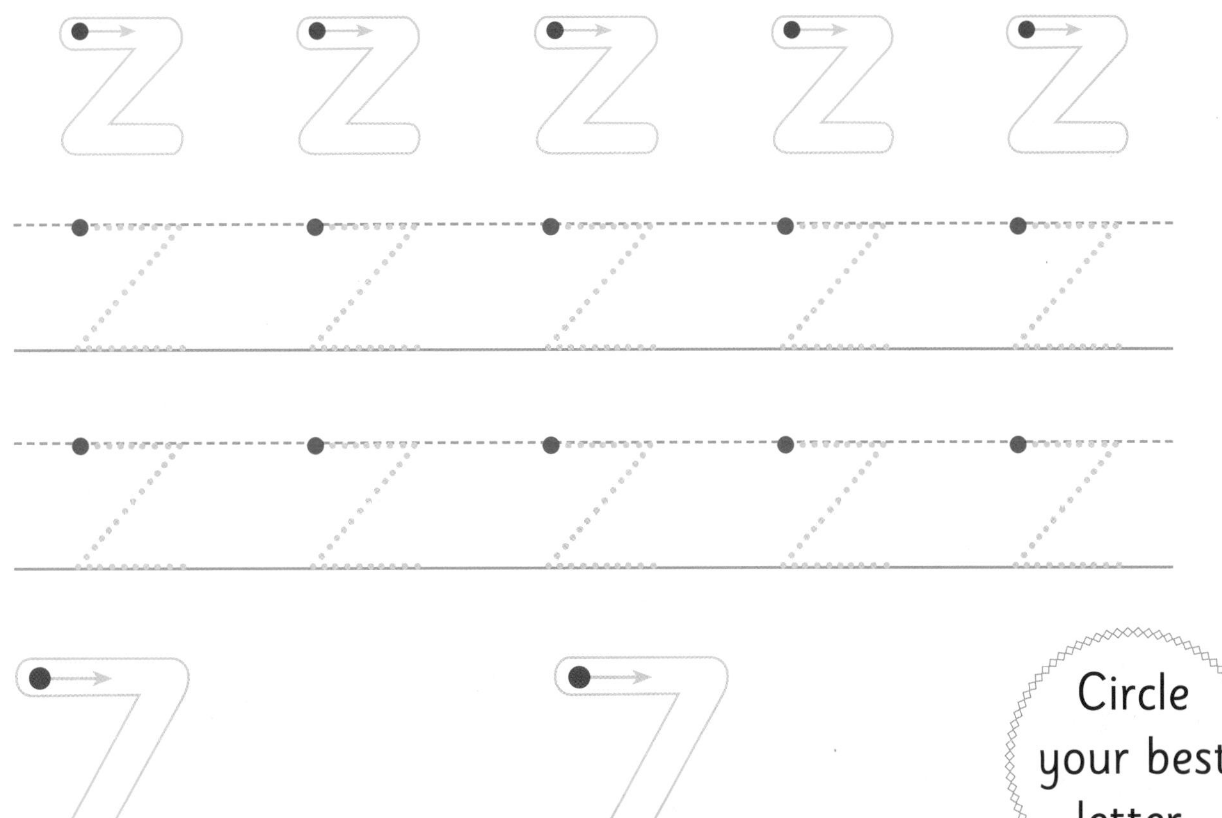

Circle your best letter.

1 Add **z**. Say the word.

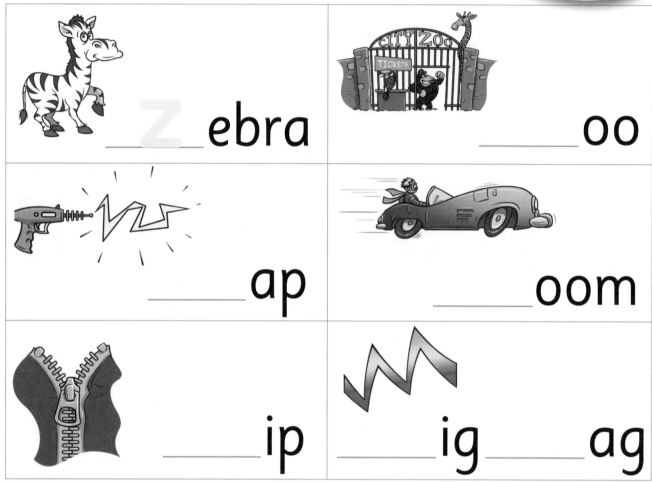

z ebra	____ oo
____ ap	____ oom
____ ip	____ ig ____ ag

2 Draw some **zzz** on the sleeping zoo.

1 Trace.

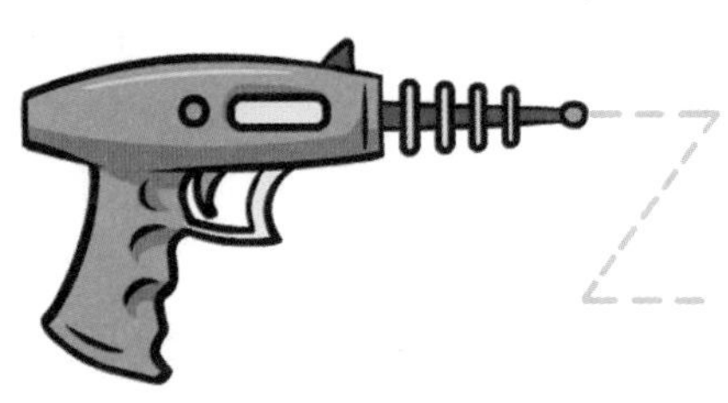

zap

2 Circle every **Z**.

Z	Z	S	Z	P
N	M	Z	I	Z

How many? ____

Circle every **z**.

z	m	z	t	s
z	p	s	z	z

How many? ____

3 Match each letter to a picture.

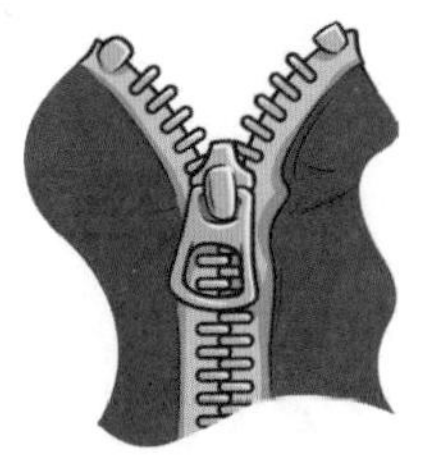

I finished this lesson online.	This egg hatched.	I know the letter sound: Zz	I can read

1 Color the eggs that begin with **e**.

2 Add **e** and say the word.

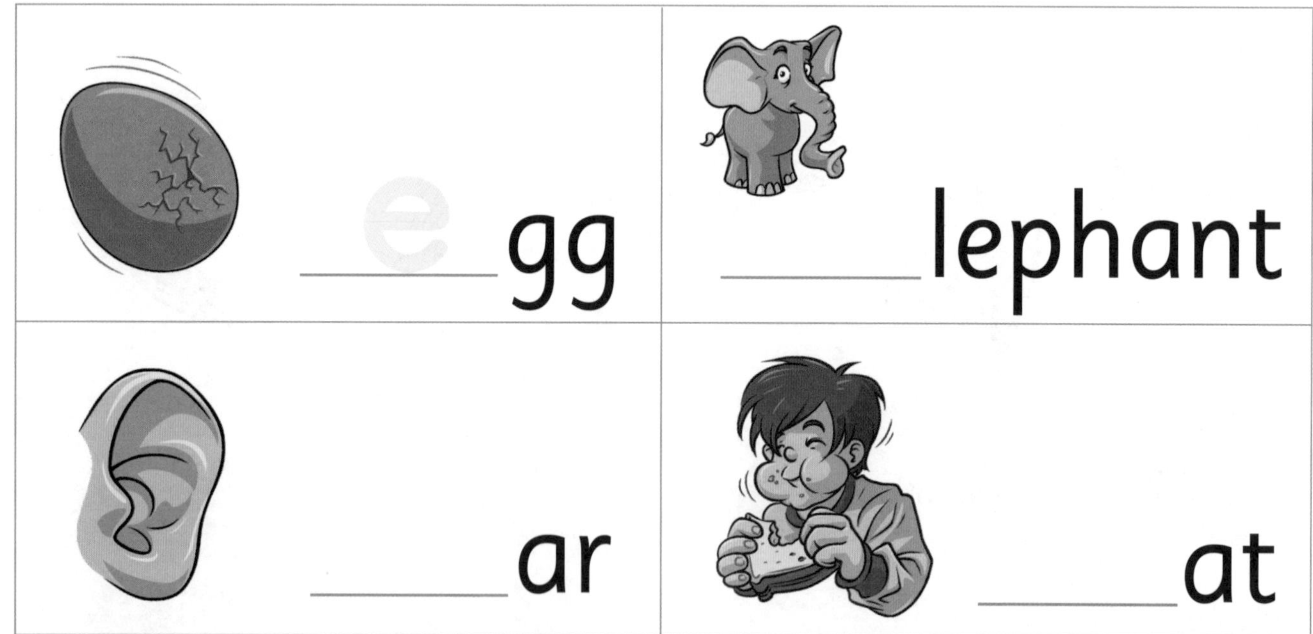

1 Complete the ladders.

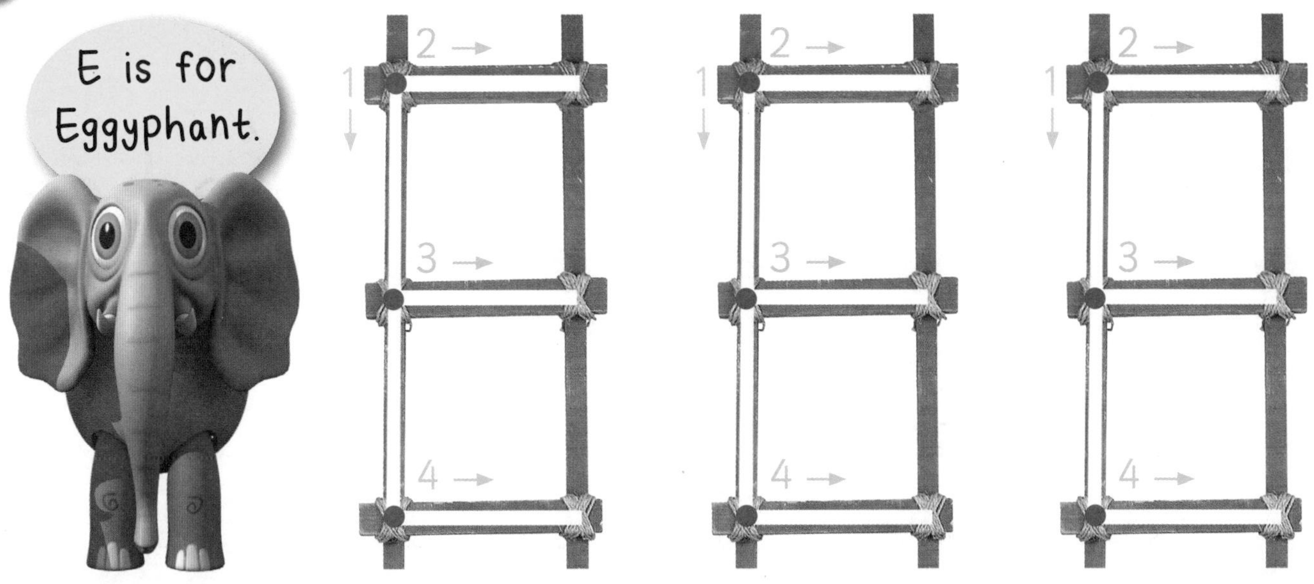
E is for Eggyphant.
2 →
1
3 →
4 →

2 Trace and write.

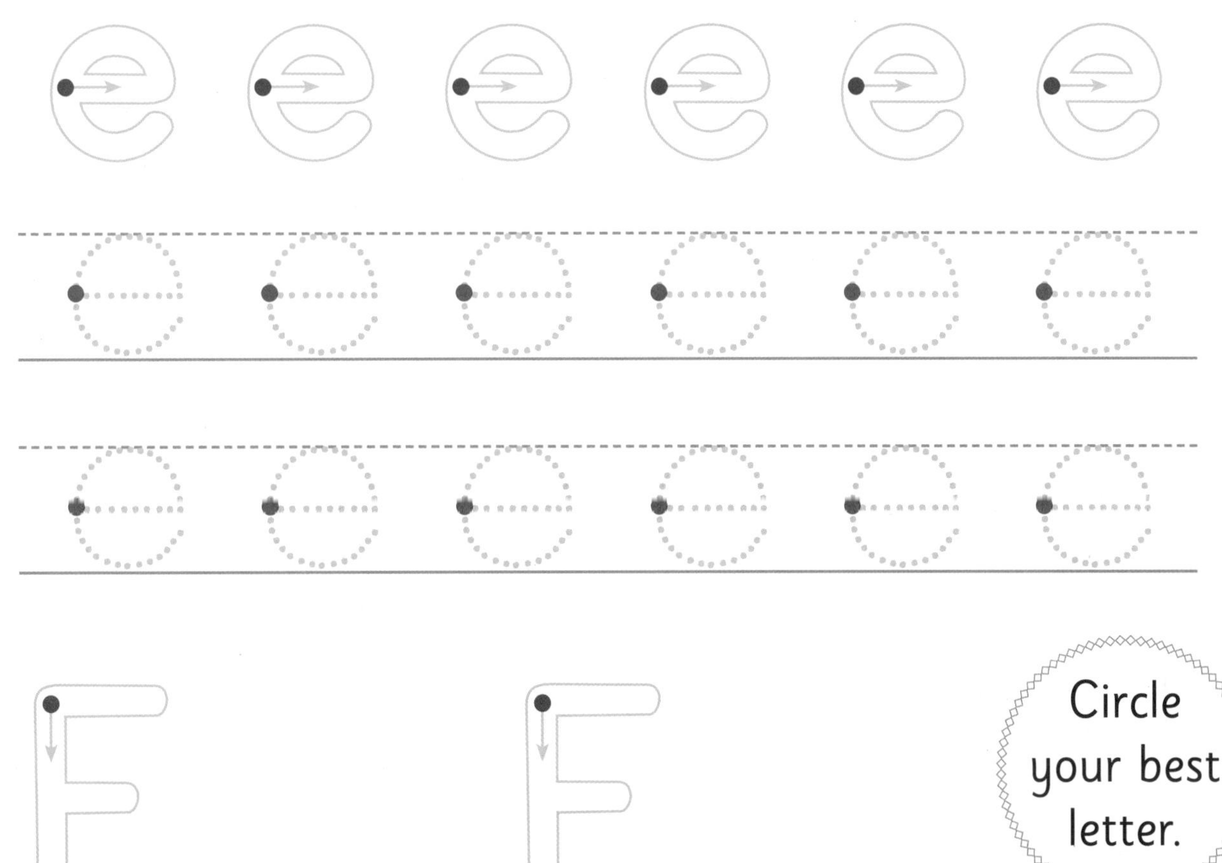
Circle your best letter.

see

1 Make a rainbow word.

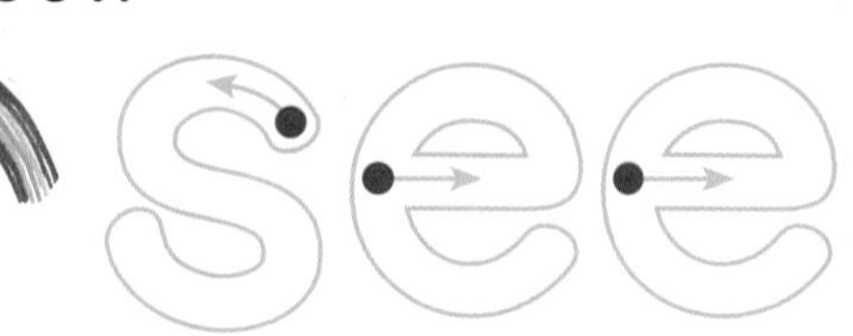

2 Read it 3 times.

See the bee.

3 Find **see**.

see	see	as	the	see
so	tree	**bee**	*is*	**as**
as	**set**	see	sat	see

4 Write **see**.

see see see

5 Draw:

The bee can see the tree.

Ee

1. Add **ee** and read the word.

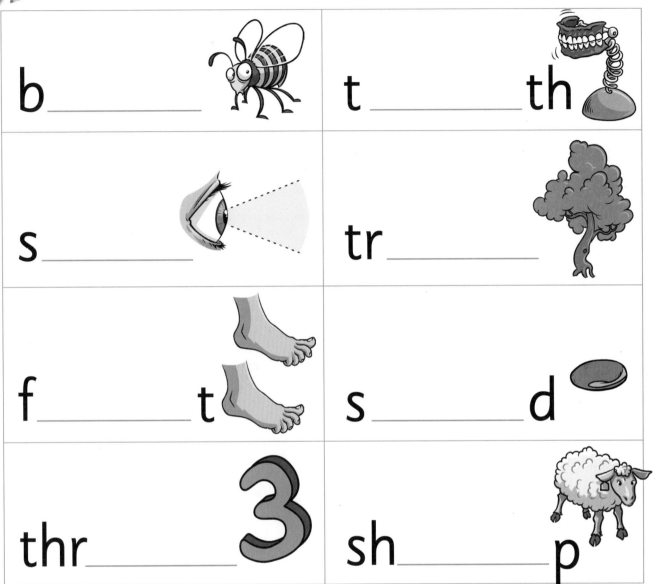

b ______	t ______ th
s ______	tr ______
f ______ t	s ______ d
thr ______	sh ______ p

2. Draw more curls.

I finished this lesson online.	This egg hatched.	I know the letter sound: Ee I can read bee, tree, see	I can read

the

1 Make a rainbow word.

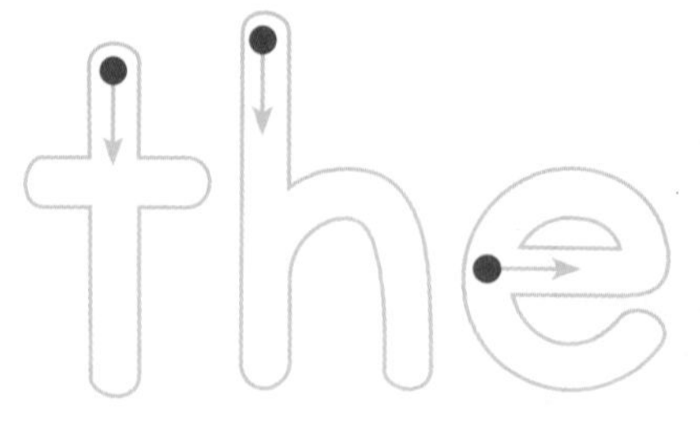

2 Read it 3 times.

the cat
the bat
the man

3 Find (**the**).

see	the	it	het	the
the	eth	**hat**	*the*	**in**
am	**hte**	am	tet	at

4 Write **the**.

the the the

5 Draw:

The cat can see the hat.

the

1 Write the matching word. Use one of these.

cat hat pan man

the

1 Use **the** or **see** to finish the sentences.

I can ________ the cat.

I can see ________ hat.

I can ________ ________ bee.

2 Color **the** in green and **see** in brown.

can	can	the	the	the	the	am	am
can	the	the	the	the	the	the	am
can	the	the	the	the	the	the	am
am	am	the	the	the	the	am	am
am	am	am	see	see	can	can	can
at	can	can	see	see	at	can	can
at	can	can	see	see	at	at	at
at	can	see	see	see	see	at	at

I can see the ________ .

1 Finish the words.

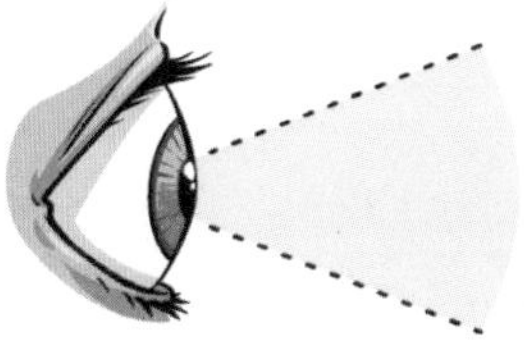

s ______	t ______
f ______	h ______
b ______	m ______
p ______	S ______

I finished this lesson online.	This egg hatched.	I can read hat, cat, man, pan	I can read

1 Trace each letter. Match to a picture that starts with that letter.

2 Color the letters you know.

a	b	c	d	e	f	g	h	i
j	k	l	m	n	o	p	q	r
s	t	u	v	w	x	y	z	★

1 Choose the right ending for the sentence.
Cross out the wrong one. Read each sentence.

Can you see

the 3 bats?

the 4 bees?

Can you see

the 5 cats?

the 5 bees?

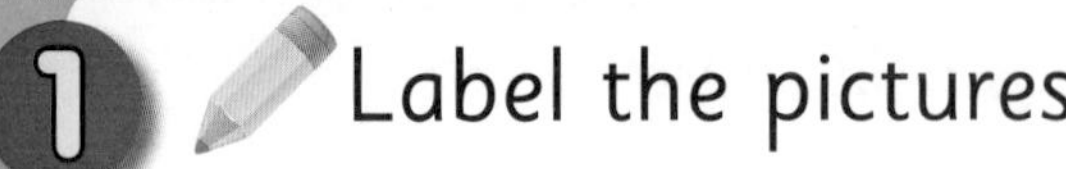

1 Label the pictures.

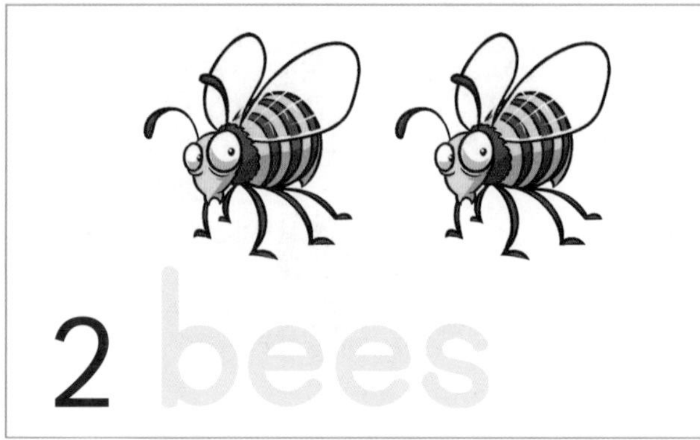

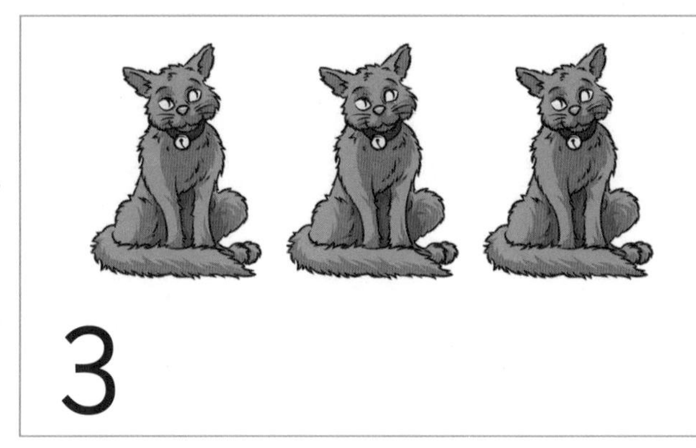

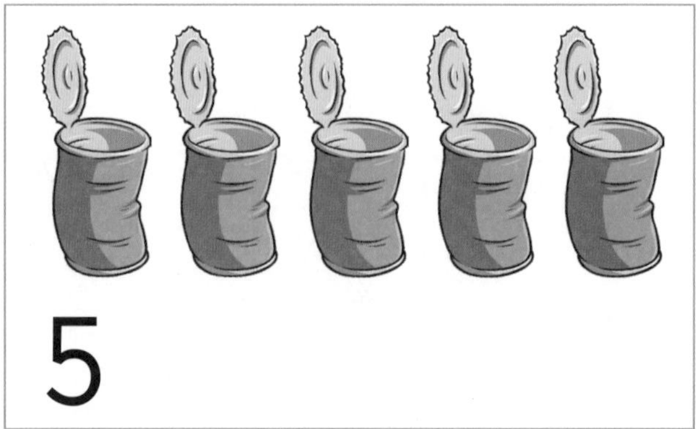

Review

Read.

See the cat

I can see the cat.
The cat is fat.
The cat has a hat.

Circle the correct answer. Write the word on the line.

1 I can see the ________ .

a dog b cat c rat

2 The cat is ________ .

a sad b big c fat

3 The cat has a ________ .

a mat b hat c ball

I finished this lesson online.

This egg hatched.

I can read cats, hats, bats, bees

I can read

1 Write the letter. Color the pictures that begin with the letter.

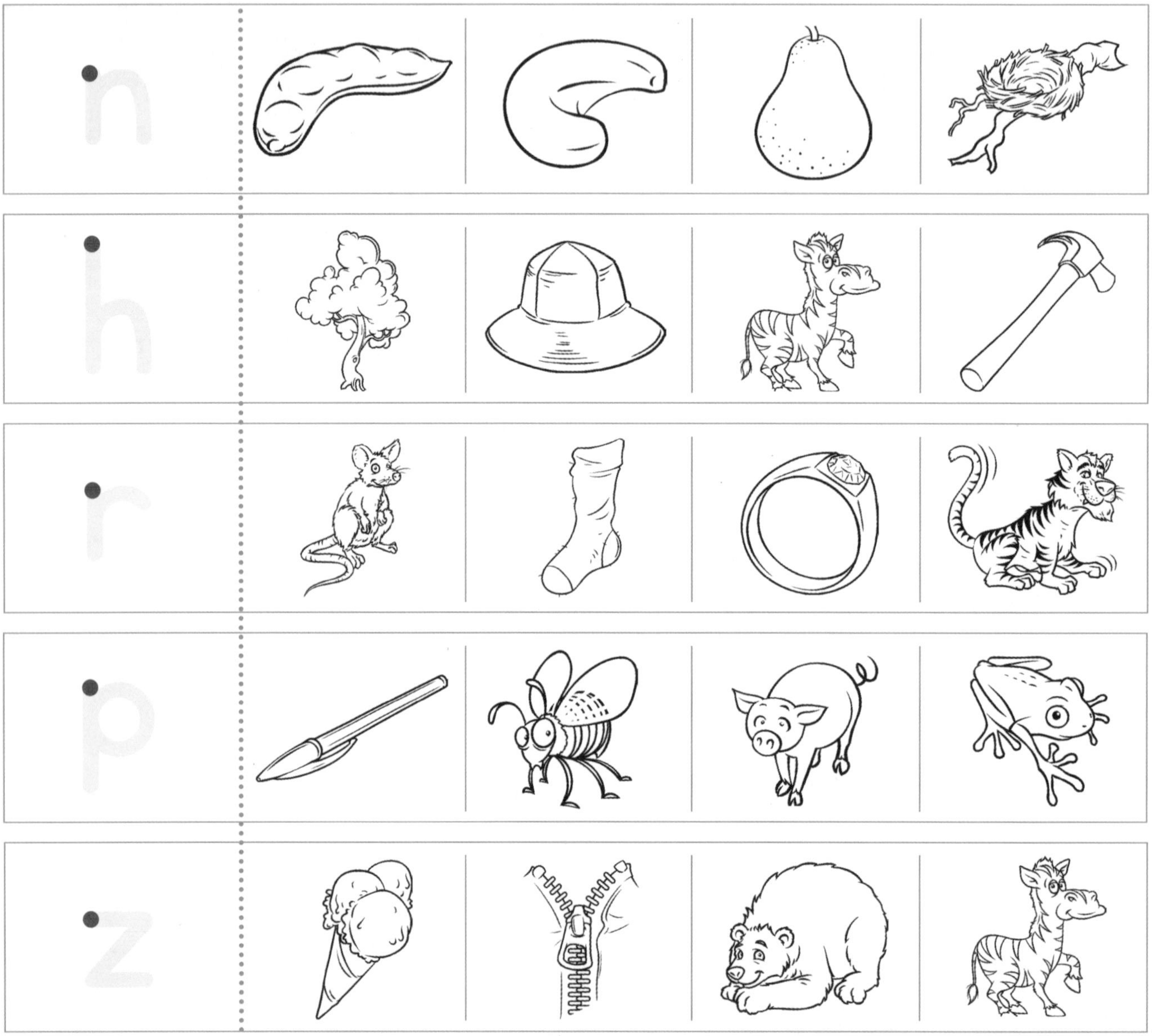

n				
h				
r				
p				
z				

2 Join the word to the picture.

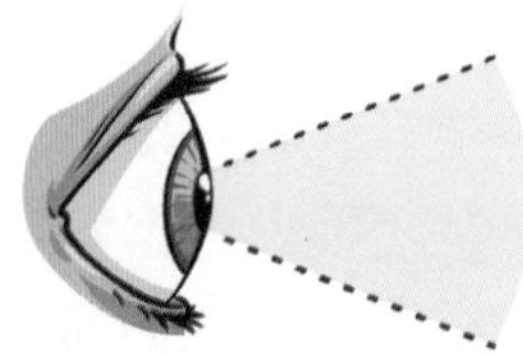

tree see bee

3 Read the word. Color the picture that matches.

man			
tap			
cats			
map			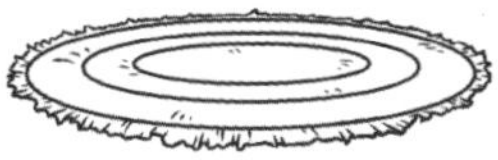

4 Read each sentence. Join to a picture.

Sam can see the hat.

Can a cat bat?

FANTASTIC!

YOU COMPLETED

MAP 2

YOU CAN:

☐ Say the letter sounds for:
a, b, c, e, f, h, i, m, p, r, s, t, z.

☐ Recognize and write the letters:
a, b, c, e, f, h, i, m, p, r, s, t, z.

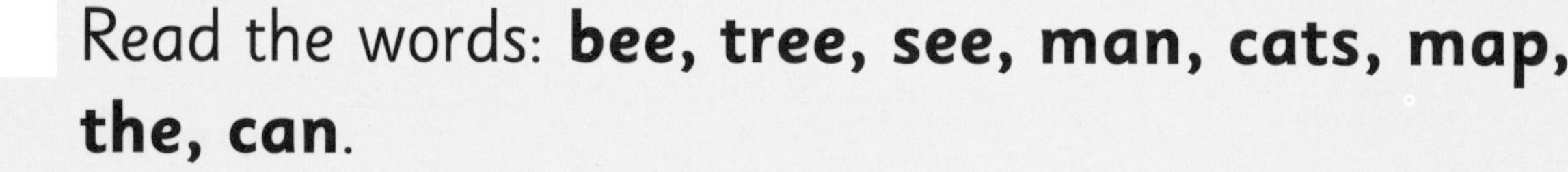

☐ Read the words: **bee, tree, see, man, cats, map, the, can**.

☐ Read the sentence: **Sam can see the hat**.

☐ Read these books:

Fun Spot 2

Follow the paths for each word.

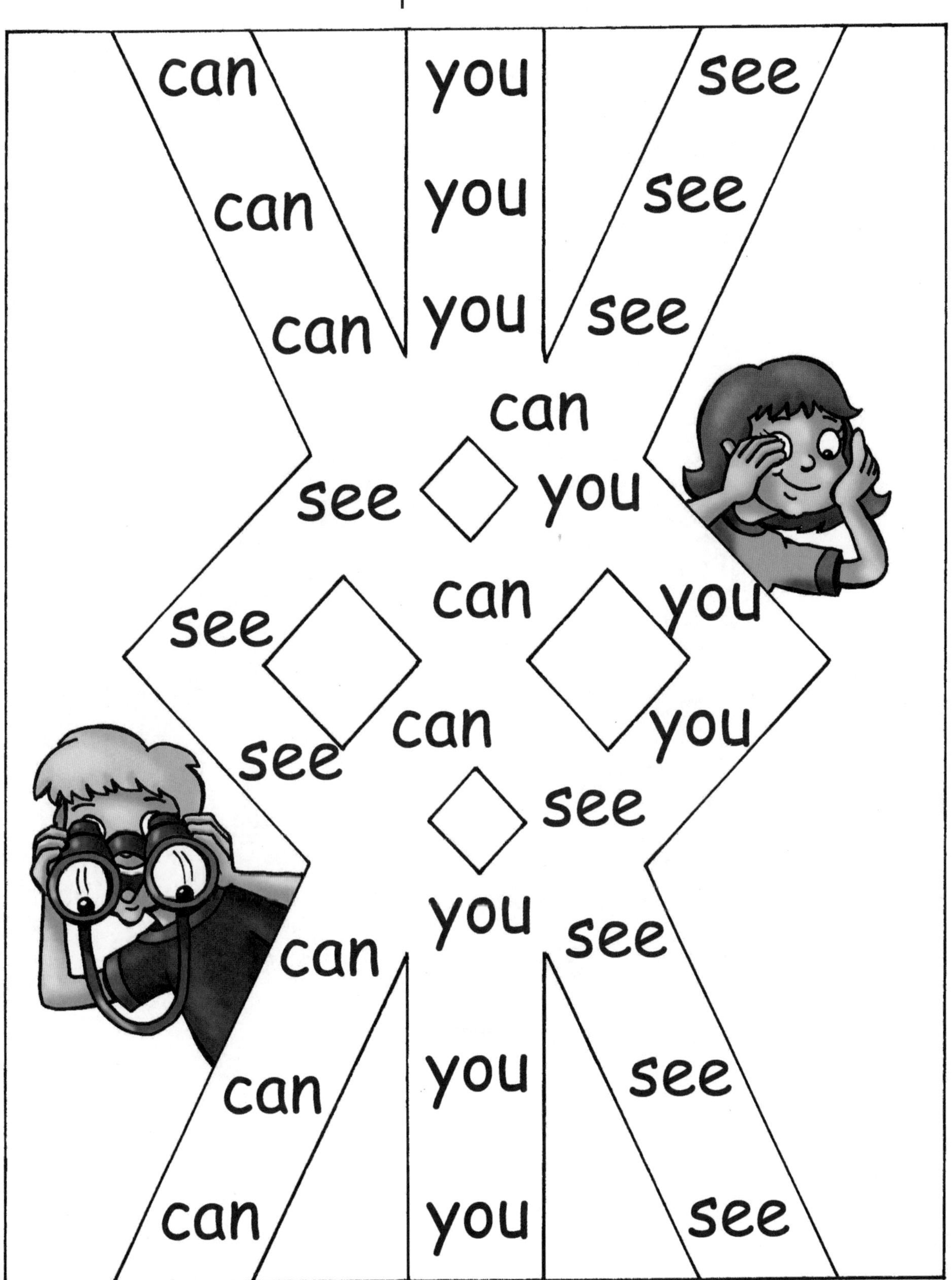

Find the hidden pictures

Ee

egg

elephant

ear

elbow

exit

engine

Find each drawing in the picture.

Ff

fish

fly

feather

frog

flower

foot

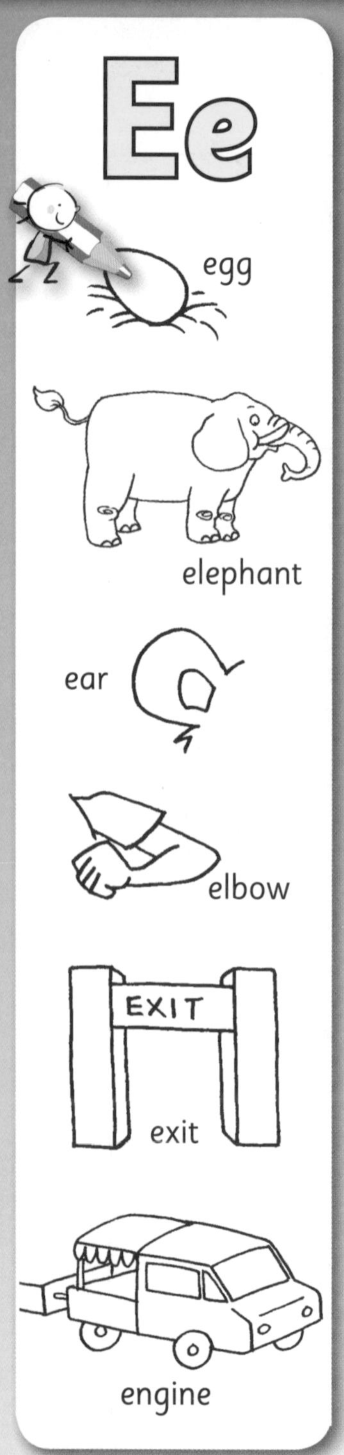

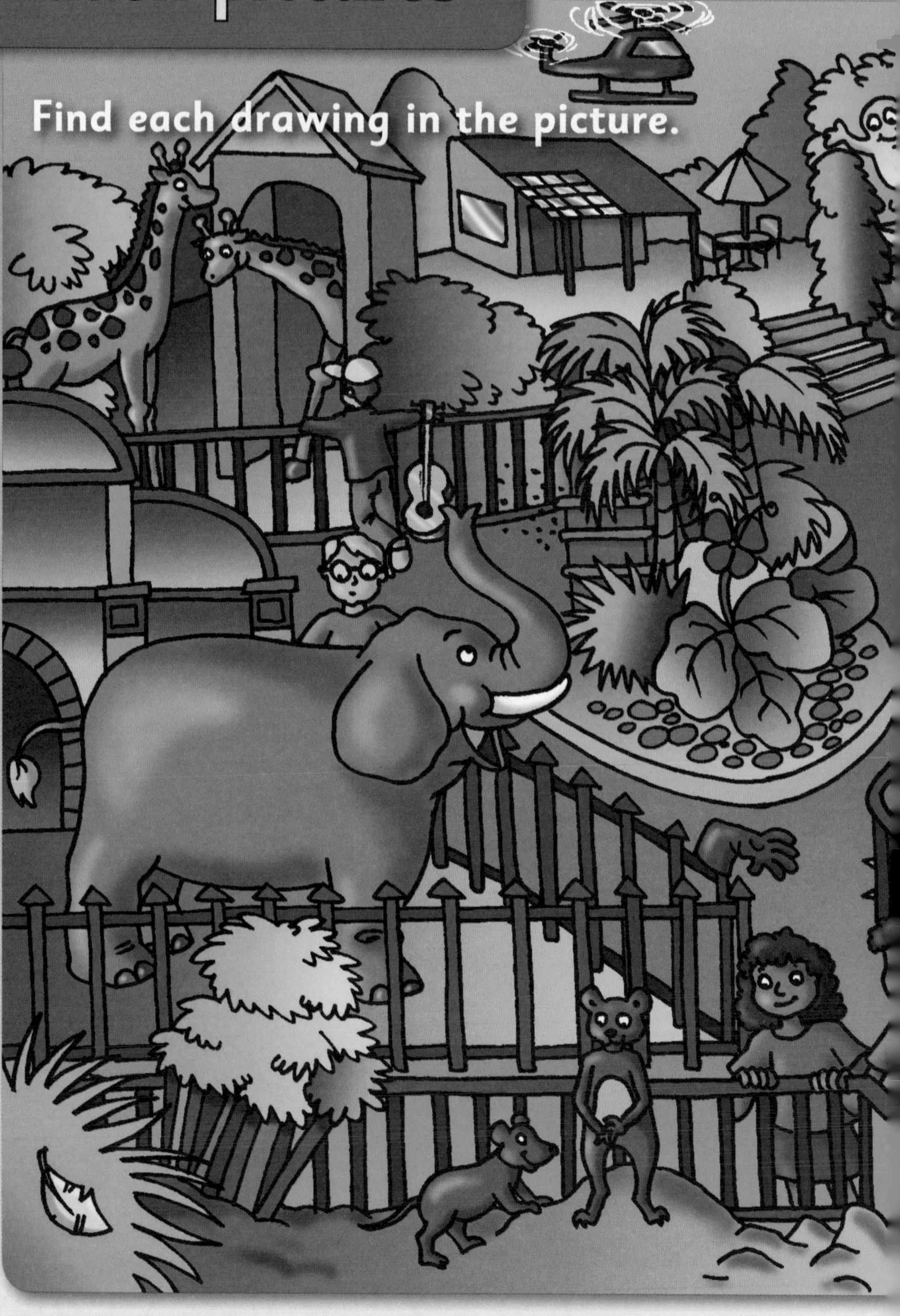

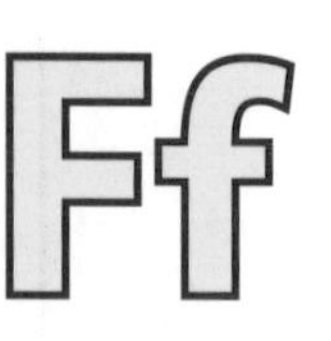

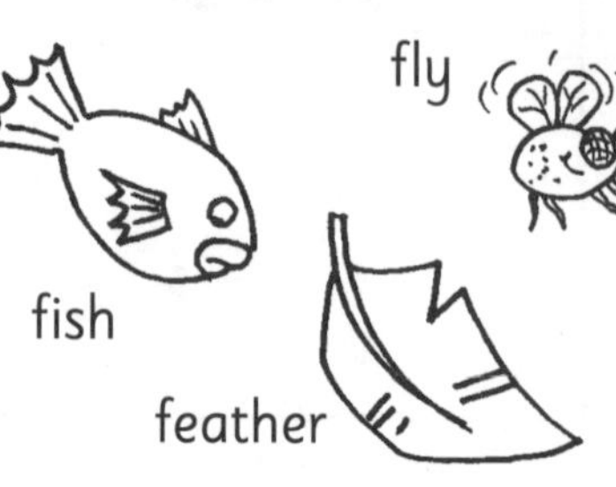

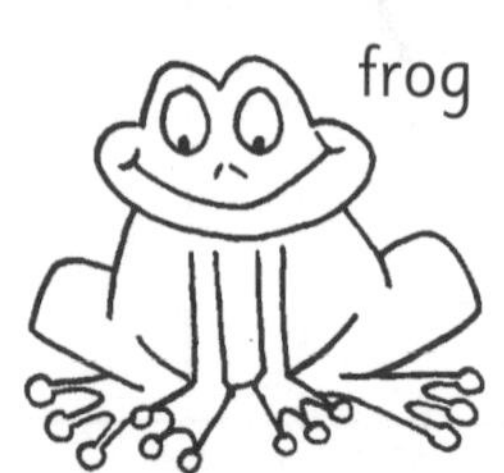

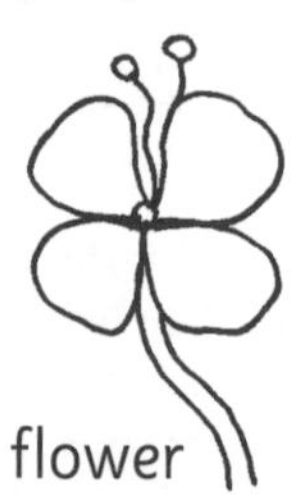

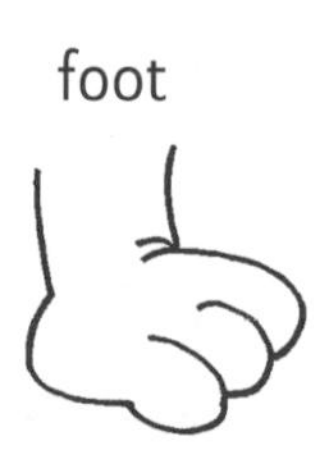

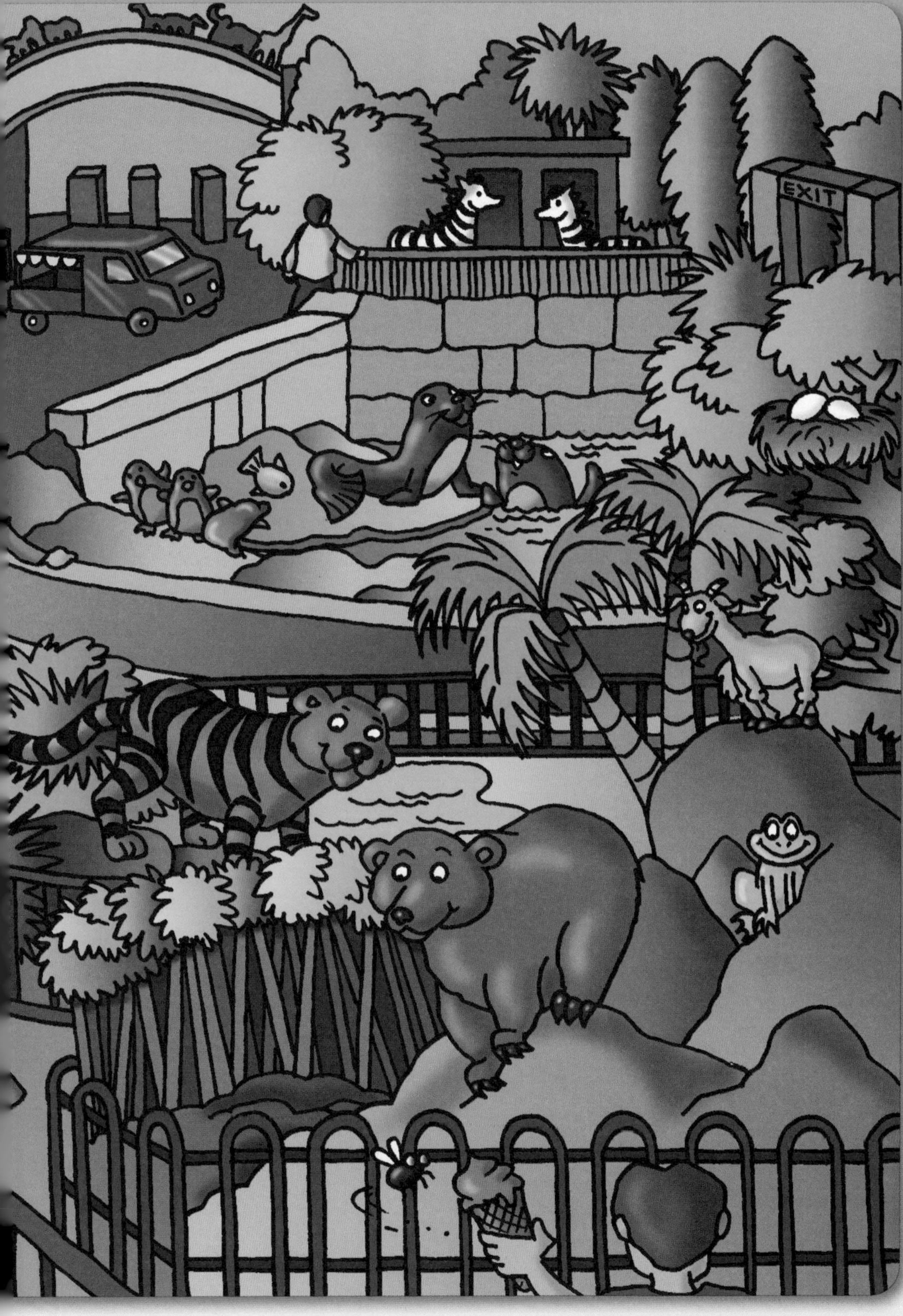

Hh
hive
hat
helicopter
hamburger
hand
house

Gg

glasses
girl
ghost

goat

glove

guitar

V is for Village Van.

1 Color things that begin with **v**.

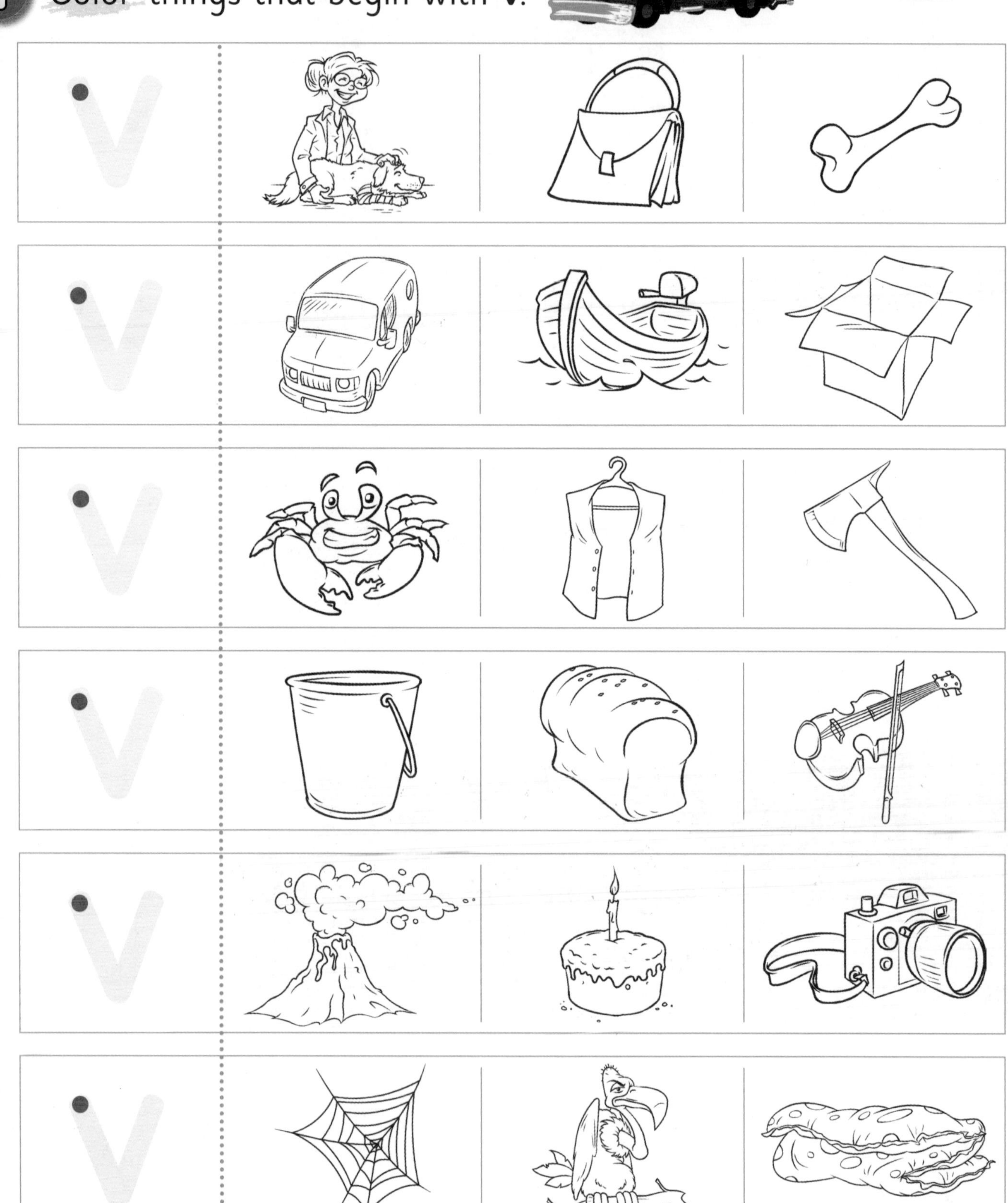

Vv

1 Trace each bird's beak.

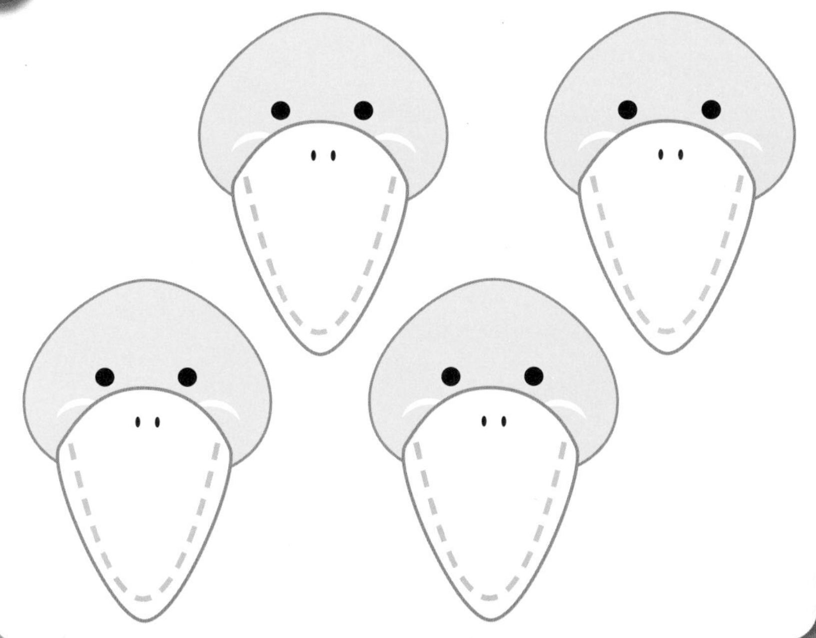

2

vase

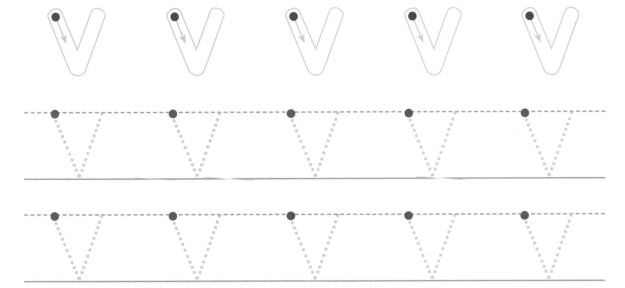

3 Trace and write.

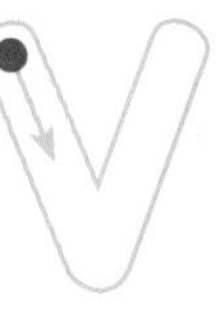

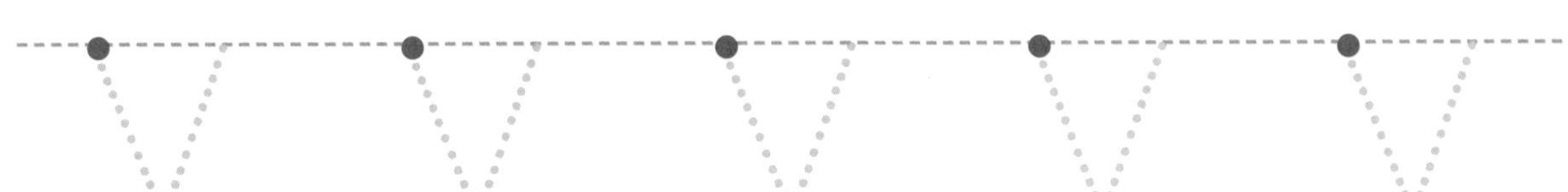

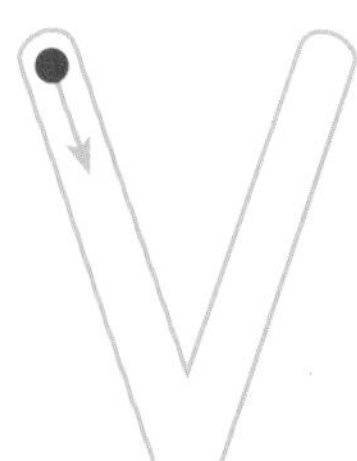
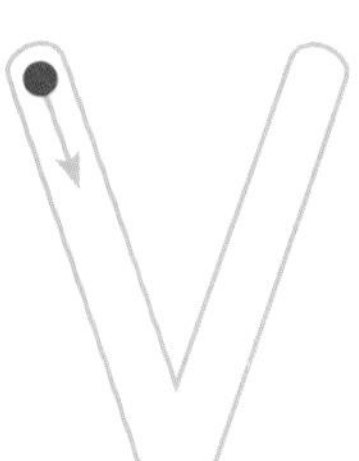

Circle your best letter.

1 Add **v** and read the word.

v____et

____olcano

____iolin

____an

____ase

____egetables

____ulture

____est

2 Draw a vase for each flower.

1 Trace and write.

v ______ V ______

2 Circle every V.

V	V	U	T	E
L	W	V	V	T

How many? ____

Circle every v.

v	v	z	v	v
n	v	w	t	v

How many? ____

3 Match each letter to a picture.

p v v v a c

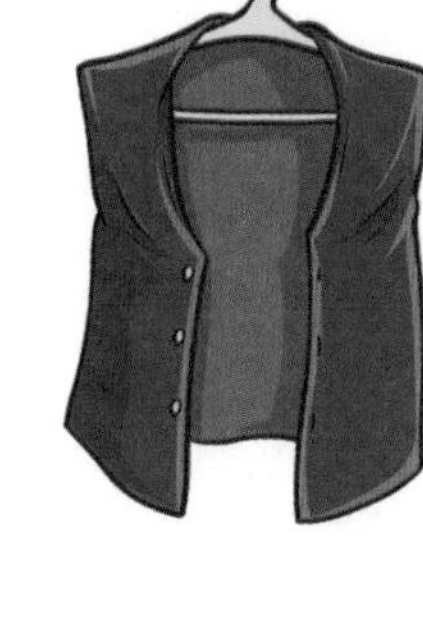

I finished this lesson online.

This egg hatched.

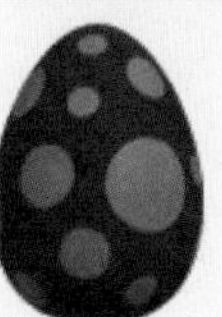

I know the letter sound: Vv

I can read

and

1 Make a rainbow word.

2 Read it 3 times.

The cat has a fan and a bat.

3 Find **and**.

jam	and	as	nap	**and**
and	trap	**hat**	*and*	**see**
see	**man**	and	see	as

4 Write **and**.

and and and

5 Draw:

Two bees and a mat.

and

1 Write the word.

and and

2 Use **and** to finish these sentences.

See the can ________ the fan.

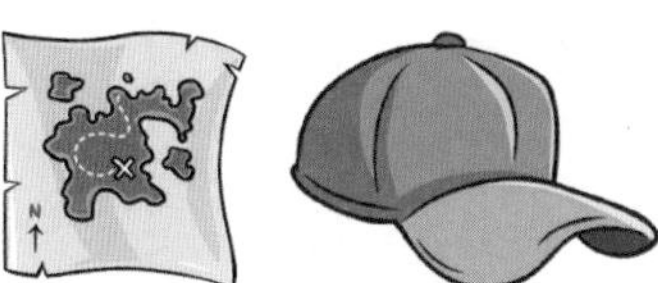

I can see a map ________ a cap.

3 Color **and** red, **the** yellow, and **see** blue.

see	the	the	the	the	the	the	see
see	see	the	the	the	the	see	see
see	see	see	the	the	see	see	see
see	see	see	and	and	see	see	see
see	see	and	and	and	and	see	see
see	and	and	and	and	and	and	see
and	and	and	and	and	and	and	and
and	and	and	and	and	and	and	and

1 Read the word. Color the picture that matches.

hand			
sand			
band			

2 Read and match to a picture.

See the hat.

See the bee.

See the band!

and

1 Finish each word.

h ______

b ______

s ______

2 In each line color the words that rhyme.

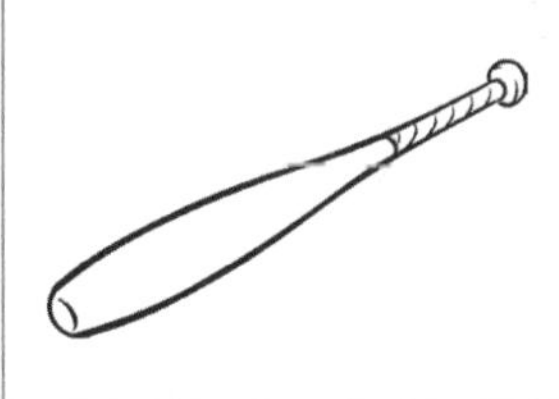	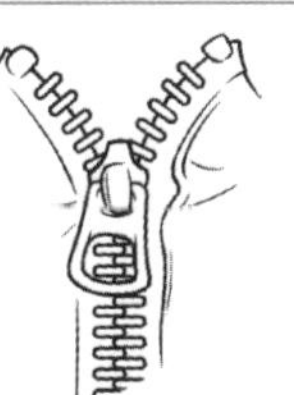		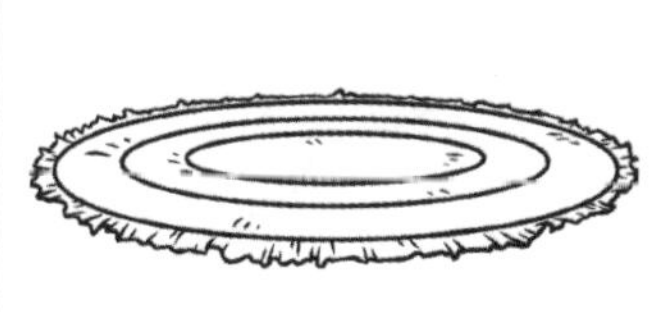

I finished this lesson online.	**This egg hatched.**	**I can read** and, sand, hand, band	**I can read**

1 Color the pictures that begin with **d**.

2 Match each letter to a picture.

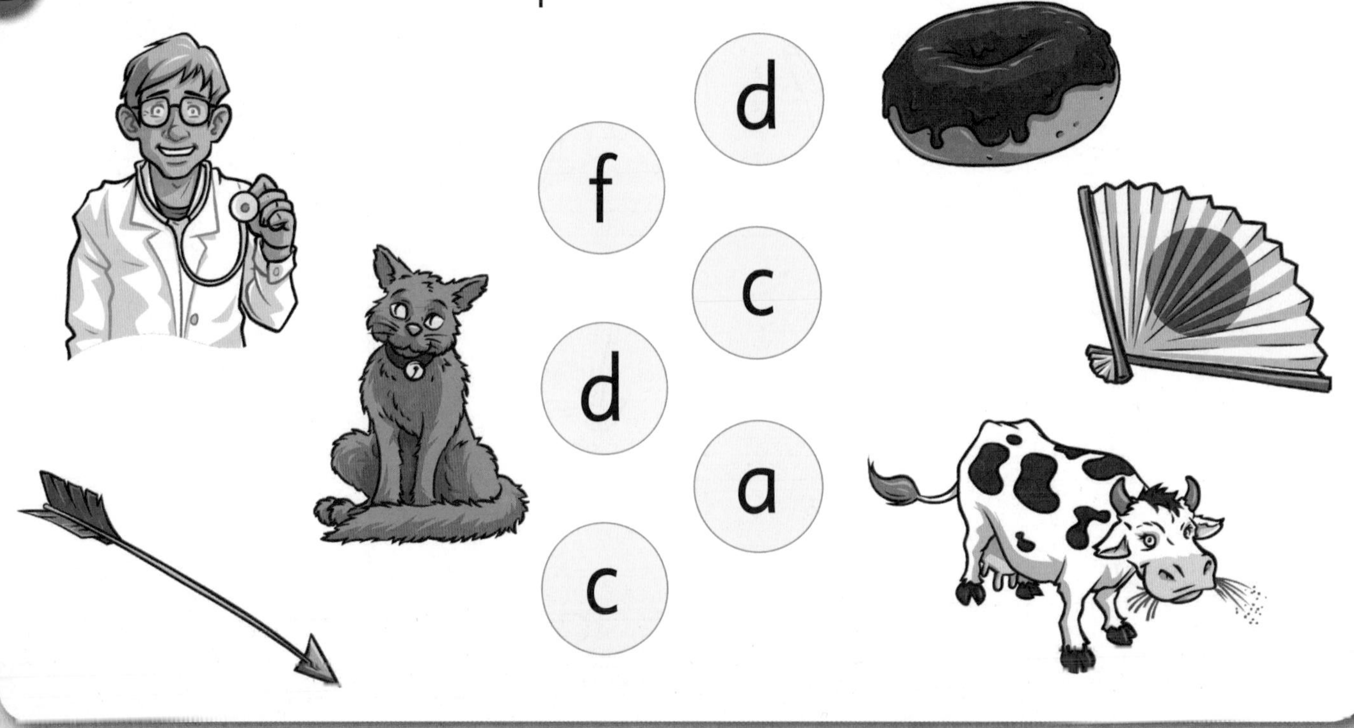

3 Circle every **D**.

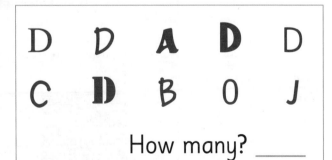

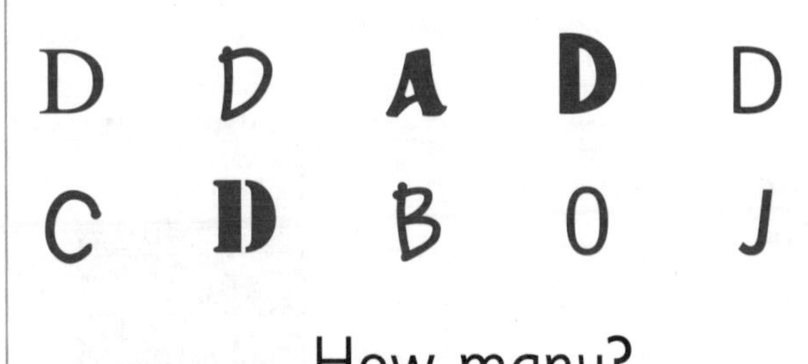

Circle every **d**.

d c d d c

d a e b d

How many? ____

1 Trace the dotted lines.

2 Trace and write.

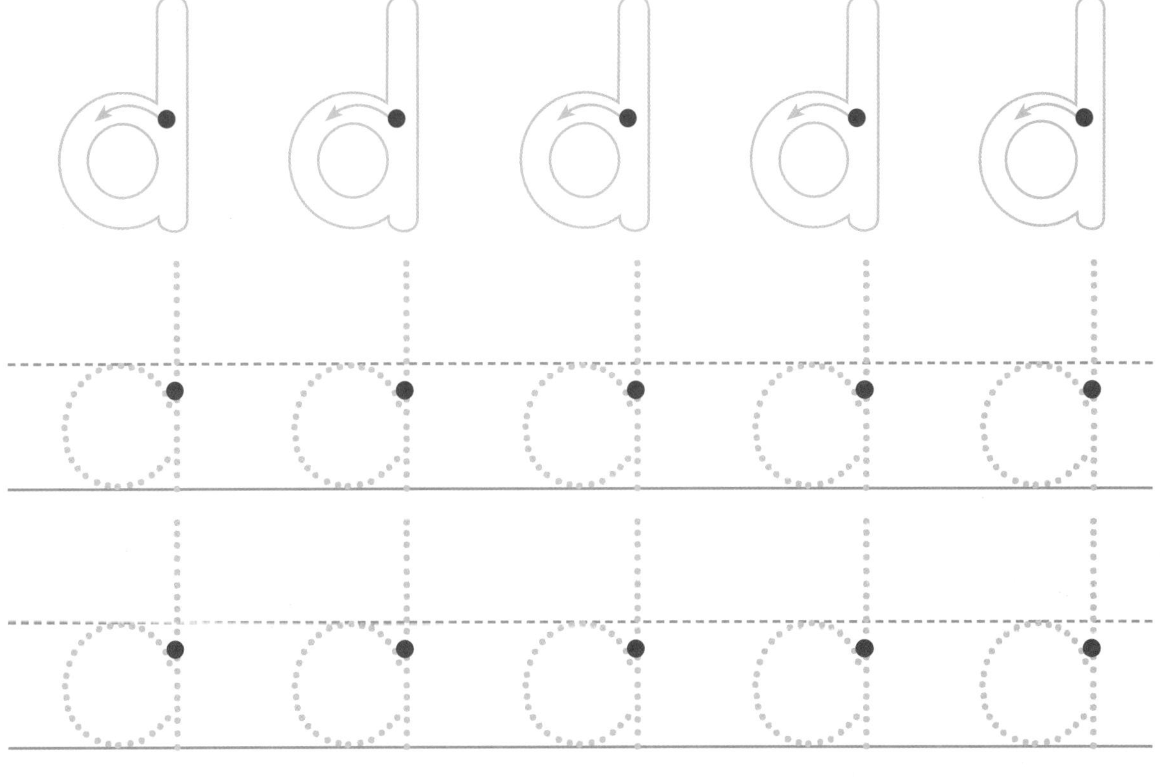

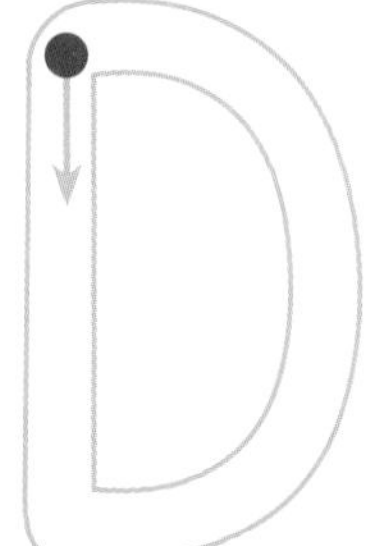

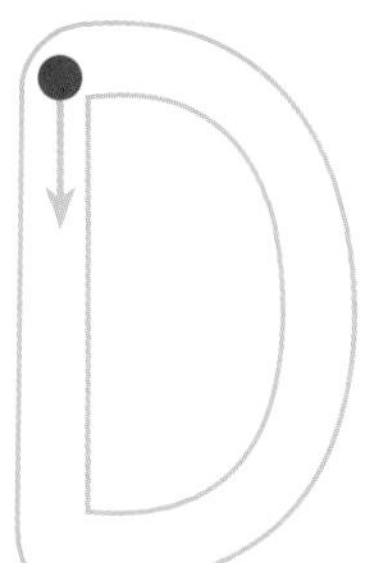

Circle your best letter.

1 Add **d**. Say the word.

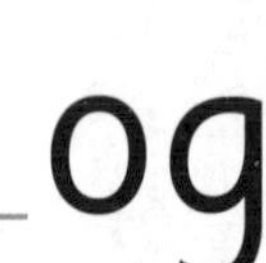

d____og

____olphin

____uck

____oor

____rum

____inosaur

sa____

see____

2 Write words that end with **d**.

____

____

1 Circle the beginning sound.

p m d	t v s	h b d
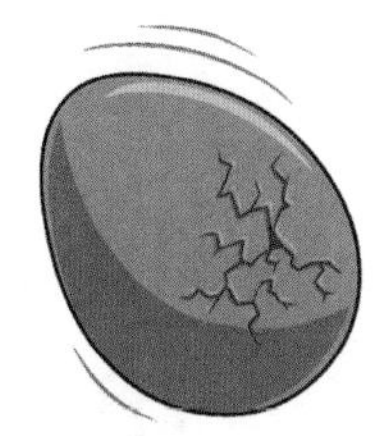	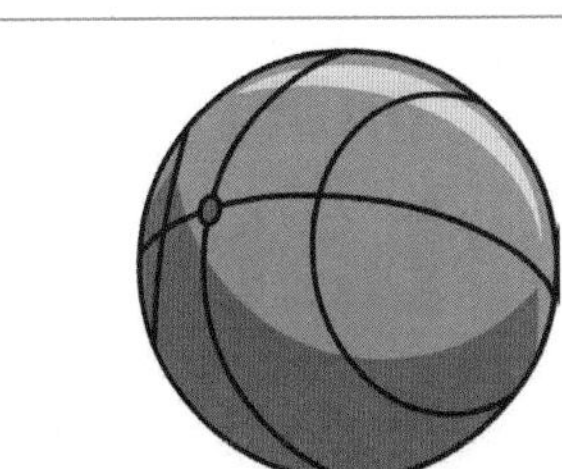	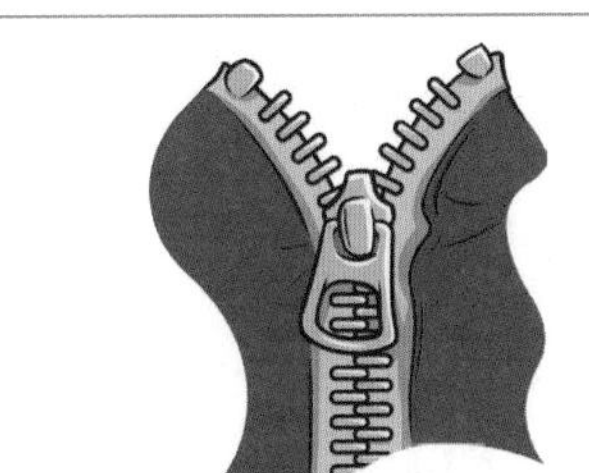
i e a	b n v	t s z
		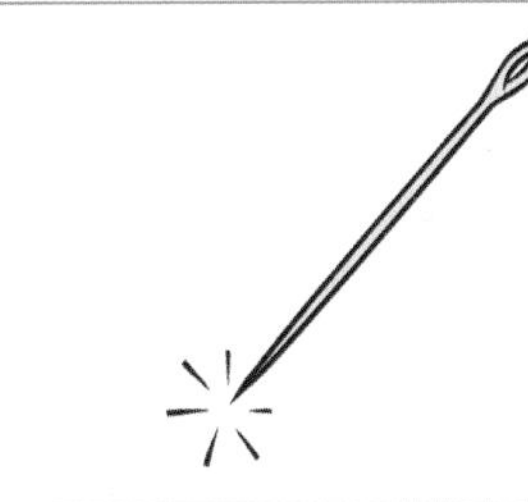
v z r	b p d	n m h

  Write the word.

bed

I finished this lesson online.	This egg hatched.	I know the letter sound: Dd	I can read

had

1 Make a rainbow word.

2 Read it 3 times.

The cat had a nap.

3 Find **had**.

has	had	man	as	jam
had	see	hat	and	had
his	as	see	had	hid

4 Write **had**.

had had had

5 Draw:

The fat cat had a hat.

had

1 Draw lines to make words. Label each picture.

h	ap	
b	an	
m	and	
c	ee	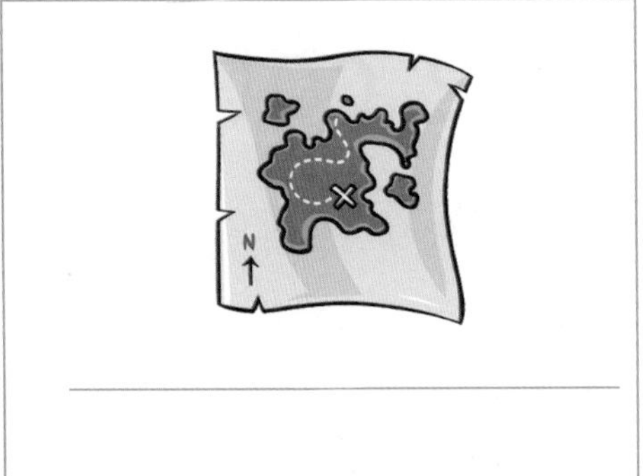

had

1 Read and write.

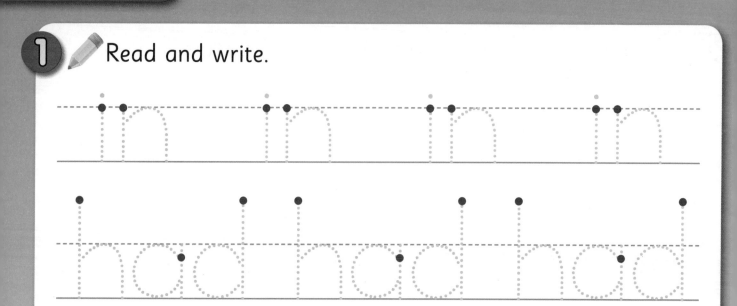

2 Use **in** or **had** to finish each sentence.

The rat __________ a hat.

The bee is __________ the tree.

The cat __________ a fan.

The egg is __________ the pan.

had

Read, then answer the questions.

The van

I can see the van.
The cat is in the van.
The cat had a nap in the van.

1. I can see the ____________ .

   a car   b tree   c van

2. In the van is a ____________ .

   a cat   b can   c pat

3. The cat had a ____________ .

   a hat   b nap   c bee

I finished this lesson online.	This egg hatched.	I can read in, had	I can read
24			

1 Color the pictures that begin with **j**.

2 Match each letter to a picture.

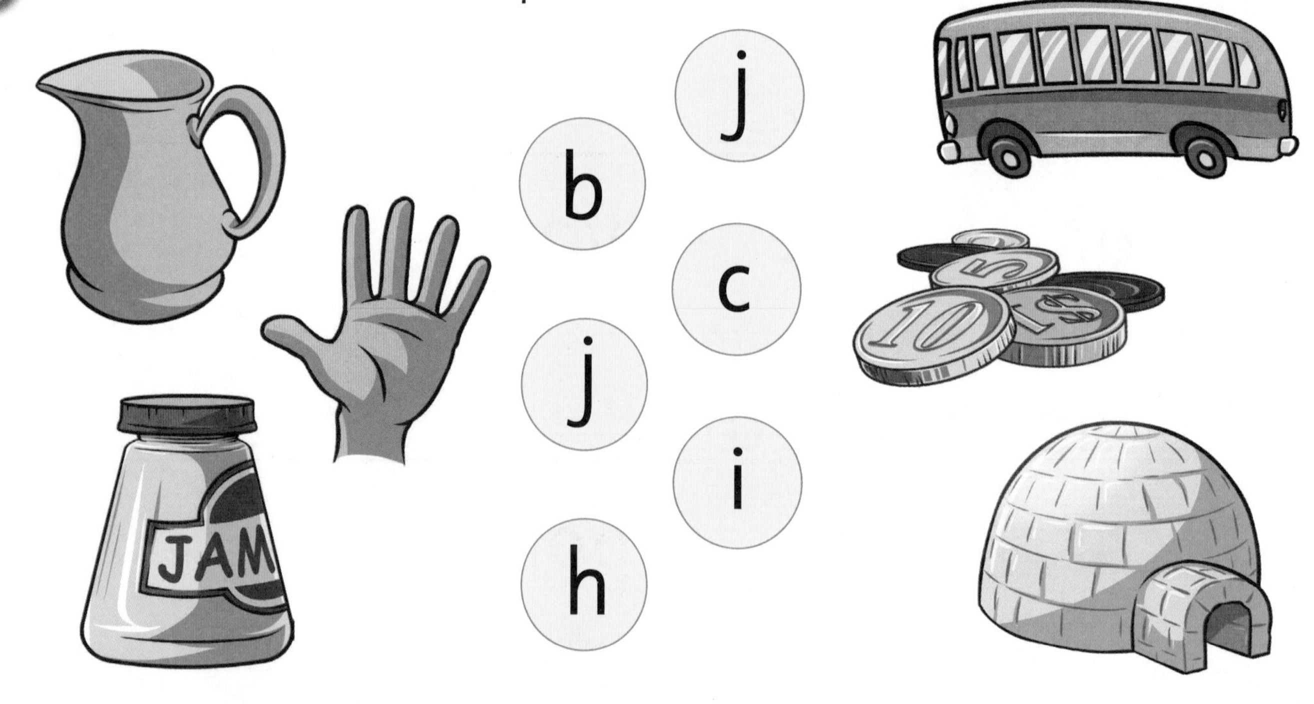

3 Circle every **J**.

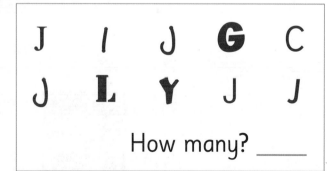

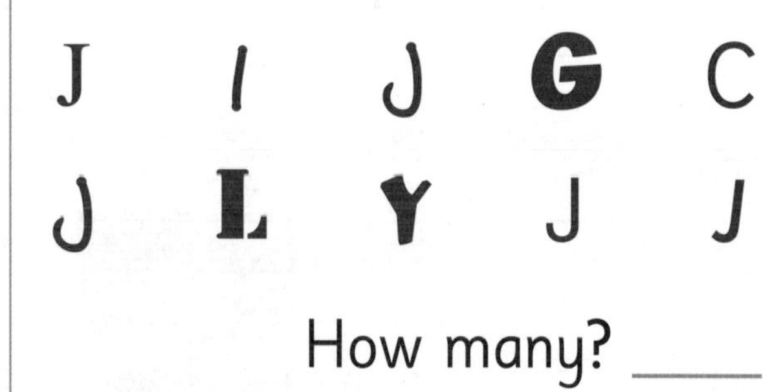

Circle every **j**.

j j j g j

i y j j b

How many? ____

1 Trace the dotted lines.

2 Trace and write.

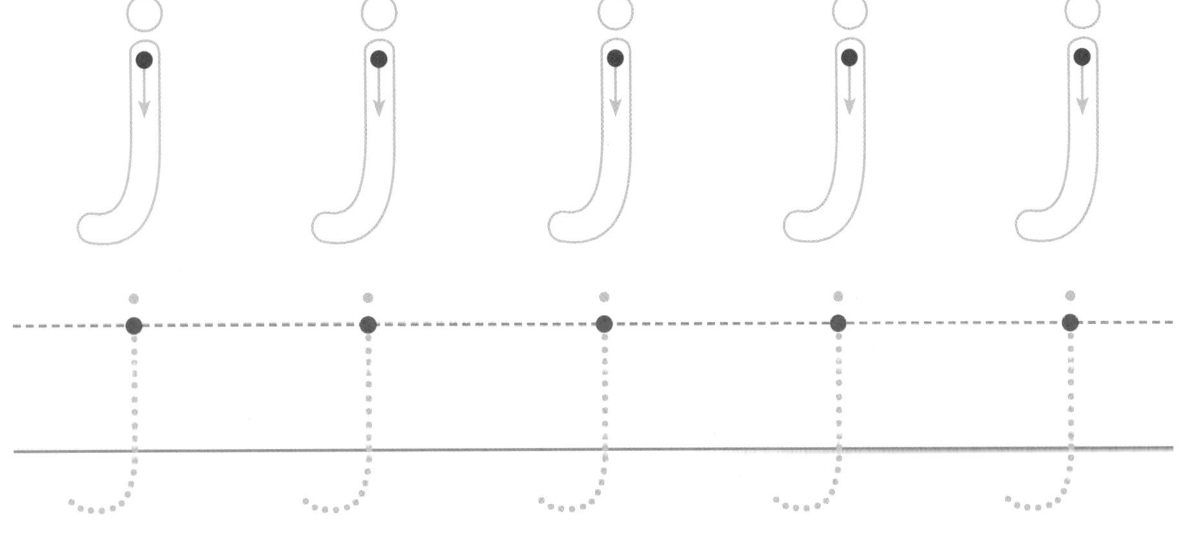

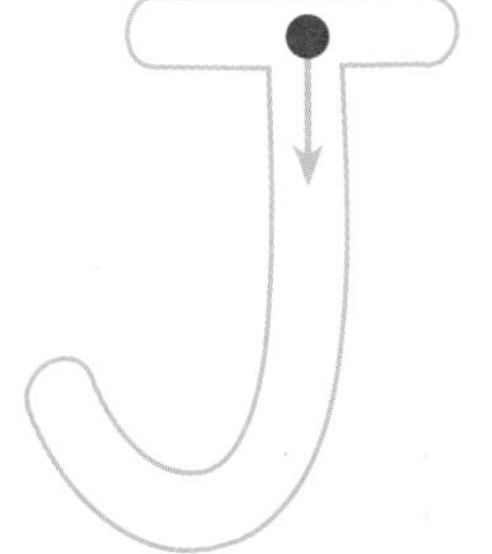

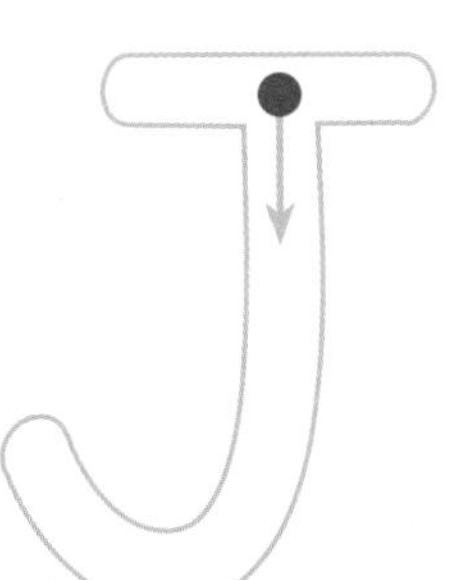

Circle your best letter.

1 Add **j** and read the word.

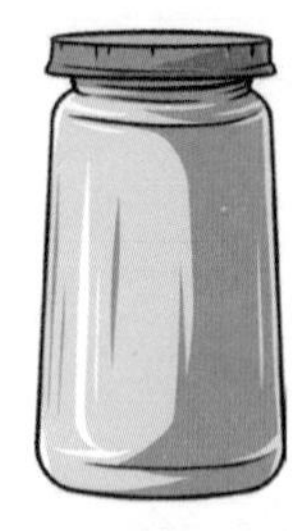

j ar

___ ug

___ ump

___ eans

2 Complete the **et** word family. Color the pictures to match.

jet

The jet is blue.

___

The dog is wet.

___

The net is red.

___

I can see the vet.

1 Circle the **beginning** sound.

h j	p d	j v	z d

t i	h r	v f	m n

3 Trace each letter. Match to a picture.

I finished this lesson online.	This egg hatched.	I know the letter sound: Jj	I can read

1 Join to the right picture.

1 rat

1 bee

2 cats

2 bees

3 ants

4 cats

3 bees

4 ants

1 Complete.

Read	Write	Color
dad		
sad		
bad		

2 Finish the sentences with an **ad** word.

The man ________ a map.

I am ________ .

I see a ________ .

1  Unjumble the letters and label each picture.

ads ____________

scta ____________

tna ____________

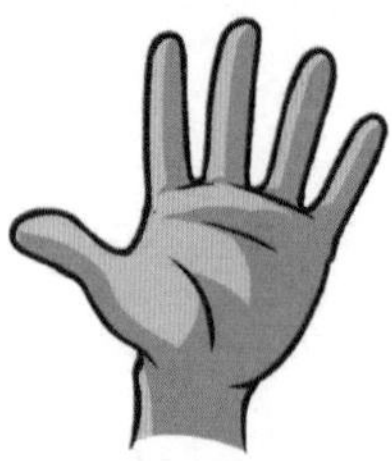

nahd ____________

sbee ____________

dda ____________

nva ____________

pac ____________

1 Join the jigsaws. Write the word. Read the word.

h a t

______

z a p

______

c a n

______

s ee d

______

2 How many sounds in each word?

cat

1 2 3

pan

egg

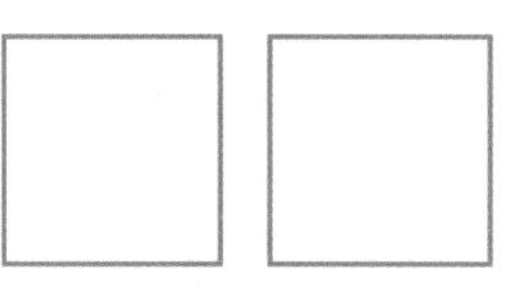

bee

I finished this lesson online.	This egg hatched.	I can read bad, sad, mad, dad	I can read

Oo

O is for
Octo Puss.

1 Add **o**. Say the word.

o range

____ctopus

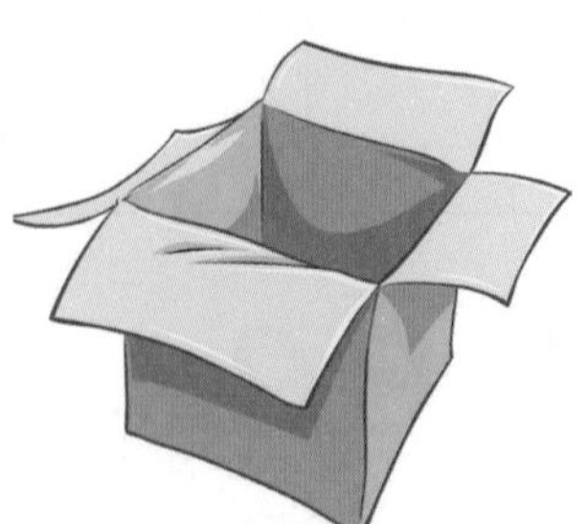

____tter

____nion

2 Color the right word. ✕ Cross out the wrong word.

bax

box

dot

dut

map

mop

tip

top

1 Buzz over to the honey.

2 Trace and write.

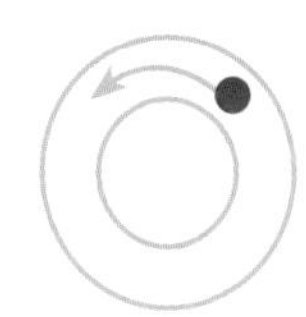
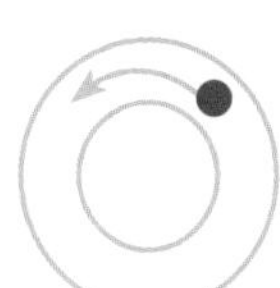
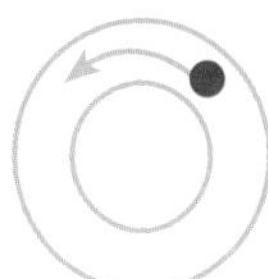
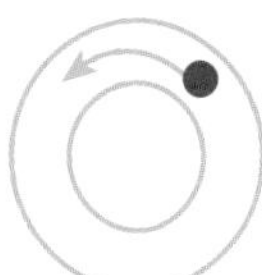
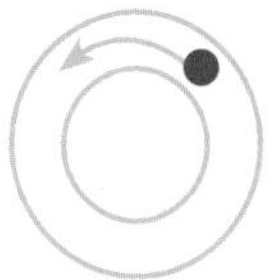
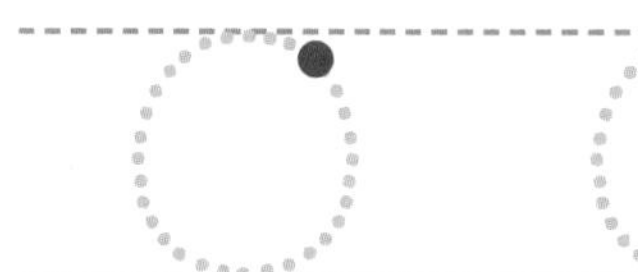
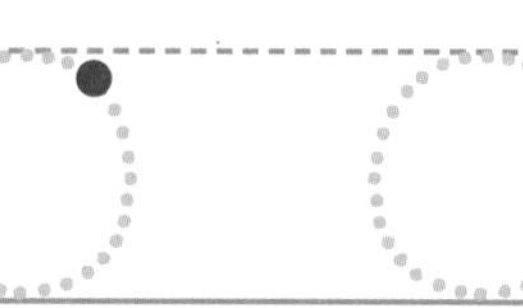
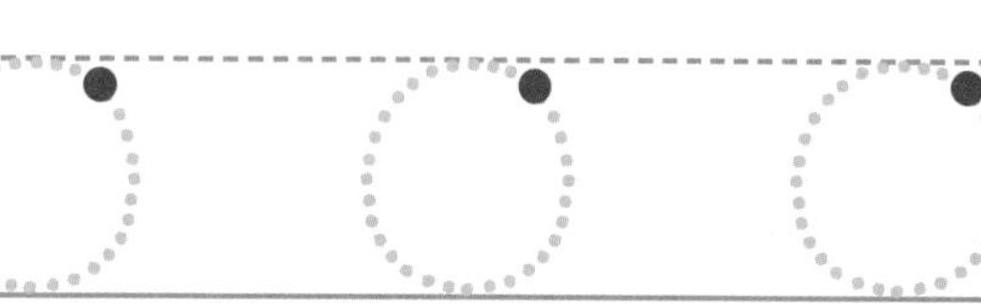

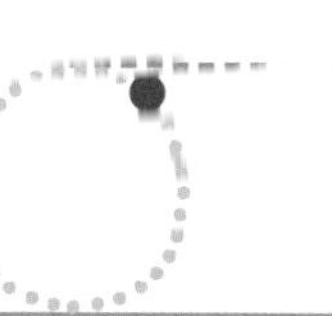
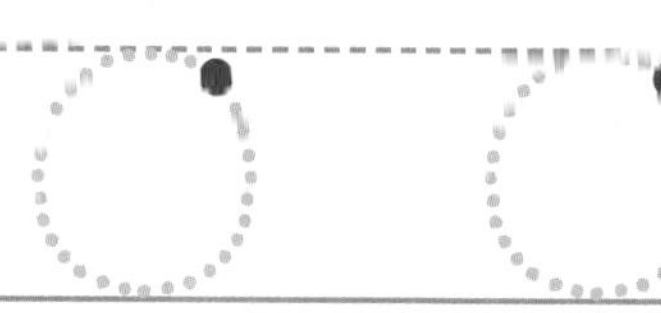
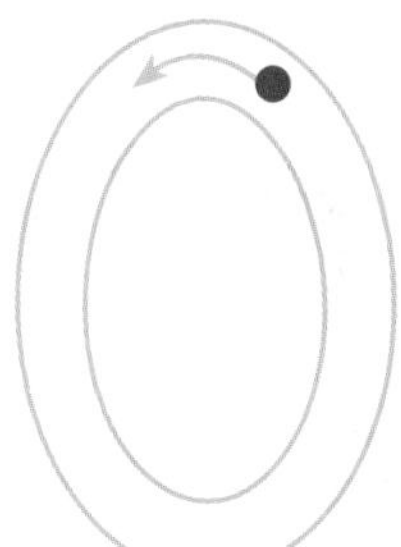
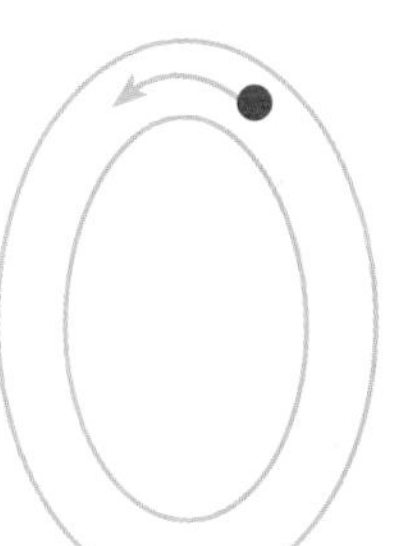

Circle your best letter.

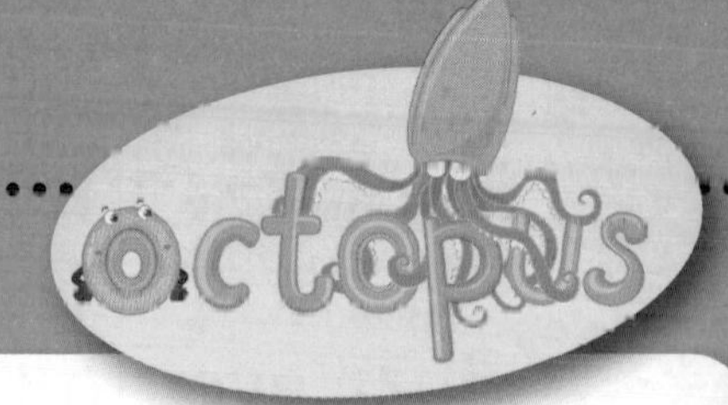

1 Write the word in the boxes. Complete the sentence.

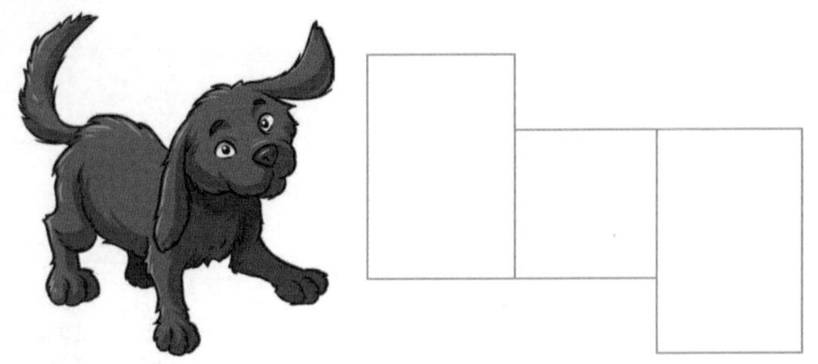

The ____________ is a pet.

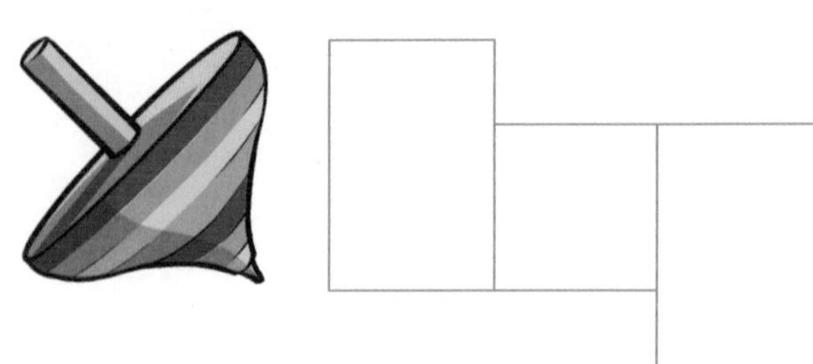

The ____________ is fun.

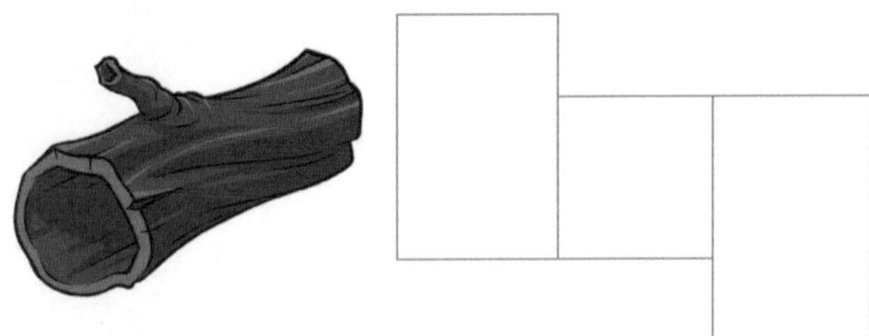

The ____________ is old.

The ____________ is wet.

2 Circle the word that matches the picture.

pig
pin

mat
mop

pen
pet

dog
dot

bet
bed

hut
hen

1 Add **o** and read the word.

_____ live

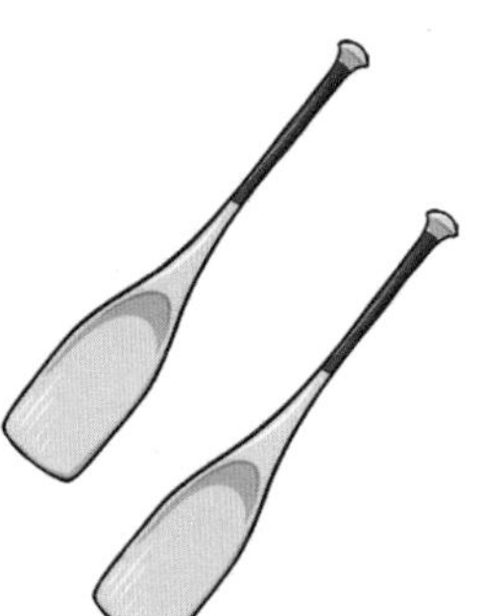

_____ ars

_____ strich

t _____ p

b _____ x

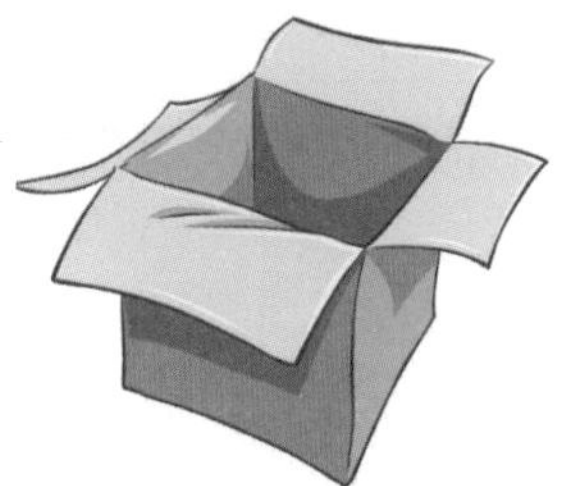

d _____ g

2 Circle every **O**.

O P C O O

O O D Q U

How many? _____

Circle every **o**.

o o a o e

b o c p o

How many? _____

I finished this lesson online.

This egg hatched.

I know the letter sound: Oo

I can read

1 Make a rainbow word.

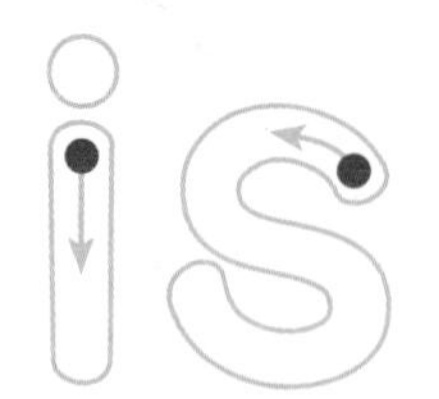

is

2 Read it 3 times.

Matt is an ant.

3 Find (is).

is	the	as	so	is
see	on	we	as	see
is	is	it	the	on

4 Write **see**.

is is is is

5 Draw:

Sam is sad.

Answer the questions. Circle yes or no.

1 Is Sam a bad ant?  yes no

2 Is the man sad?  yes no

3 Can you see a cat?  yes no

4 Is this a bee?  yes no

5 Can you see 2 eggs?  yes no

6 Complete the sentence.

I can see ______________ .

1 Color by word family.

at op ee an

Read, then answer the questions.

Bob

I am Bob.
Bob can hop.
Bob can see the cat.

1. I am ____________ .

   a Ted   b Bob   c cat

2. Bob can ____________ .

   a run   b top   c hop

3. Bob can see the ____________ .

   a cat   b dog   c ram

I finished this lesson online.

This egg hatched.

I can read hop, dog, top

I can read

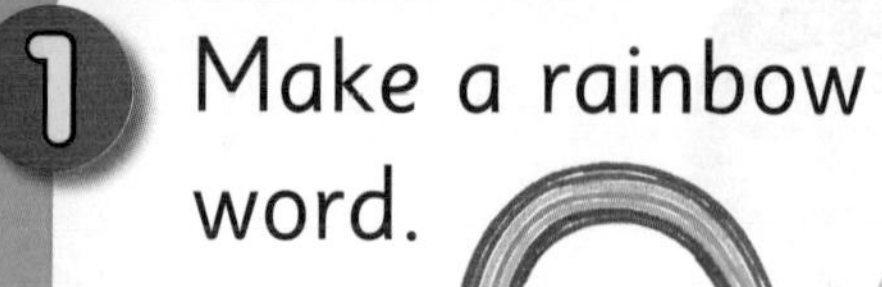

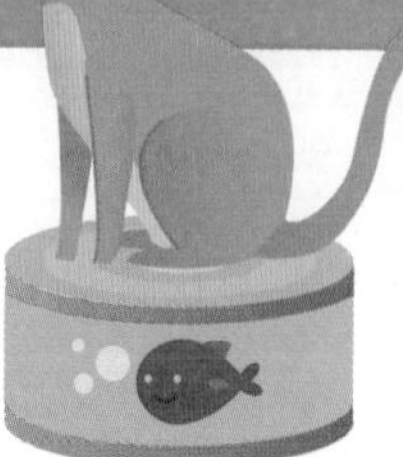

1 Make a rainbow word.

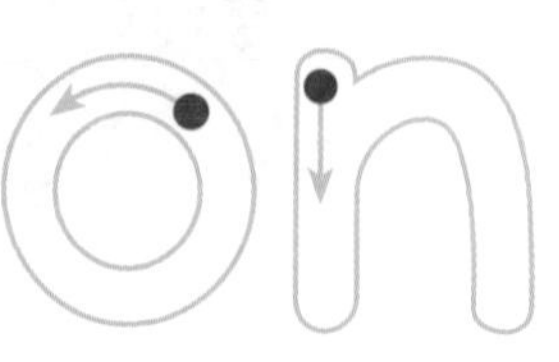

2 Read it 3 times.

A cat on a can.

3 Find **on**.

of	to	in	an	on
and	on	**it**	on	**in**
on	**old**	on	it	to

4 Write **on**.

on on on on

5 Draw:

Dots on a pot.

1 Join the picture to its sentence.
Draw a picture for the other sentence.

Zee is a bee.

Sam is an ant.

Sam the ant is on the mat.

Zee the bee is on the mat.

1 Write the words.

cat		

WORD BANK

jet pen bee rat man
cap van cat fan

Read, then answer the questions.

Sam the ant

Sam is an ant.
Sam is on the mat.
Sam can see a bee.

1. Sam is an ________.

   a ant   b egg   c fan

2. Sam is on the ________.

   a bee   b mat   c can

3. Sam can see a ________.

   a hat   b bat   c bee

I finished this lesson online.

This egg hatched.

I can read on, the, and, is, a

I can read

Qq LESSON 30 INITIAL SOUNDS

queen

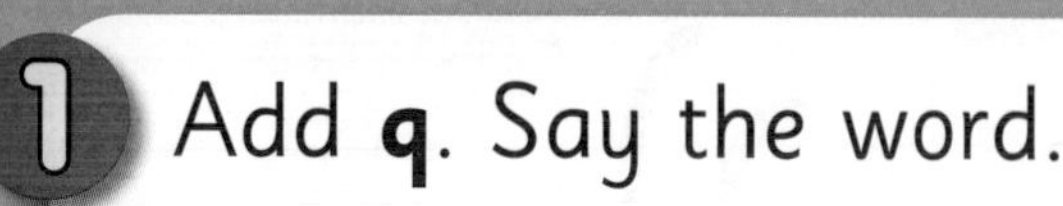

1 Add **q**. Say the word.

_____ueen

_____uail

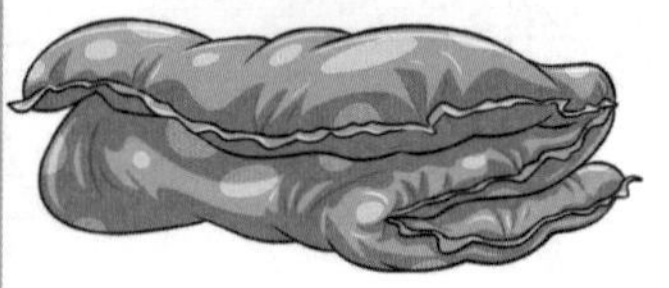

_____uilt

_____uack

2 Match each letter to a picture.

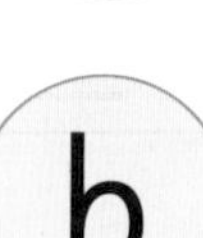

q c b q o d

3 Color the letters you know.

a	b	c	d	e	f	g	h	i	j	k	l	m
n	o	p	q	r	s	t	u	v	w	x	y	z

1 Complete the balloons.

2 Trace and write.

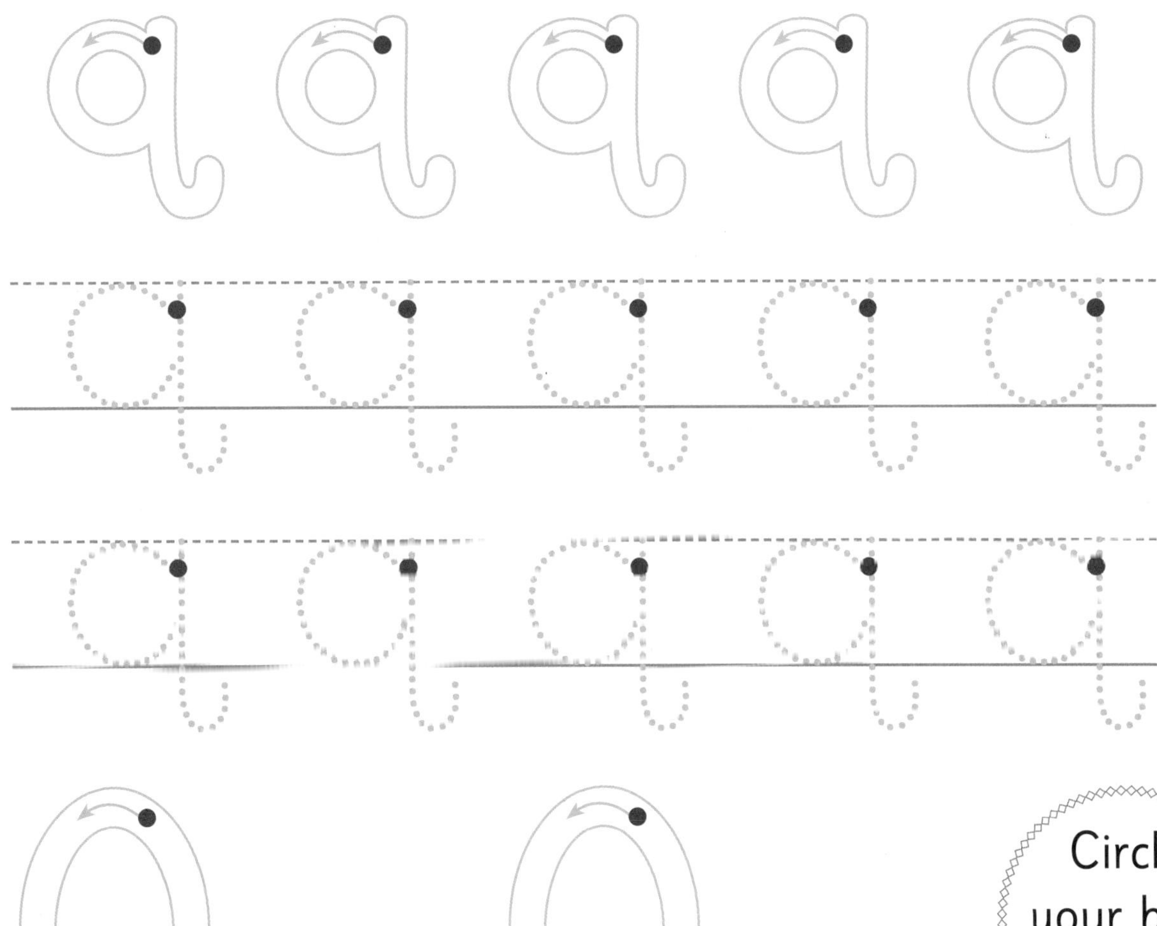

Circle your best letter.

1 Color the pictures that start with the letter.

is had on and in

1 Read and write.

and in had

is on

2 Put each word in a sentence.

I see a rat ______ a cat.

The cat is ______ the tree.

The cat ______ a nap.

The rat is ______ the mat.

I finished this lesson online.	This egg hatched.	I know the letter sound: Qq	I can read

1 Write the letter. Color the pictures that begin with the letter.

v	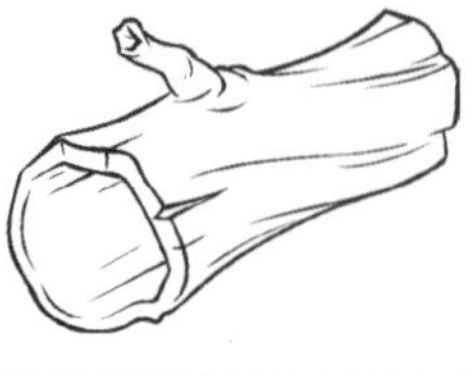		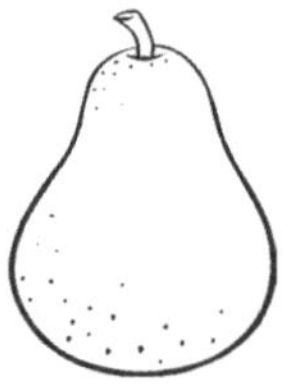	
d				
j				
o				

2 Write each sentence. Put the words into the correct order.

cap. Sam a had

band! See the

Quiz

3 Read the word. Color the picture that matches.

bee			
sad			

4 Sound it out. Circle the beginning, middle, and end sounds.

Write the word.

Say	Circle the letters			Write
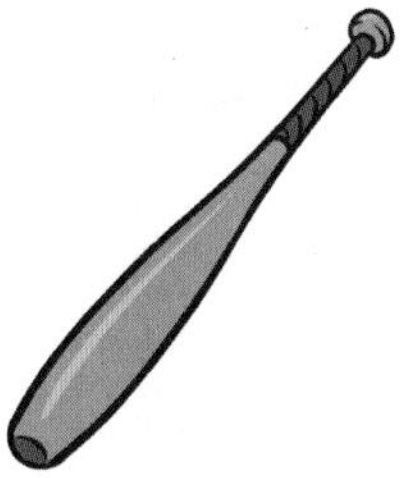	b z	a e	n t	______
	m j	a e	t b	______
	h t	o a	s p	______

Great Work!

YOU COMPLETED

MAP 3

YOU CAN:

- ☐ Say the letter sounds for: **a, b, c, d, e, f, h, i, j, m, o, p, r, s, t, v, z**.
- ☐ Recognize and write the letters: **a, b, c, d, e, f, h, i, j, m, o, p, r, s, t, v, z**.
- ☐ Read the words: **and, hand, sand, band, bed, had, is, in, on**.
- ☐ Read the sentence: **Zee the bee is on the mat**.
- ☐ Read these books:

Fun Spot 3

Match the upper and lower case letters.

B c a m C p b A J M G d f j D P F g

A	B	C	D	E	F	G	H	I	J	K	L	M	N	O	P
a	b	c	d	e	f	g	h	i	j	k	l	m	n	o	p

Find the hidden pictures

Find each drawing in the picture.

Nn

nut

nest

nose

necklace

net

nail

Oo

orange

octopus

onion

ostrich

otter

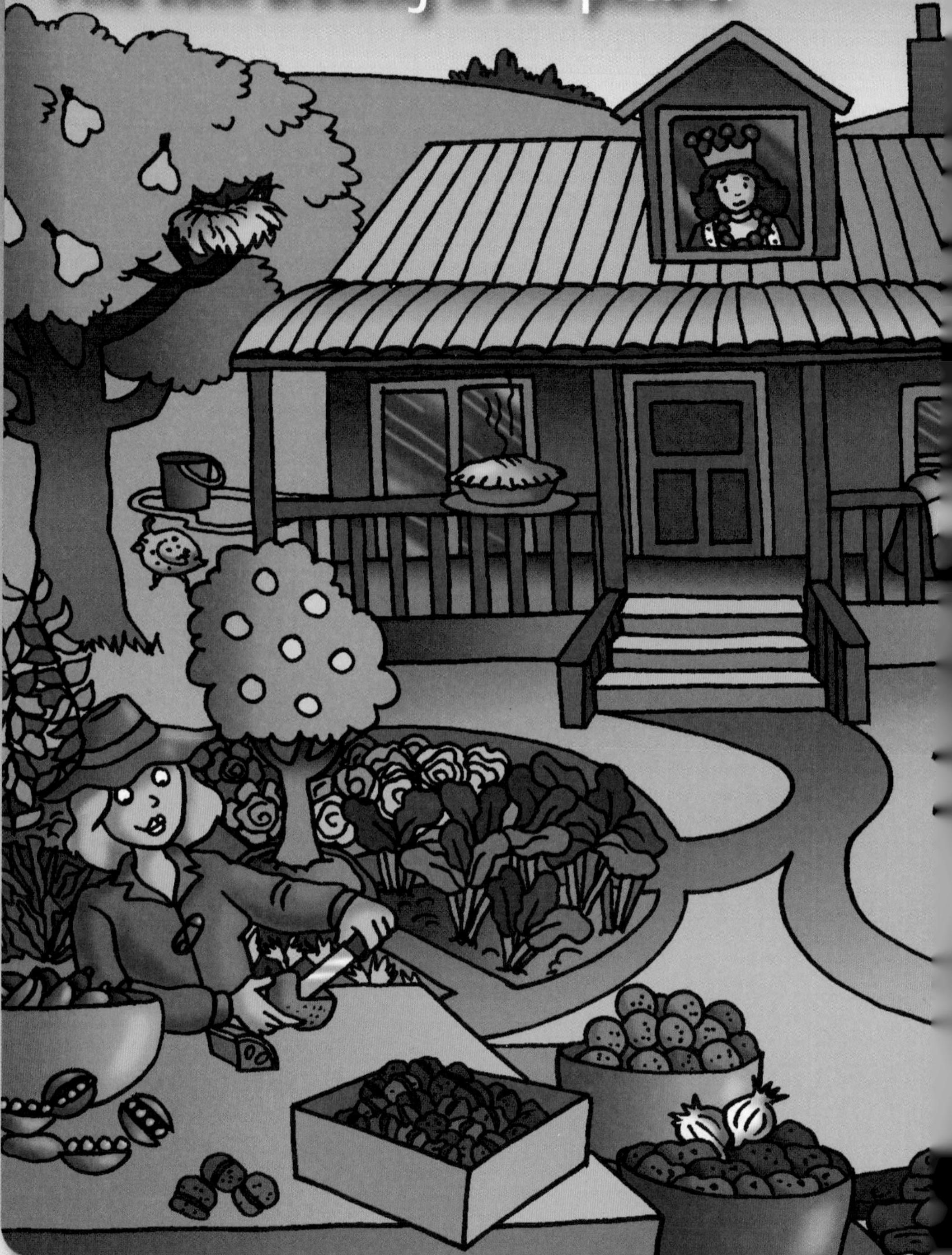

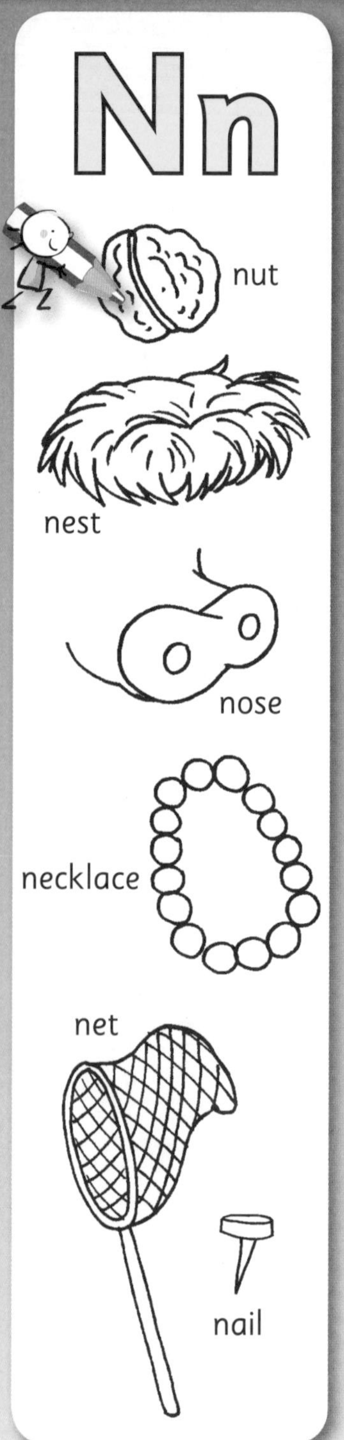

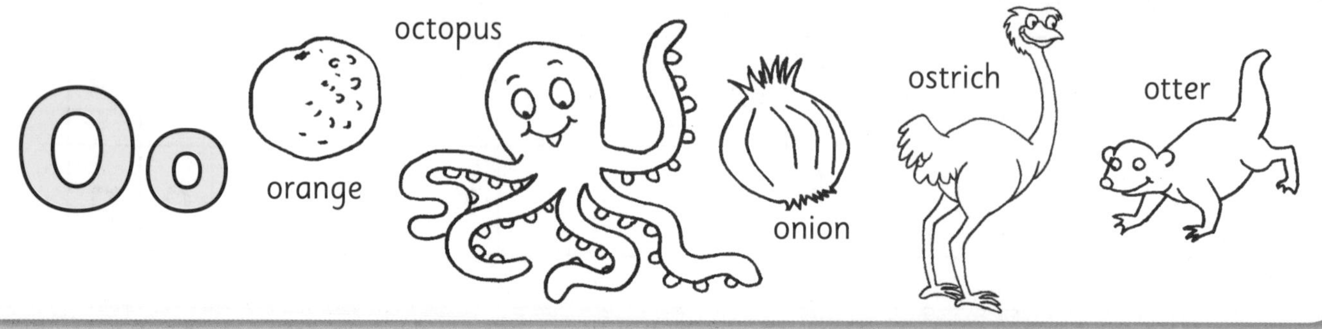

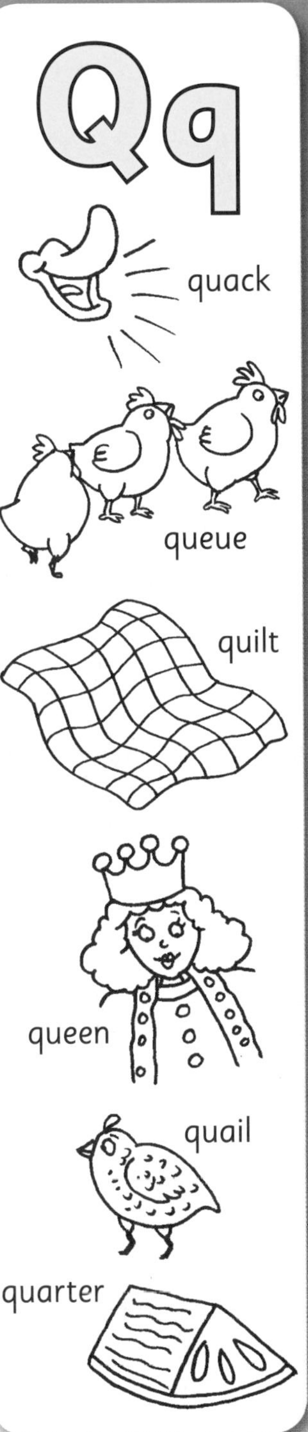
Qq
quack
queue
quilt
queen
quail
quarter

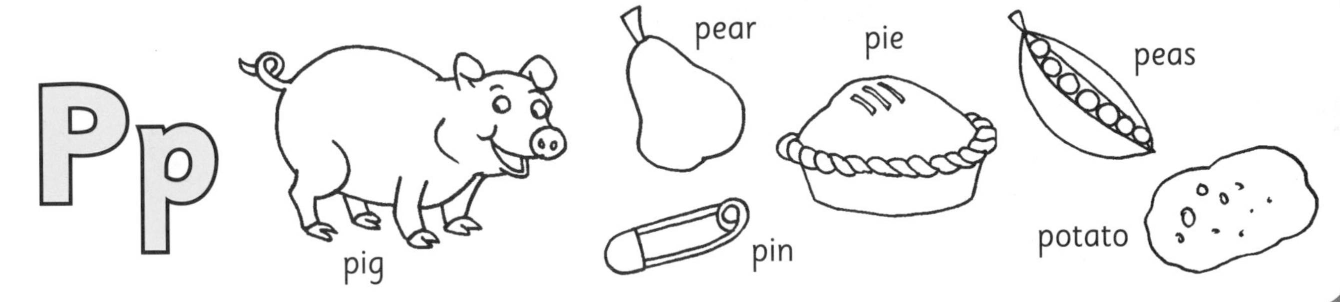
Pp
pig
pear
pie
pin
peas
potato

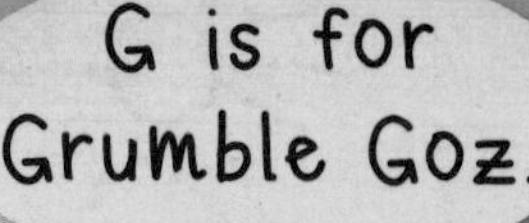

1 Match each letter to a picture.

c

b

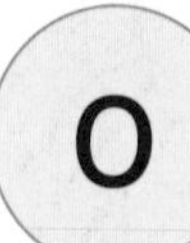

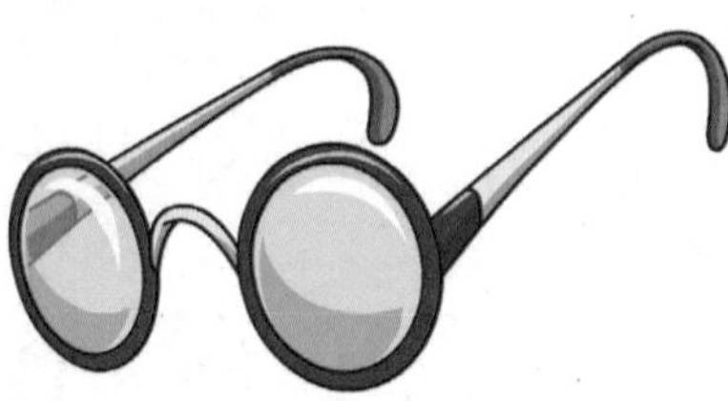

2 Join **g** things to Grumble Goz.

3 Color the **g** goldfish.

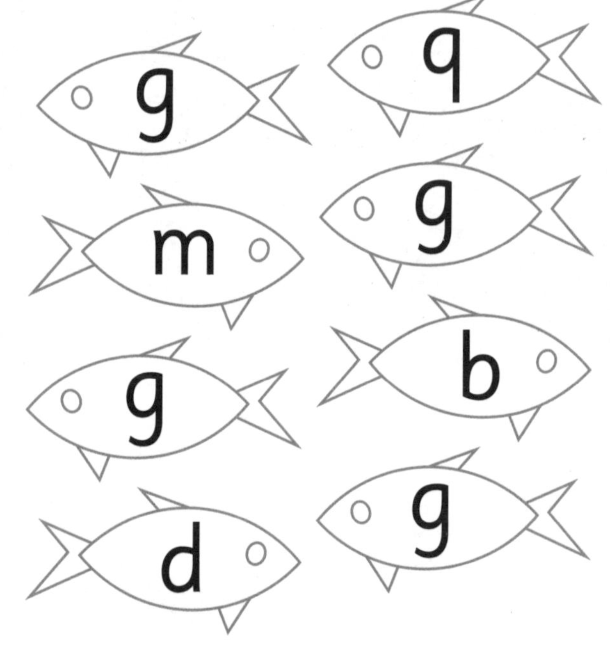

1 Trace the wings of Grumble Goz's friends.

2 Trace and write.

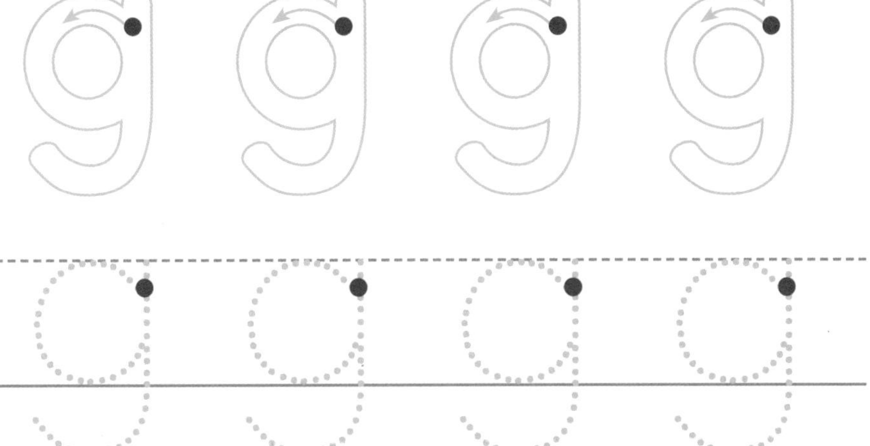

Circle your best letter.

3 Color Go Go Gizmo's garden.

1 Add **g**. Say the word.

g irl

_____ uitar

_____ oose

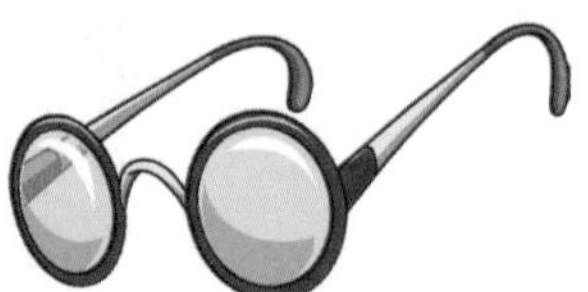

_____ lasses

2 Complete the **og** family.

	dog	The dog is a good dog.
	j	I can jog.
	fr	The frog is on the log.

1 Trace and write.

2 Circle every **G**.

G	D	G	**G**	C
G	C	G	Q	G

How many? ____

Circle every **g**.

g	g	g	y	g
j	b	g	a	g

How many? ____

3 Color the pictures that start with **g**.

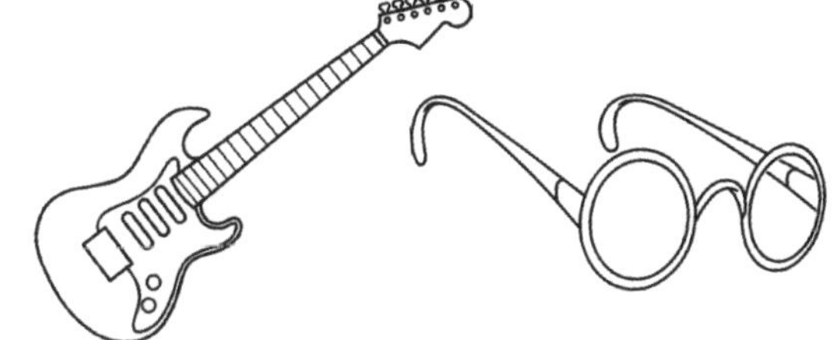
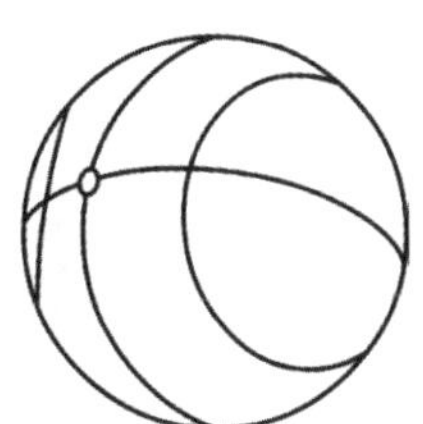

4 Add **g** then say the word.

 ____ift

 ____oose

I finished this lesson online.	This egg hatched.	I know the letter sound: Gg	I can read

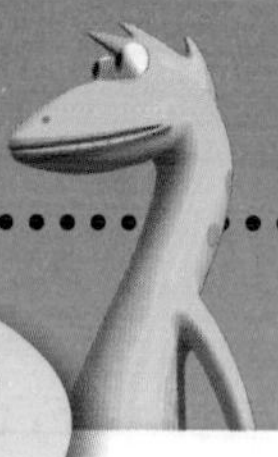

Look out! It's Lemon Lizard.

1 Match each letter to a picture.

l

e

b

l

l

g

2 Join l things to Lemon Lizard.

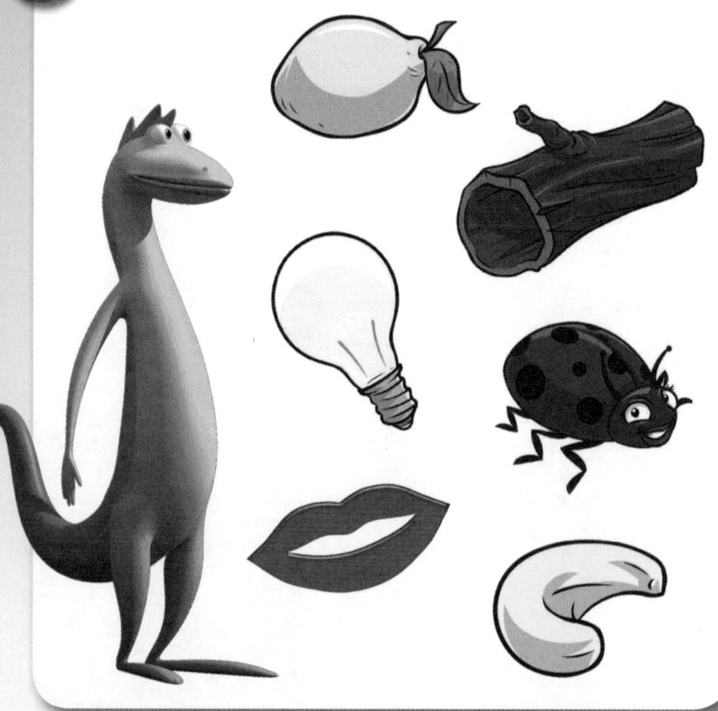

3 Color the l lemons.

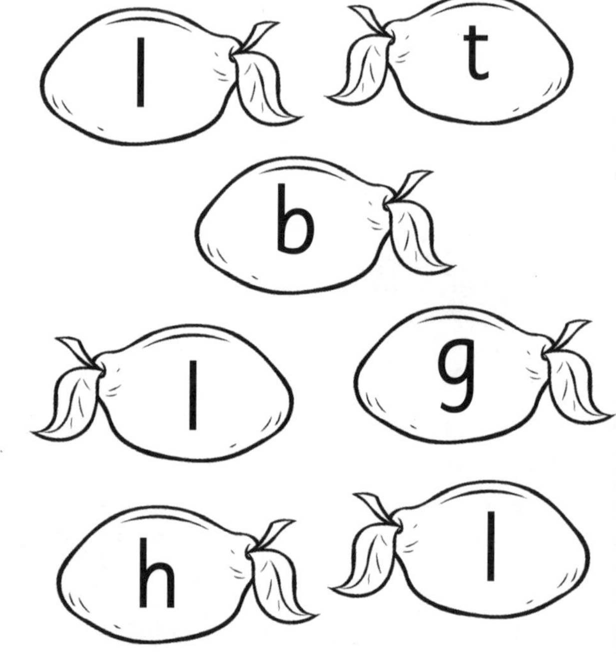

1 Trace the dotted lines.

2 Trace and write.

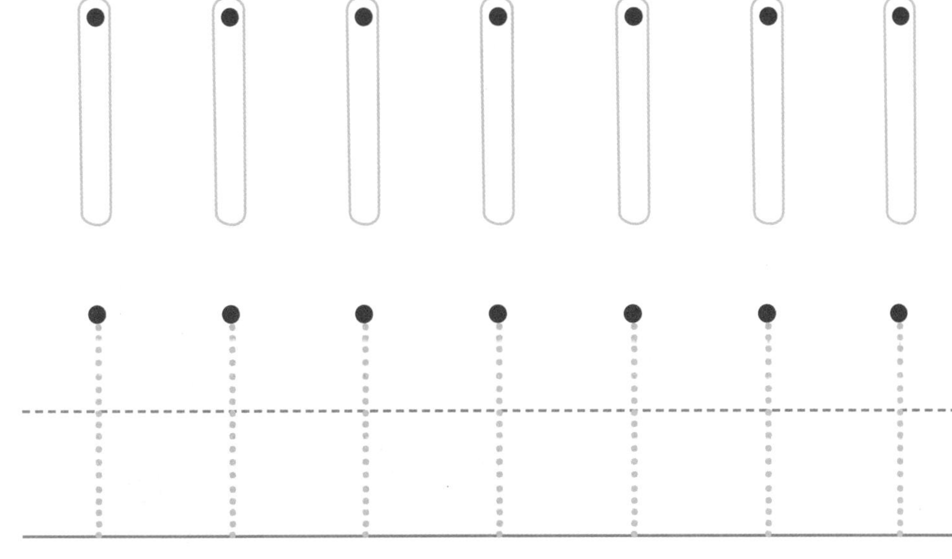

Circle your best letter.

LESSON 32 INITIAL SOUNDS

1 Add l. Say the word.

l____emon

____izard

____eg

____adder

____amp

____ips

2 Draw 4 legs on the lion.

A lion has 4 legs.

1 Trace and write.

2 Circle every L.

L	N	E	F	L
L	L	L	I	J

How many? ____

Circle every l.

How many? ____

3 Circle the word that matches the picture.

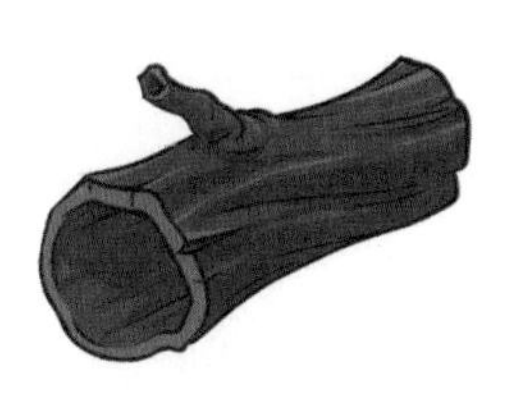 lid log	 dig dog	 bell ball
 cot cat	 flag foot	 leg led

I finished this lesson online.	This egg hatched.	I know the letter sound: Ll	I can read

1 Color **he** in green, **she** in yellow.

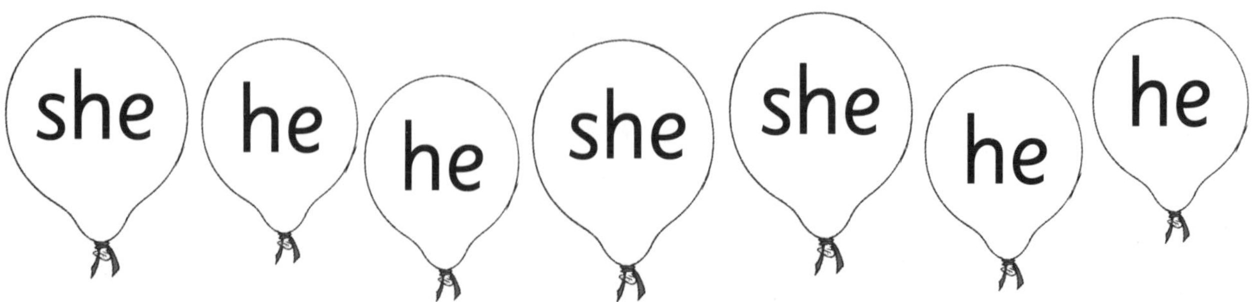

2 Trace and write.

he he she she

3 Match the word to its picture.

he

she

Cans

1 Color the right ending for the sentence. Read each sentence.

The cat can see

- a cat on a can.
- a man on a can.

The cat can see

- jam in a can.
- a tap on the can.

1 Circle the word that matches the picture.

mat man

map tap

ham jam

sat hat

fan can

bat fat

2 Complete the sentences.

in on

The bee is ________ the flower.

See a rat ________ a hat.

The cat is ________ the mat.

Read, then answer the questions.

Tom

Tom is a man.
He is hot.
He can get a fan.

1. Tom is a ____________ .

   a fan   b mat   c man

2. He is ____________ .

   a hot   b top   c hit

3. He can get a ____________ .

   a fin   b fan   c man

I finished this lesson online.	This egg hatched.	**I know** the words: he, she, in, on, see, is	**I can read**
	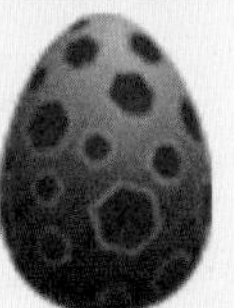		

kite

1 Match each letter to a picture.

2 Join **k** things to Kangako.

3 Color the **k** keys.

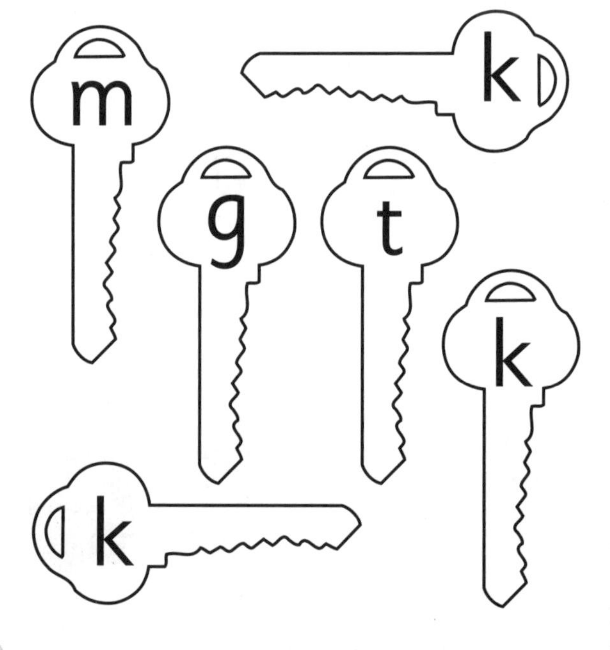

1 Give each koala a kite.

Koalas with kites.

2 Trace and write.

k k k k k k

k k k k k k

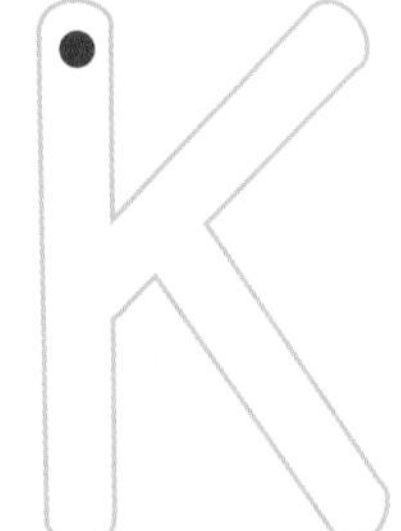

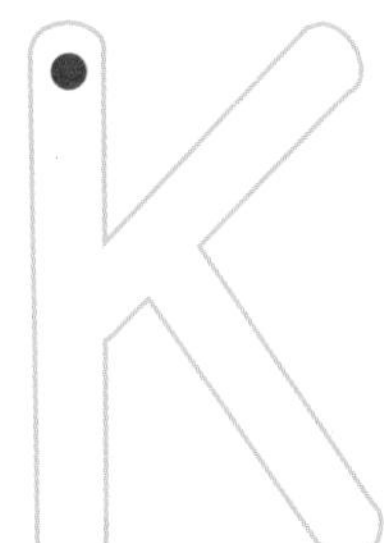

Circle your best letter.

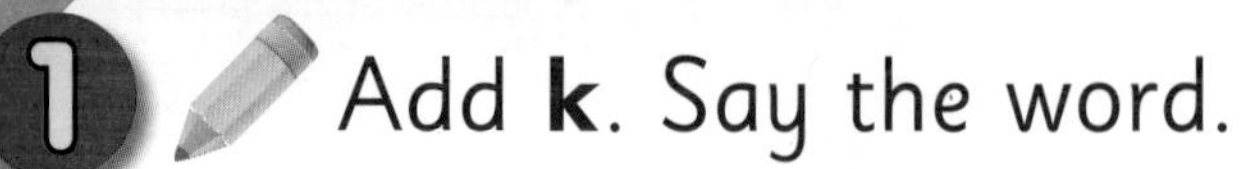

1 Add **k**. Say the word.

k____angaroo

____oala

____ey

____iss

____ite

____itten

2 Match.

A	B	C	D	E	F
b	a	f	c	d	e

G	H	I	J	K	L
h	i	g	l	j	k

Read, then answer the questions.

Ben has a pet

Ben is ten.
He has a pet hen.
The hen is red.

1 Ben is ________ .

a hen b ten c red

2 He has a pet ________ .

a cat b dog c hen

3 The hen is ________ .

a wet b red c ill

I finished this lesson online.	This egg hatched.	**I know** the letter sound: Kk	I can read
34			

as has

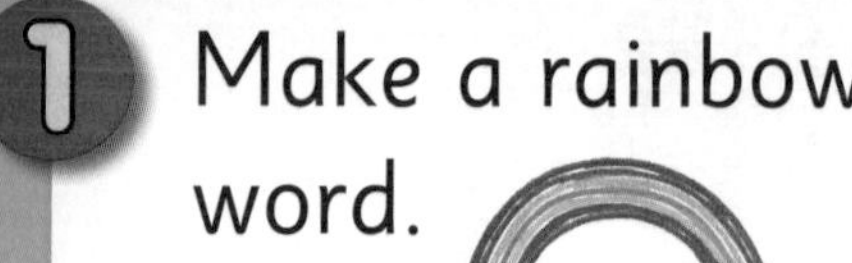

1. Make a rainbow word.

2. Find **has**.

sah	has	**am**	hat	has
am	as	**has**	*had*	**hot**
has	**had**	at	sad	*has*

3. Write **has**.

has has has

4. Complete the sentence.

Sam has a ________.

as has

1 Draw

a fan on the cat.

a tap on the can.

a man on the map.

a rat on the mat.

as has

LESSON 35 CHECK

1 Join the words that rhyme.

map	mat
fat	tap
ham	man
can	jam

2 Color the correct word. ✕ Cross out the wrong word.

She has as a map. 

I am has as good as Sam. 

3 Say the name of each picture. Color its end sound.

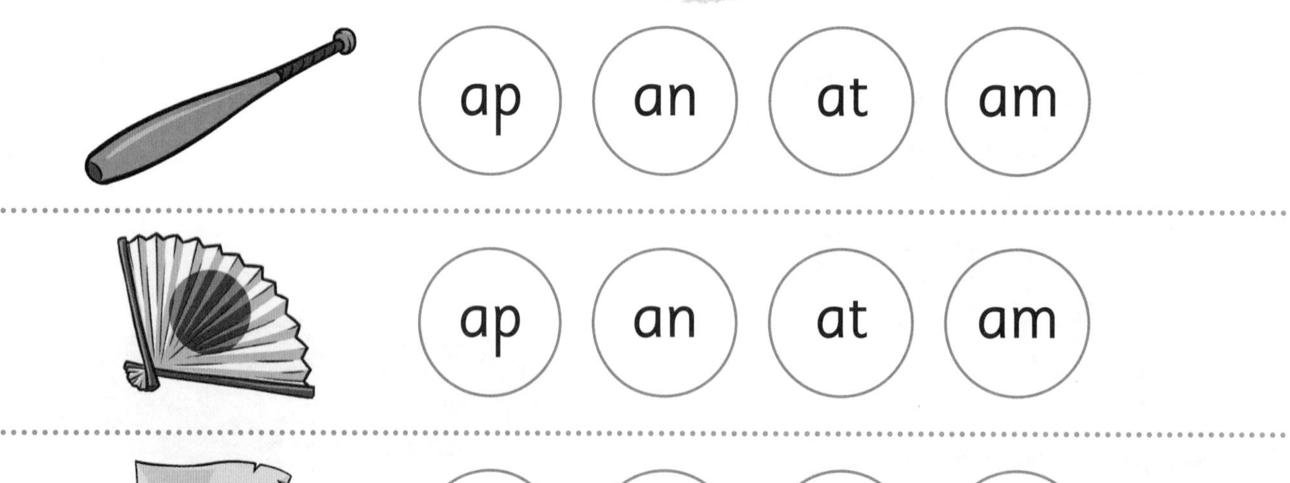

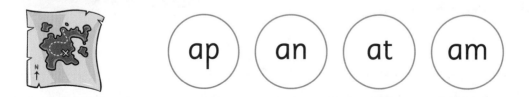

ap an at am

as has

Read, then answer the questions.

The dog and cat

The dog has a hat.
The cat has a fan.
The fan is on.

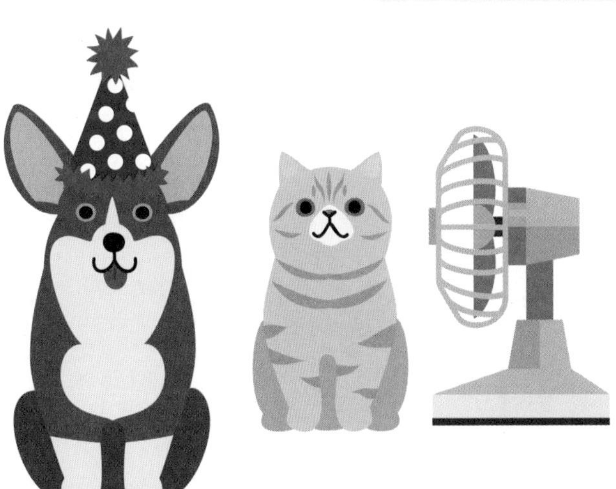

1. The dog has a ________ .

   a tap   b hat   c fan

2. The cat has a ________ .

   a fan   b sun   c fish

3. The fan is ________ .

   a red   b on   c off

I finished this lesson online.

This egg hatched.

I **know** the words: as, has

I can read

1 Color **Y** green and **y** red.

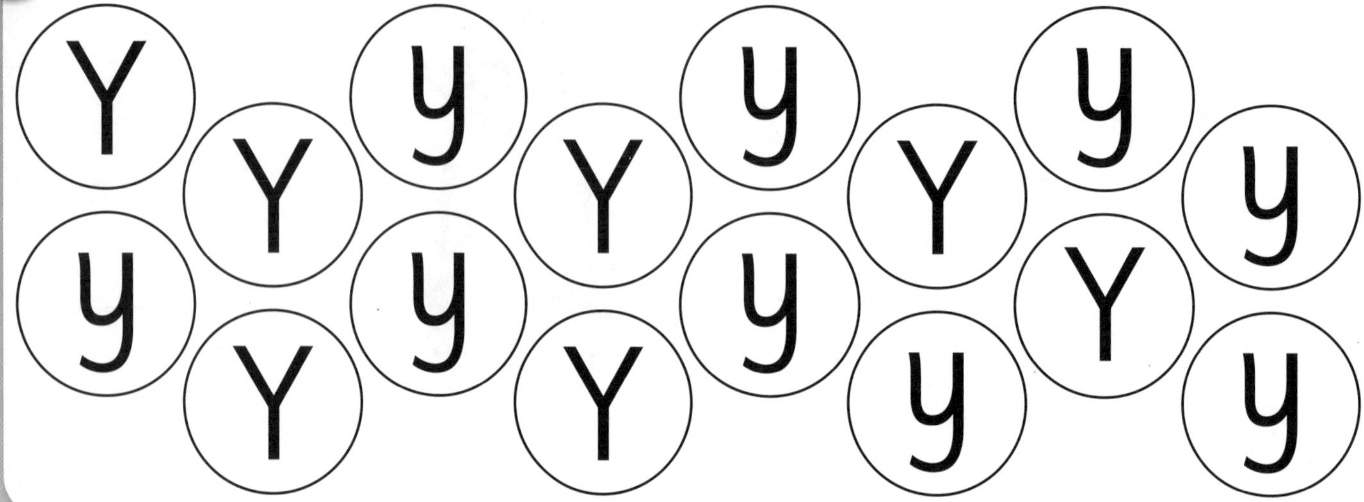

2 Color things that begin with **y**.

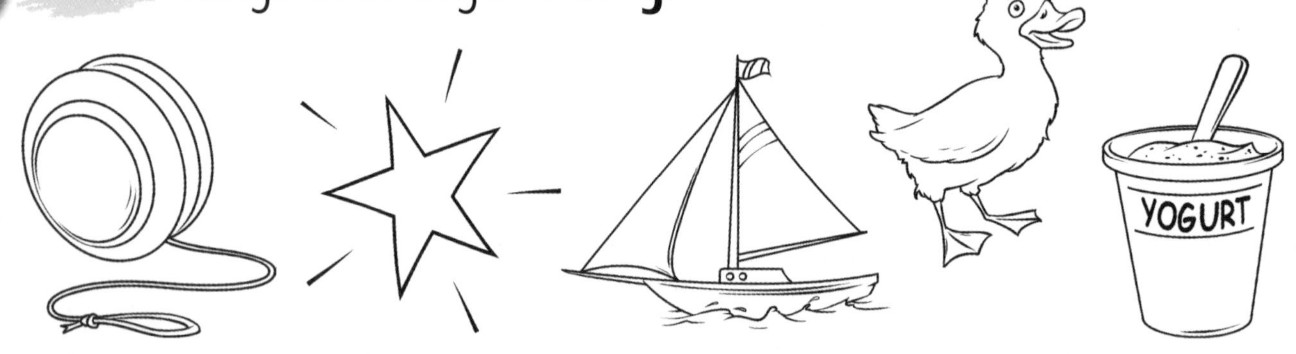

3 Color these letters on the keyboard. Y E S

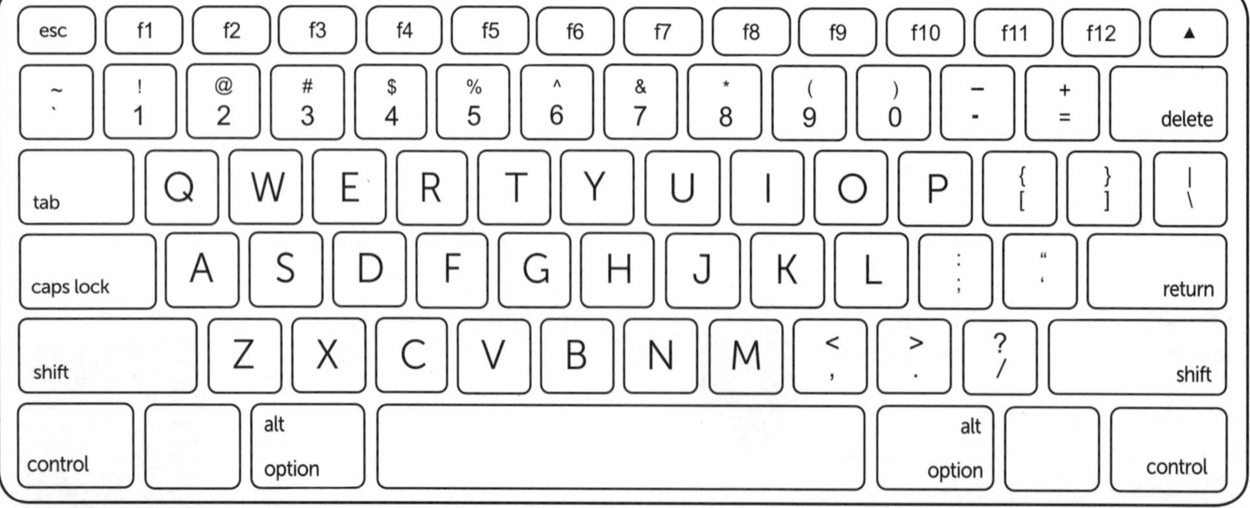

1 Trace and write.

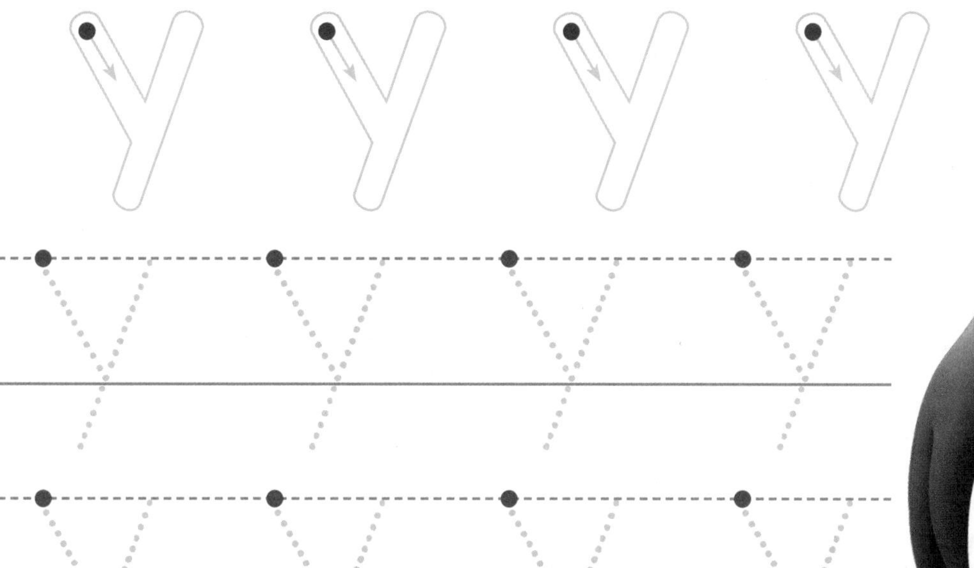

2 Add **y** to the beginning. Say the word.

____ak

____ellow

3 Add **y** to the end. Say the word.

bo____

to____

1  Trace and write.

 ______  ______

2 Circle every **Y**. Circle every **y**.

Y	W	Y	**Y**	T
I	H	Y	S	Y

How many? ____

y	y	g	o	y
o	o	y	u	y

How many? ____

3 Say the name of each picture. Circle the beginning sound.

s y m	p b g	k v f

t b d	m h n	n l i

Read, then answer the questions.

The yak

I can see a yak.
The yak has a hat.
The hat is yellow.

1. I can see a __________ .

   a yak b yes c dog

2. The yak has a __________ .

   a map b yoyo c hat

3. The hat is __________ .

   a red b yellow c blue

I finished this lesson online.	This egg hatched.	I know the letter sound: Yy	I can read

yes you

1 Make rainbow words.

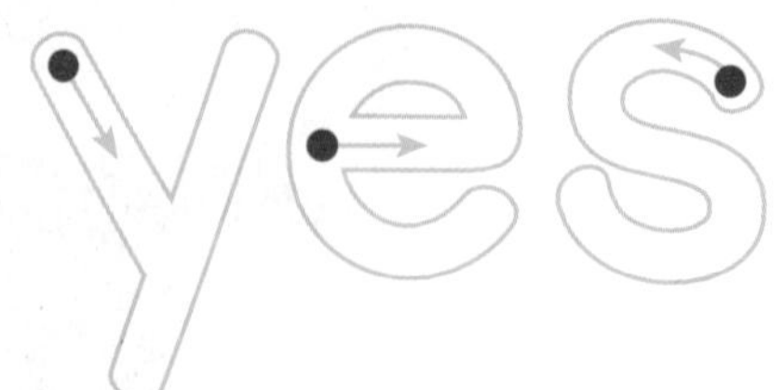

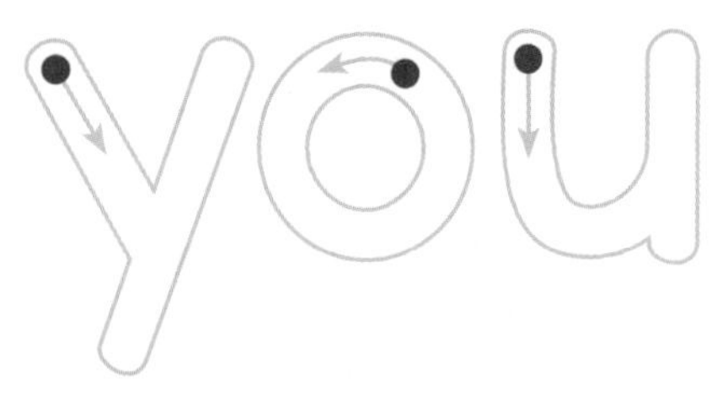

2 Color **you** in red, **yes** in yellow.

yes	our	you	in	yes
yeou	yes	see	yes	you
yet	said	yes	of	jet
you	yak	you	set	you

3 Write one of the words.

Can __________ see Sam?

Can you see six fish?

____

1 Finish each sentence with a word from the box. Read each sentence.

cat map van

Dan has a

______________________.

Dan has a

______________________.

Dan has a

______________________.

LESSON 37 CHECK

1 Write each word in the correct boxes.

yes
ant
van
you

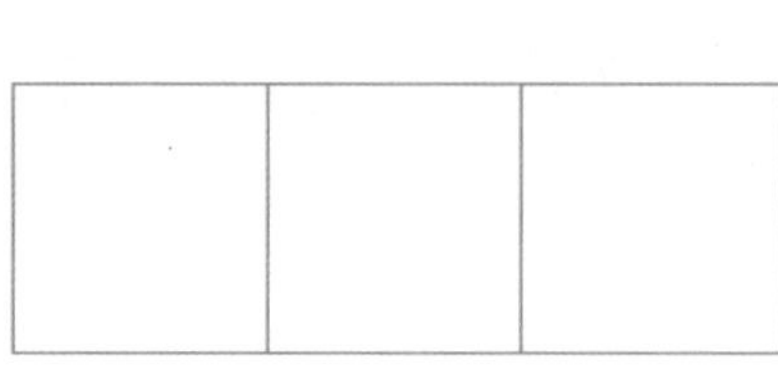

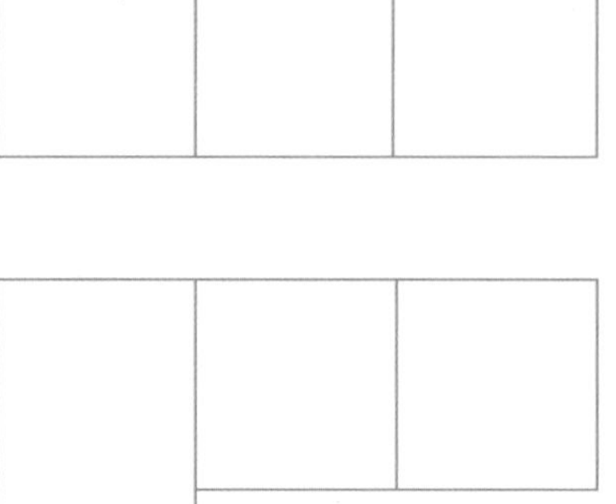
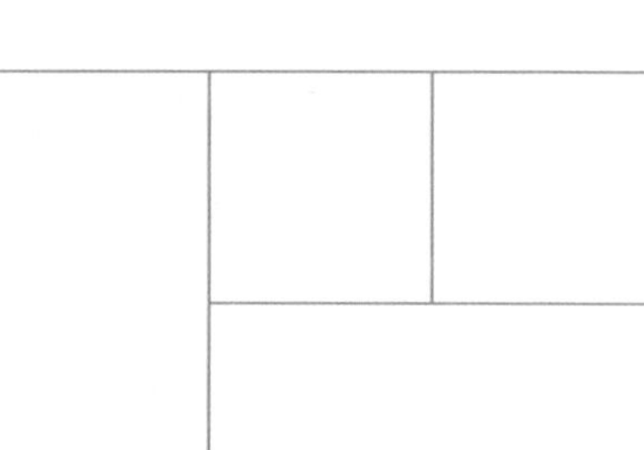

2 Join the jigsaw pieces. Write the word.

y o u ____________

y e s ____________

3 Complete the sentence.

Dan has an ant

Read, then answer the questions.

The map

Can you see the map?

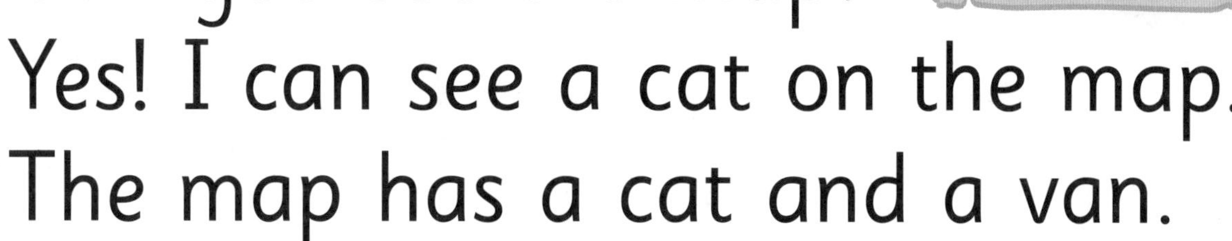

Yes! I can see a cat on the map.
The map has a cat and a van.

1. Can you see a fan on the map?

   a yes   b no   c tan

2. Can you see a cat on the map?

   a map   b yes   c no

3. The map has a cat and a ________ .

   a dog   b van   c cap

I finished this lesson online.	This egg hatched.	**I know** the words: yes, you	**I can read**

Say hello to Xpanda!

1 Match each letter to a picture.

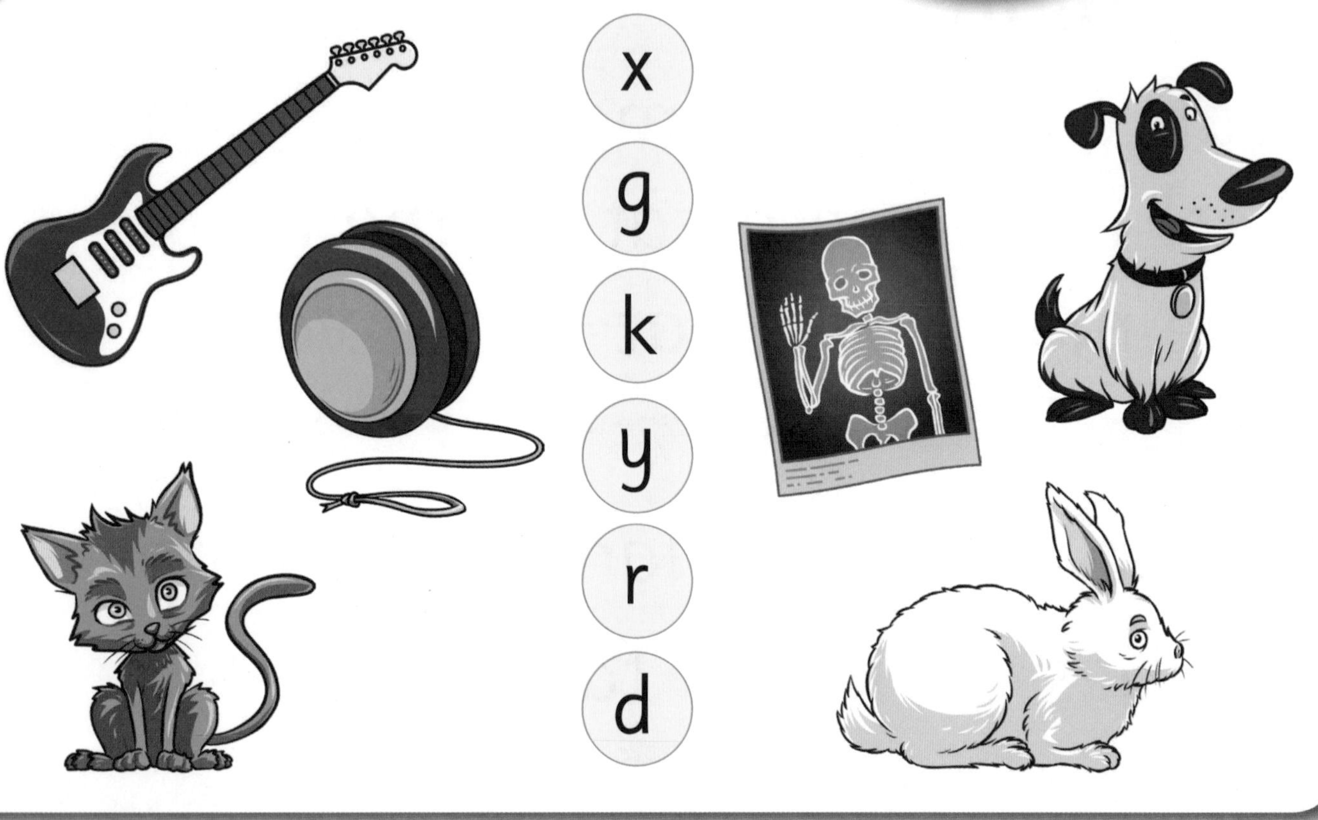

2 Which words end in **x**? Join to Xpanda.

3 Color the **x** boxes.

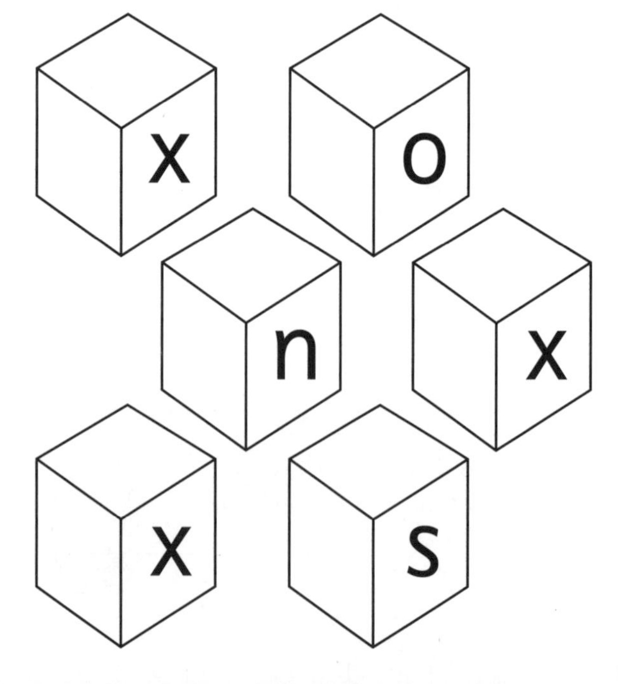

1 Help Sixty six reach the finish line. Follow the track.

2 Slice the pizzas.

3 Trace and write.

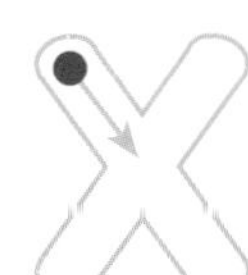

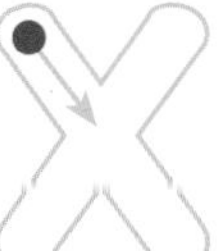
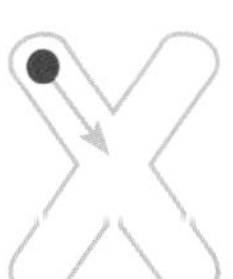

Circle your best letter.

1 Finish each word with an **x**.

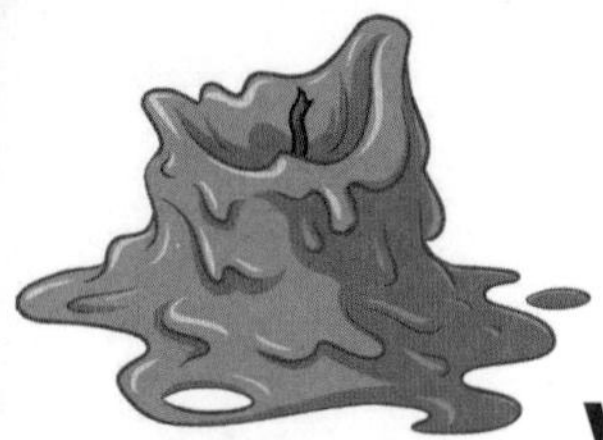

wa x

ta ___ i

mi ___ er

e ___ it

fo ___

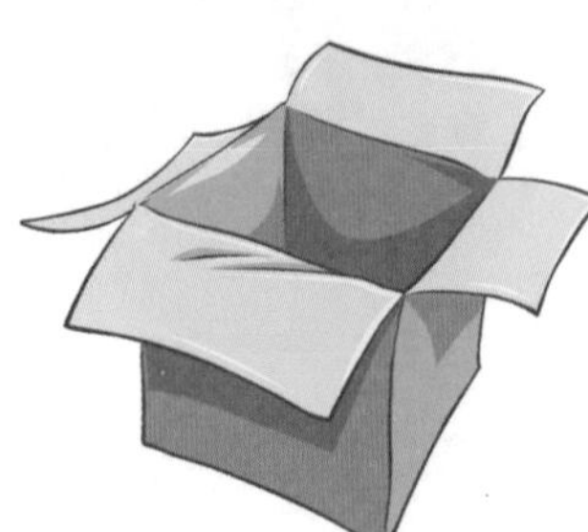

bo ___

2 Put an **x** on every box.

1 Trace and write.

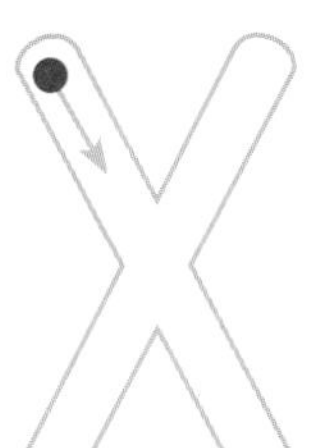

X ______ x ______

2 Circle every X. Circle every x.

X	M	I	T	X
L	X	X	O	X

How many? ____

x	x	i	x	t
a	x	m	x	l

How many? ____

3 Add an **x** then say the word.

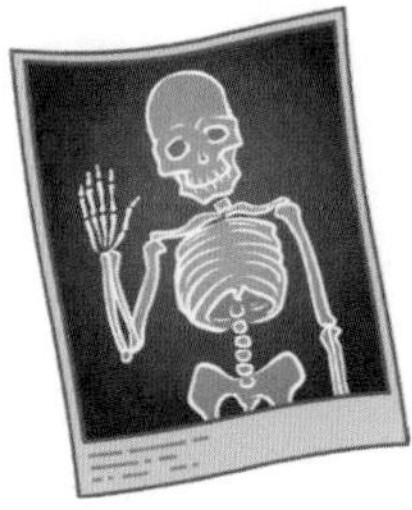

______ -ray

si ______

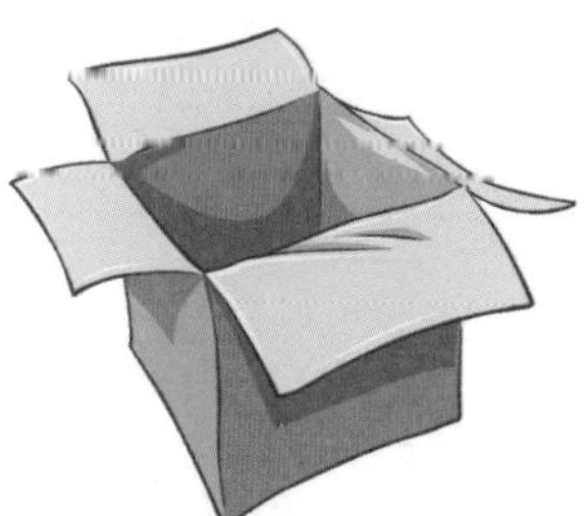

bo ______

mi ______

I finished this lesson online.

This egg hatched.

I know the letter sound: Xx

I can read

1 Match each letter to a picture.

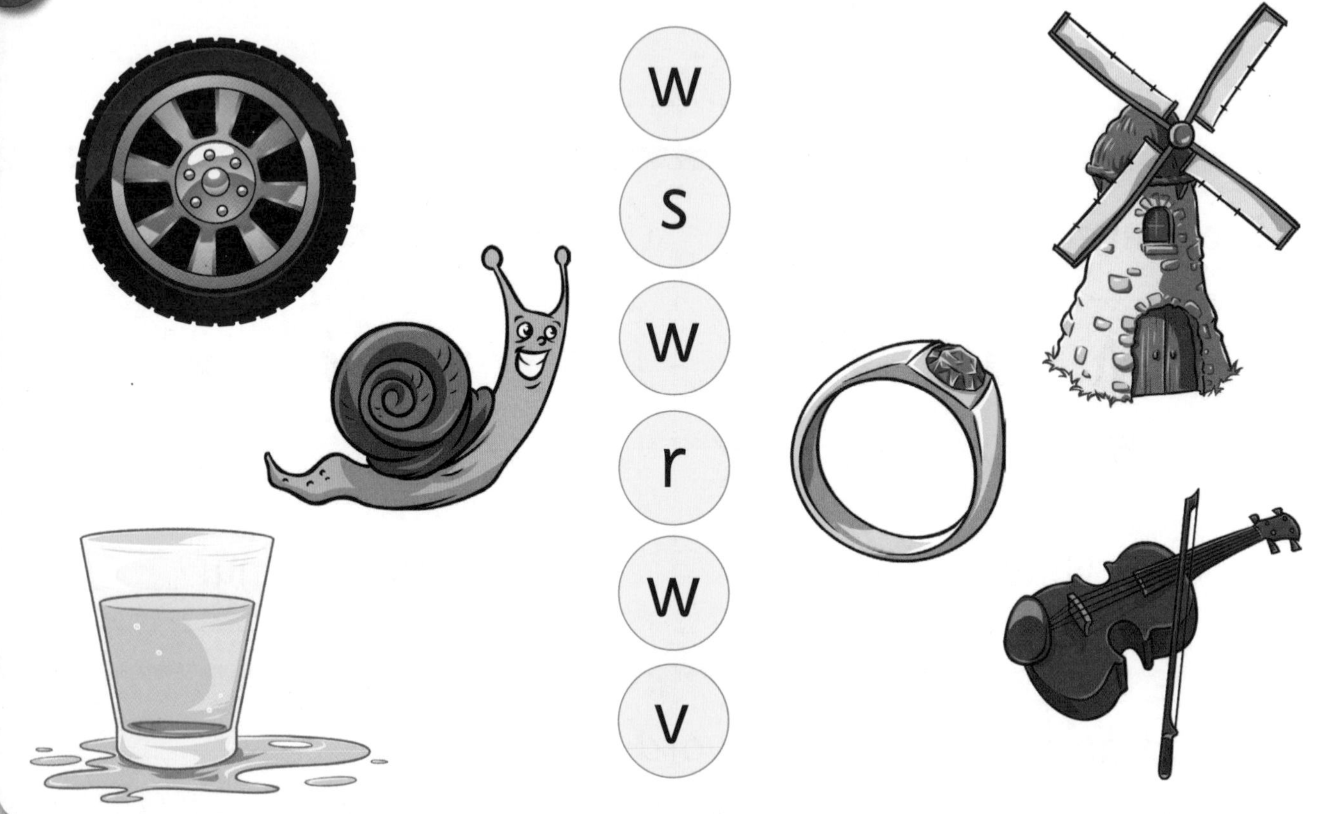

2 Join **w** things to Wheely Whale.

3 Color the **w** whales.

Ww

1 
Draw waves for Wheely Whale.

2 Trace and write.

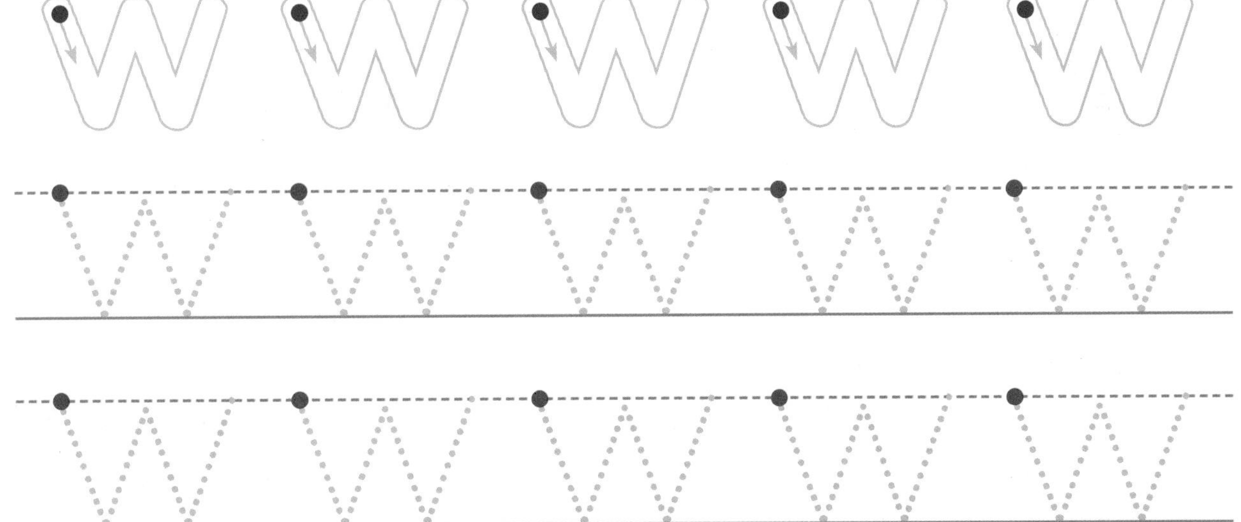

Circle your best letter.

1 Add **w** and then say the word.

w eb

____hale

____in

____orm

____ell

____ig

2 Draw some whiskers on the wolf.

A wolf with whiskers.

Ww

1 Trace and write.

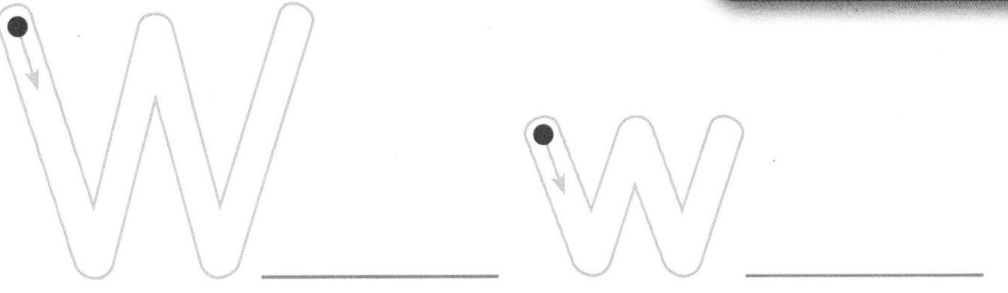

2 Circle every **W**.

How many? ____

Circle every **w**.

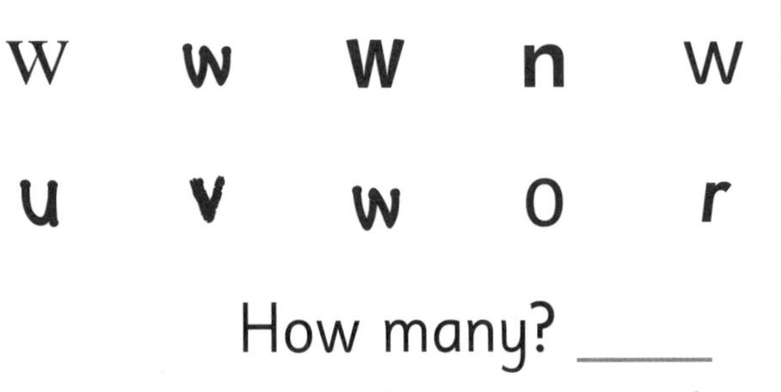

How many? ____

3 Color the words in the web that begin with **w**.

I finished this lesson online.

This egg hatched.

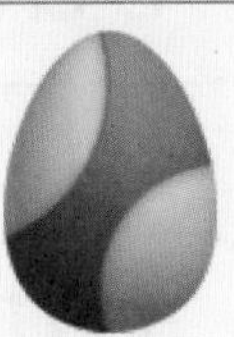

I know the letter sound: Ww

I can read

1 Use color to match words that rhyme.

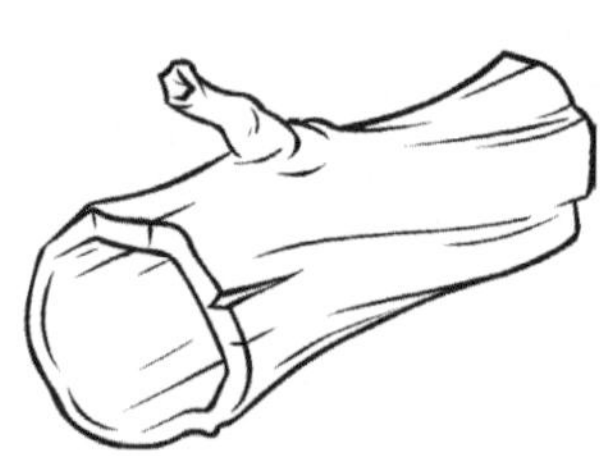

2 Color the odd one out in each row.

ran	man	pat	can
mad	bad	had	van
zap	dam	jam	ham
hat	can	bat	sat
tap	map	rat	gap

Review

1 Match to a picture.

The fish
has fins.

The fish has a tin.

Dan has an ant in a hat.

A rat has a hat.

The cat can see a cat on a can.

1 Trace and write the words.

he the she

2 Join Sandy Can to the word **can**.

can no yes  can can can on

3 Write the words in the correct box.

as you
has on
yes see
in is

2 letter words	3 letter words

1 Circle the pictures that start with the letter.

g  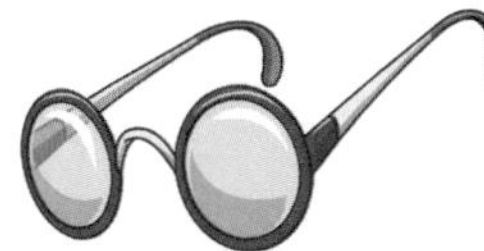  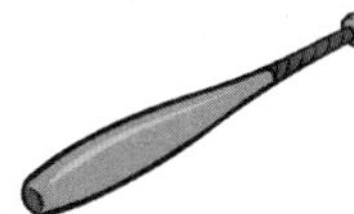 

k     

2 Write each word in a box.

has see

 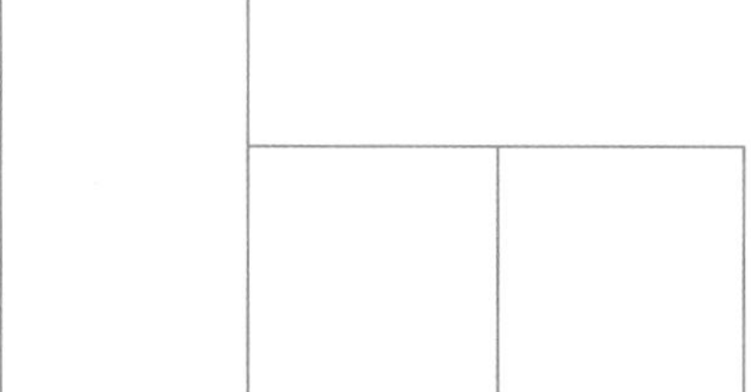

3 Draw a picture for each sentence.

The fish has a fin.	
The cat can see the fish.	

I finished this lesson online.	This egg hatched.	I know the alphabet	I can read

Quiz

1 Write the letter. Color the pictures that begin with the letter.

g				
k				
l				
y				
w				

2 Join the word to a picture.

web fish box

Quiz

Read, then answer the questions.

Dan

Dan has a cat and a fish.
He can see the fish.
The fish is big.

3 Dan has a cat and a ________ .

a dog b fish c fan

4 Can you see the fish?

a yes b no

5 Can you see the cat?

a yes b no

6 The fish is ________ .

a big b little c black

SUPER!

YOU COMPLETED

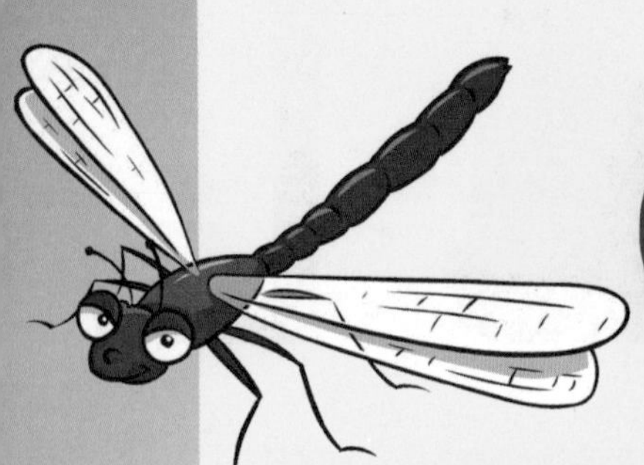

MAP 4

YOU CAN:

- ☐ Read and write the alphabet.
- ☐ Read these words: **yes, you, fish, she**.
- ☐ Read lots of sentences, such as:
  The cat can see the fish.
- ☐ Read these books:

Secret Sentences

Find the sentence that matches the picture.
Color each word. Write the sentence.

A	the	see	top
bee	is	in	ran
pan	mat	the	and
pop	bad	tree	on

A

The	vet	on	the
you	can	see	box
is	sun	the	cat
bed	bee	had	I

The

Find the hidden pictures

Find each drawing in the picture.

Ii

ice

ice-cream

insects

Jj

jug

juice

jet

Kk

kangaroo

kite

kitten

key

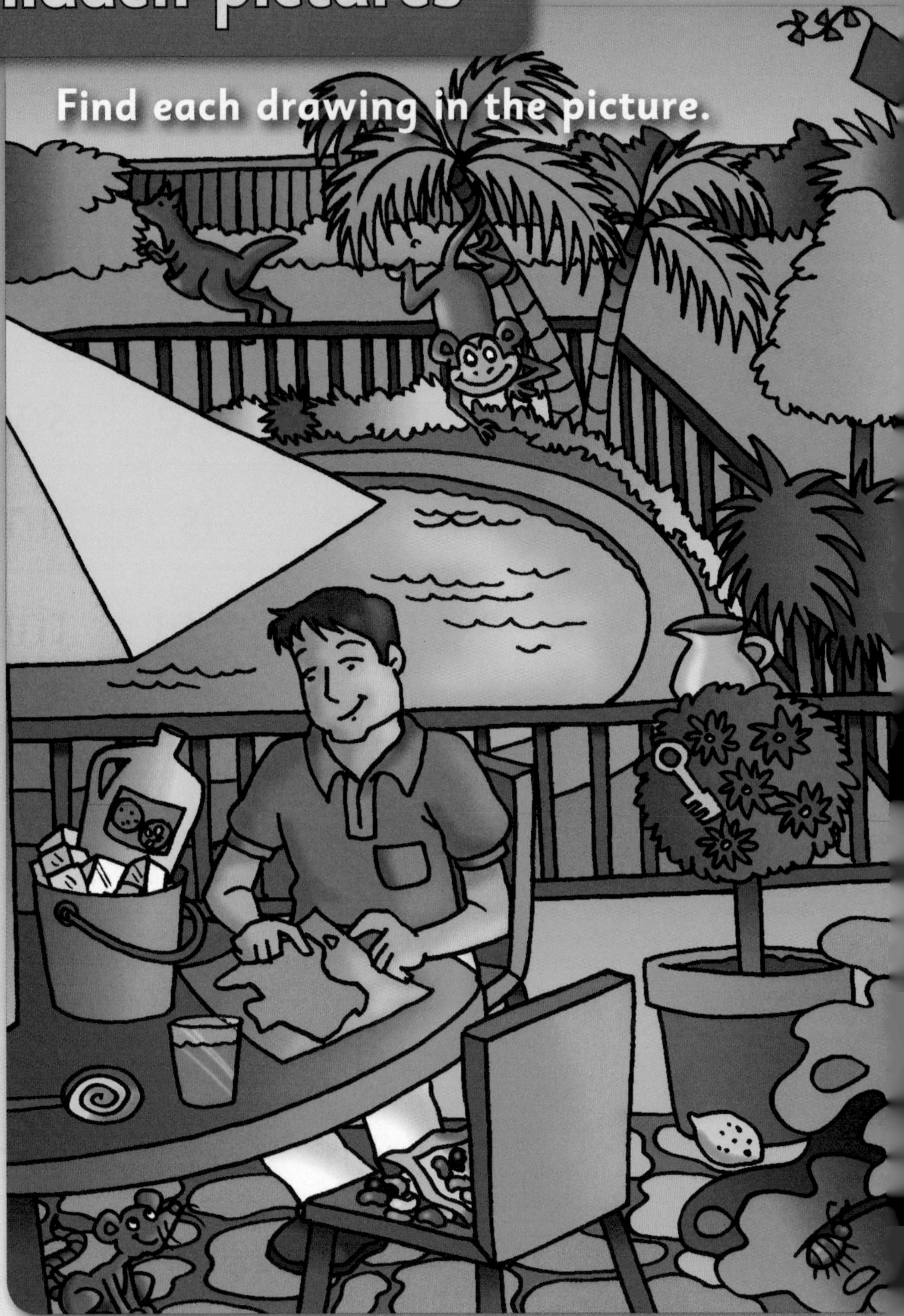

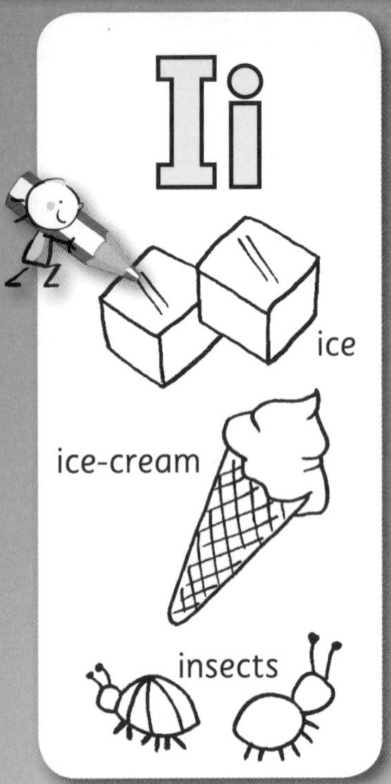

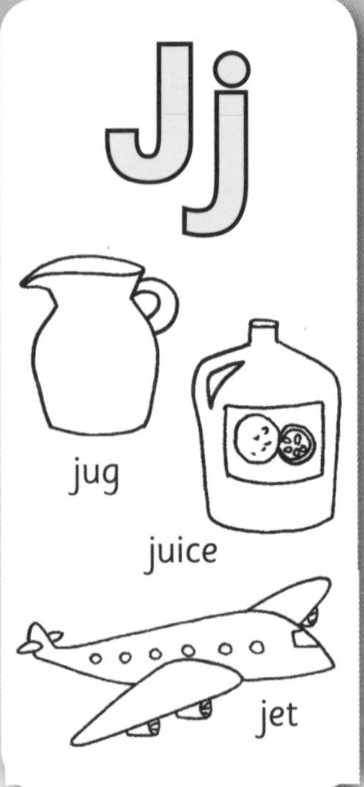

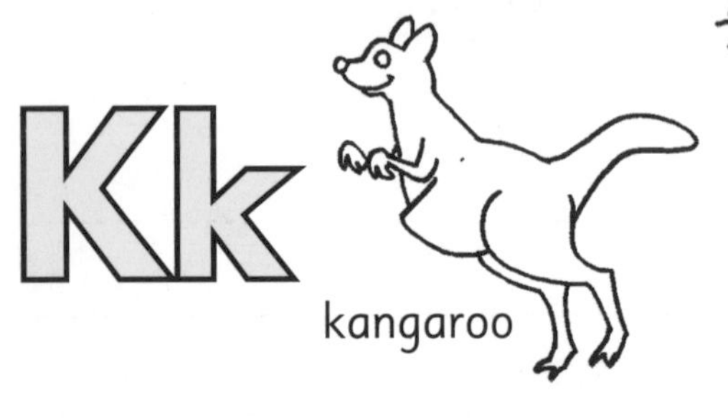

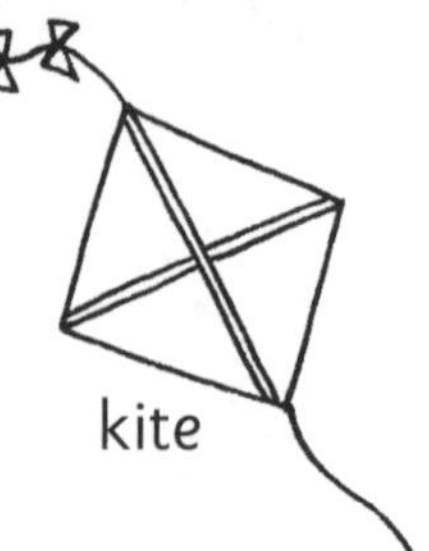

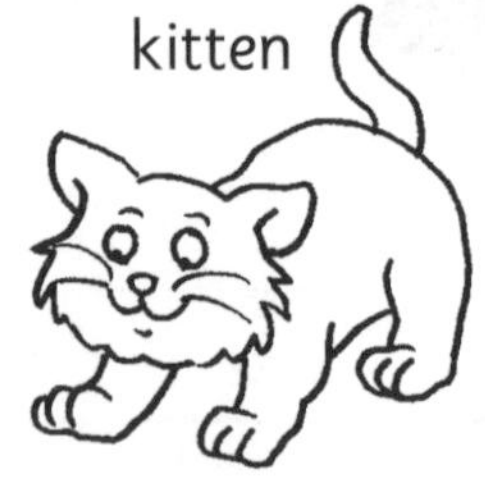

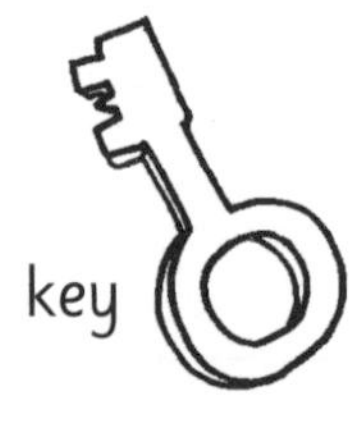

Mm
milk
MILK
mouse
monkey
man
map

Ll

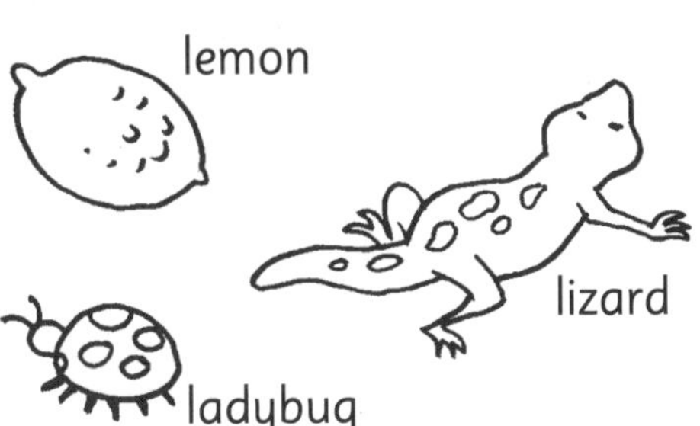
lemon
lizard
ladybug

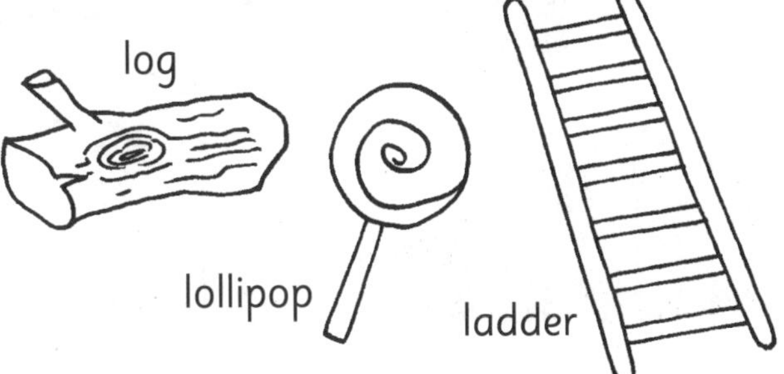
log
lollipop
ladder

1 Match each letter to a picture.

u

g

u

l

u

c

2 Join **u** things to Underting.

3 Color the **u** umbrellas.

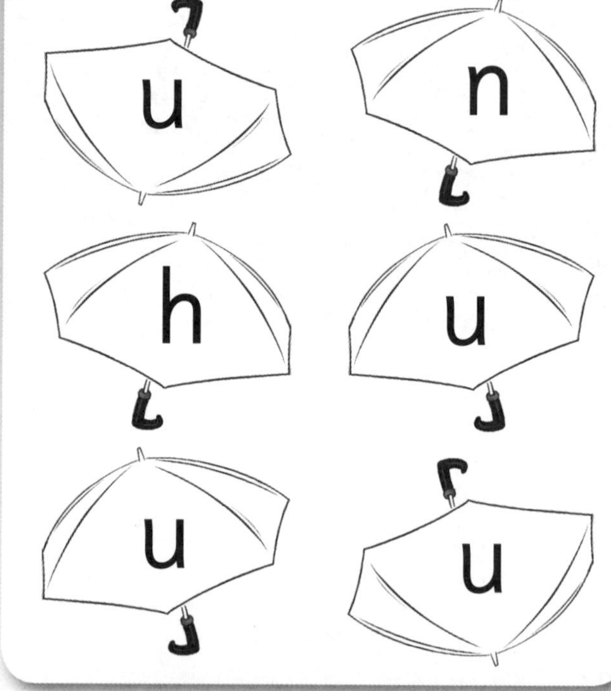

1. Trace the upside down umbrella.

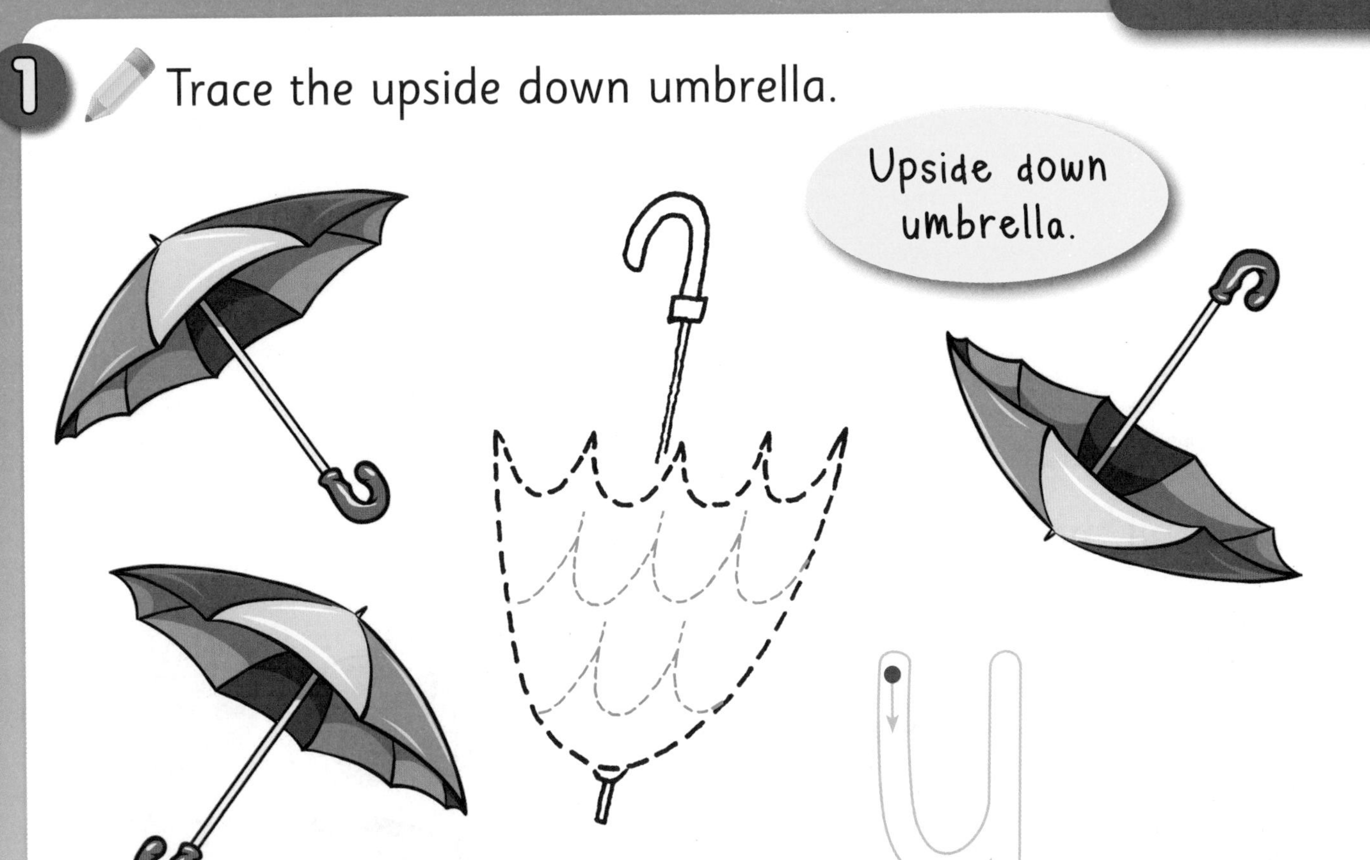
Upside down umbrella.

2. Trace and write.

u u u u u u

1 Trace and write.

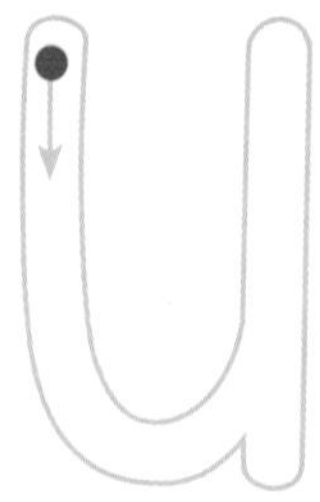

2 Circle all the **u** words.

3 Match each picture to a word.

cup

bun

umbrella

sun

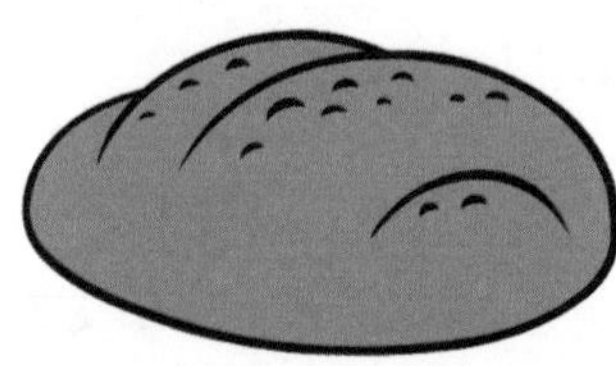

Read, then answer the questions.

Jazz and Sam

Jazz has a cup.
Sam has a cup and a bun.
Sam cut the bun.

1 Jazz has a ____________ .

a bun b cup c hat

2 Sam has a cup and a ____________ .

a cap b cup c bun

3 Sam cut the ____________ .

a bun b fun c bat

I finished this lesson online.	This egg hatched.	I know the letter sound: Uu	I can read
41			

1 Complete the alphabet snakes.

a b ___ d e ___

g h ___ j k ___

m ___ o ___ q ___ s

t u ___ w ___ y ___

2 Draw lines to match.

1 Say the word. Write the beginning sound.

1 In each group color two pictures that rhyme.

2 Circle every **Qq**.

q u S c Q
q Q Q 0 q

How many? ____

Circle every **Uu**.

U u j v U
n U s U i

How many? ____

3 Circle the word that matches the picture.

fin
fan

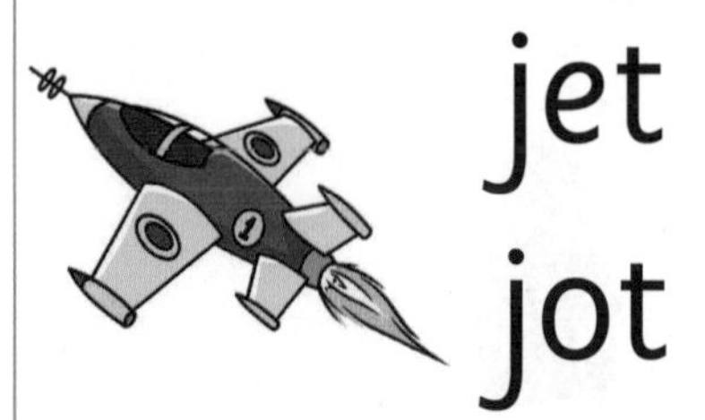

jet
jot

bug
big

1 Draw lines to match.

K E Y Q N A

2 Color **at** words red, **an** words blue.

cat	hat	man	fan
van	rat	pan	tan

3 Complete the sentences.

hat fat can

I ________ see Sam.

She has a ________ .

The rat is ________ .

I finished this lesson online.

This egg hatched.

I know the alphabet

I can read

id

1 Trace.

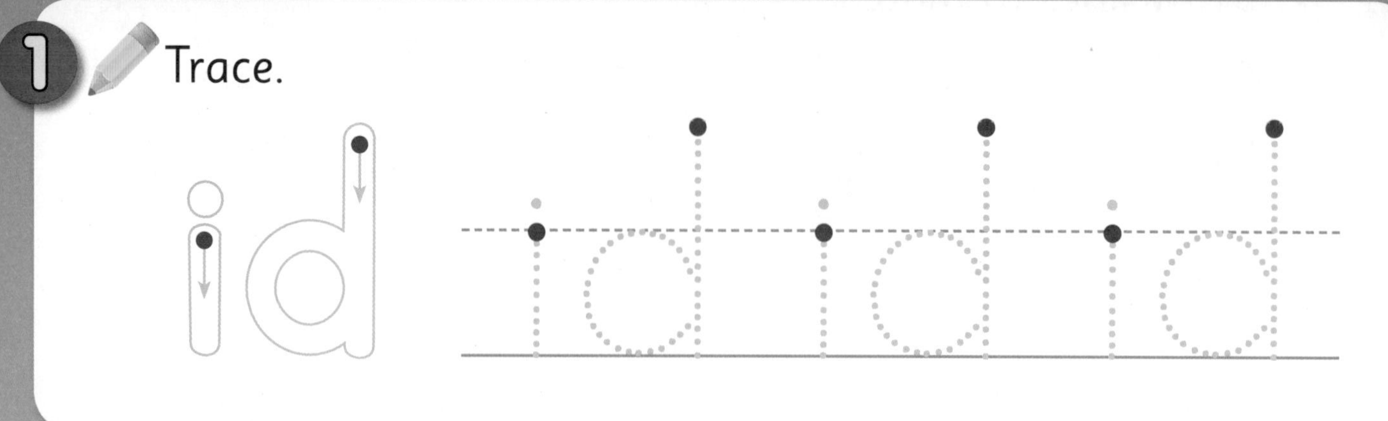

2 Color **id** words.

did	Sid	fat	cup	hid
sat	lid	man	kid	van

3 Match the word to its picture.

lid

hid

kid

did

1 Complete the sentence.

I am Sid the

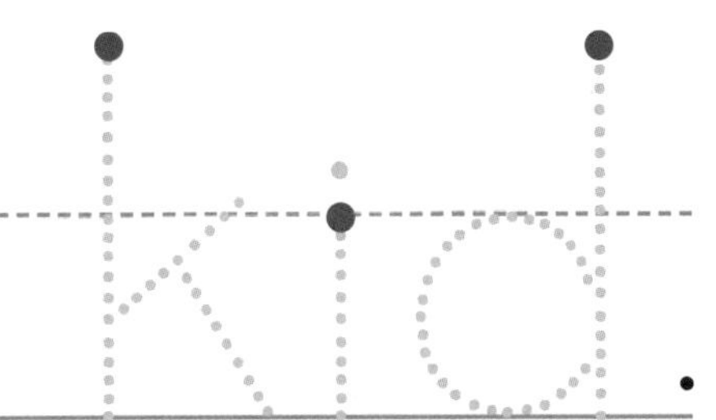

2 Complete the sentences.

did Sid lid

Sid has a bat.

Can Sid hit the ___________ ?

Yes! Sid ___________ hit the lid.

1 Complete the words. Use Sid the kid's letters.

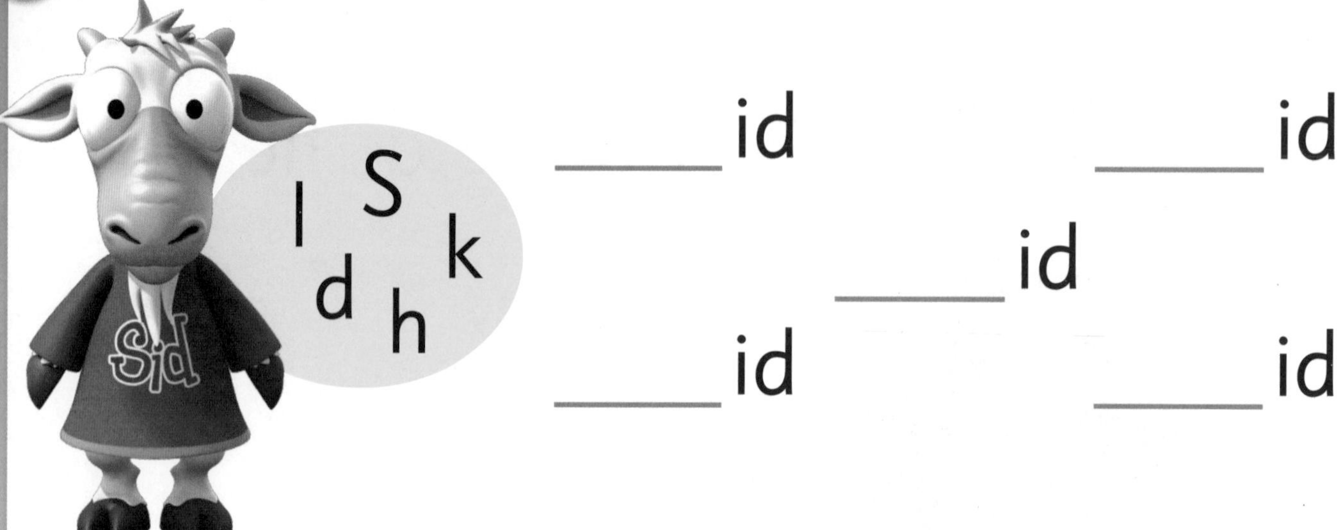

____id ____id

____id

____id ____id

2 Color the odd one out in each row.

lid	had	kid	Sid
did	rid	sad	bid

3 Complete the sentence.

Sid hit the

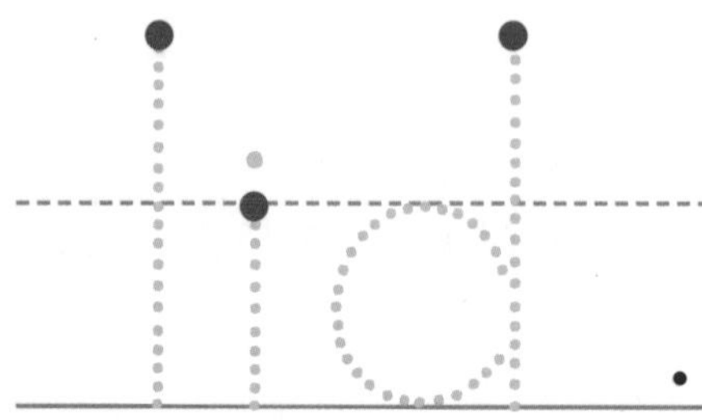

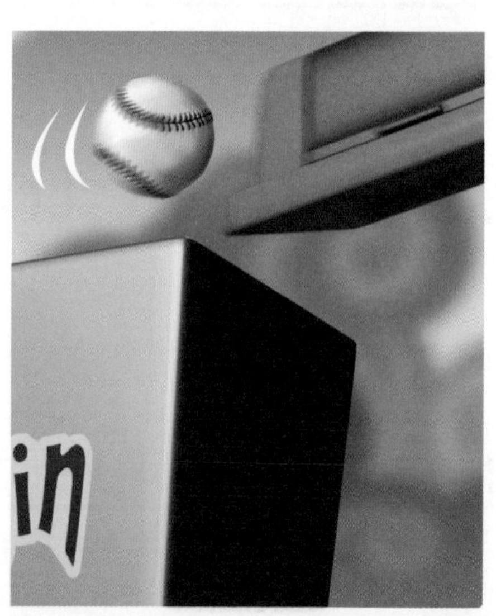

Read, then answer the questions.

Sid the kid

Sid is a kid.
He has a hat.
Sid hid in a log.

1 Sid is a ________.

a kitten b did c kid

2 He has a ________.

a log b hat c hot

3 Sid hid in a ________.

a leg b log c lid

I finished this lesson online.	This egg hatched.	I know the **id** word family: kid, hid, Sid, did	I can read

1 Complete.

Read	Write	Color
six		
mix		
win		
pin		

2 Draw

a six pins.

b a big tin.

1 Match each picture to a word.

six

mix

win

pin

2 Write the words on the correct tin.

fix win
bin six
mix pin

3 Complete each word family.

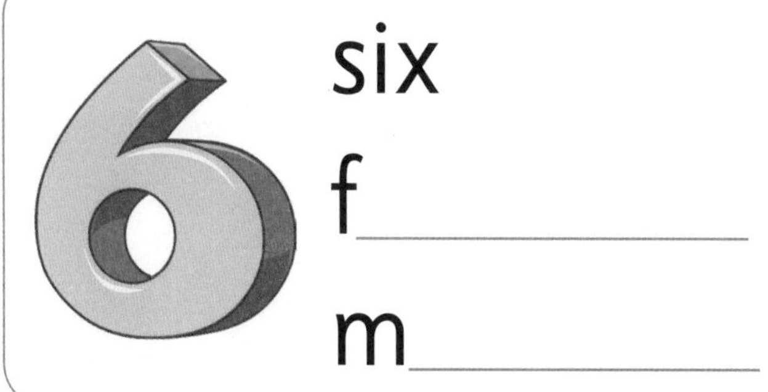

six
f__________
m__________

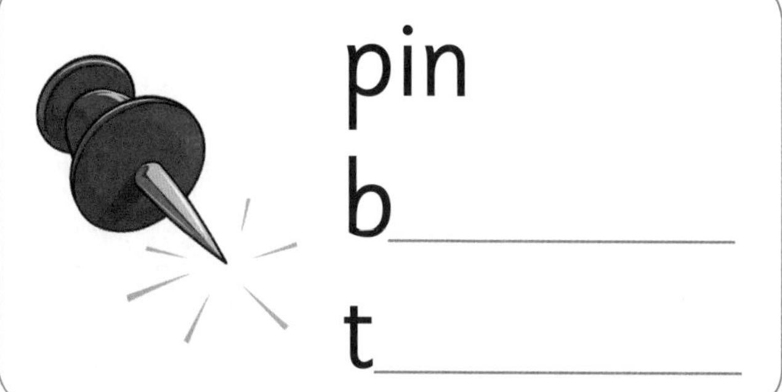

pin
b__________
t__________

1 Complete.

Read	Write	Color
Sid		
lid		
hid		
kid		

2 Draw

a a lid on the bin.

b Sid the kid.

1 Find the words. Color **you** = blue, **can** = red, **see** = green.

y	o	u	s	e	e	c	a	n
s	e	e	c	a	n	y	o	u
c	a	n	y	o	u	s	e	e
s	e	e	c	a	n	y	o	u

2 Make a word with the letters on the fridge.

_____ix _____in

_____in _____ix

3 Draw a picture for this sentence.

I can see six pink pigs.

I finished this lesson online.	This egg hatched.	I know the word families: ix, in, id	I can read

1 Complete.

Read	Write	Color
sit		
bit		
hit		
fit		

2 Color the **it** words blue and the **in** words red.

pin	spin	it	tin	sit
bit	fit	bin	hit	fin
skin	win	lit	in	kit

1 Write the words in the boxes. Complete the sentences with the word.

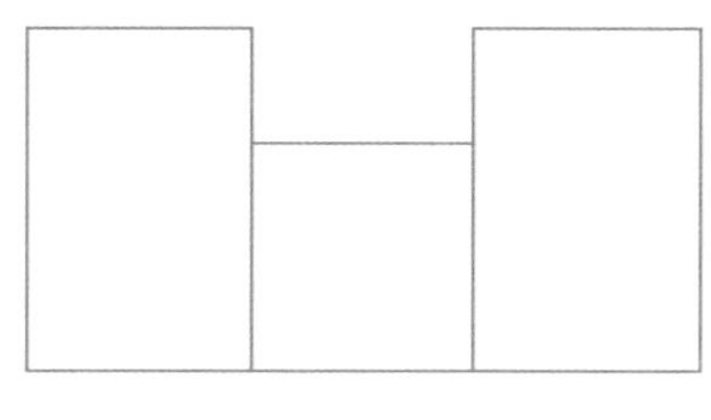

I am ________ .

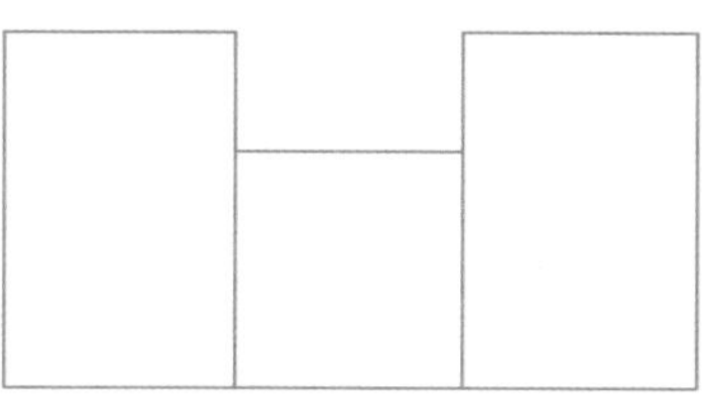

He ________ the apple.

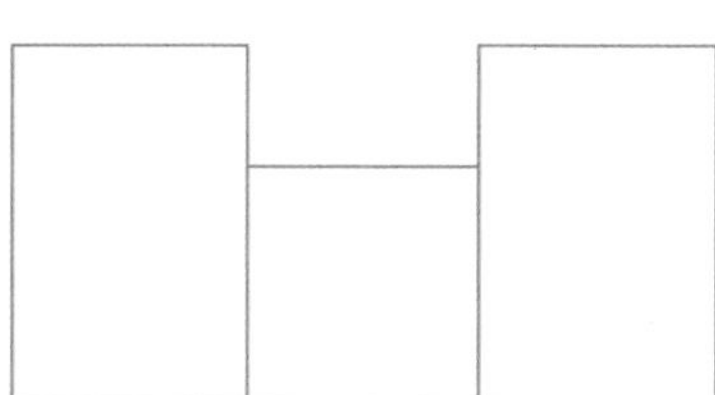

She ________ the ball.

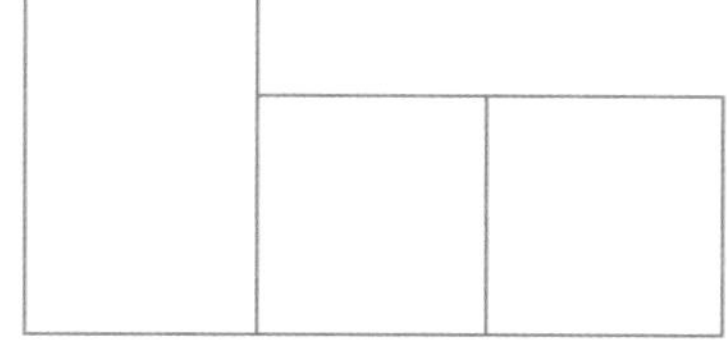

The fish has a ________ .

2 Color the correct word.

Can you

on it?

Can it

?

We can
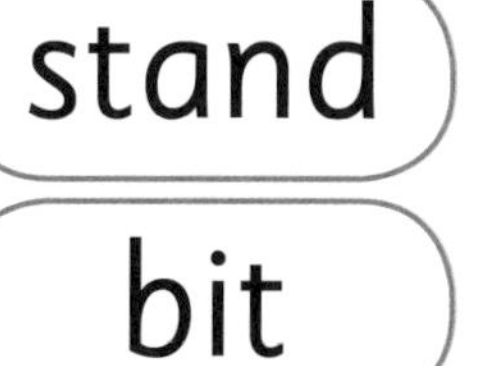

on it.

We can swing / win ?

1 Color by word family.

Read, then answer the questions.

The red top

Sam has a top.
It is big and red.
It can spin.

1 Sam has a ________ .

a tip b top c tap

2 The top is ____________ .

a a bit b little c big and red

3 The top can ________ .

a spin b bin c fin

I finished this lesson online.	This egg hatched.	I know the word: it	I can read
45			

1 Complete.

Read	Write	Color
wig		
dig		
pig		
fig		

2 Circle the word that matches the picture.

wig
win

pit
pig

lit
leg

1 Make rainbow words. 

2 Color **like** in blue and **said** in orange.

said	like	said	see
like	ill	like	like
said	like	it	like
add	sed	said	like

3 Write **like** and **said**.

like like like

said said said

1 Complete the sentence.

“This is Matt the ant,”

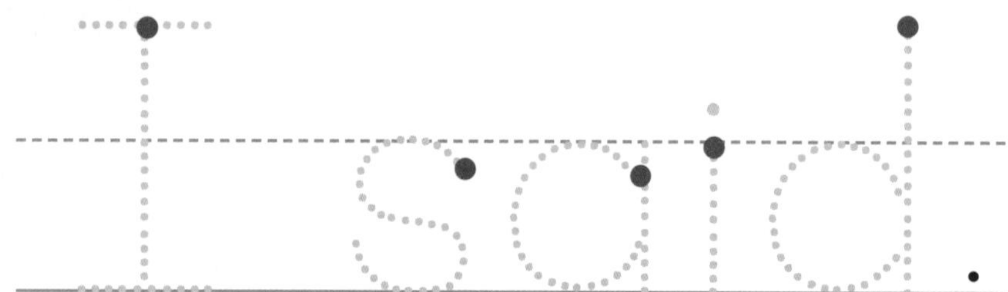

2 Complete the sentences.

big said like

I ____________ my big horse.

I like my ____________ bed.

“I like my big ring,”
she ____________.

said
like

Read, then answer the questions.

Sam's bed

Sam has a bed.

"I like my big bed," said Sam.

"I can sit on it."

1. Sam has a __________ .

   a wig   b box   c bed

2. Sam said, "I like my __________."

   a boxes   b big bed   c Tom

3. Can Sam sit on his bed?

   a yes   b no

I finished this lesson online.	This egg hatched.	I know the words: like, said	I can read
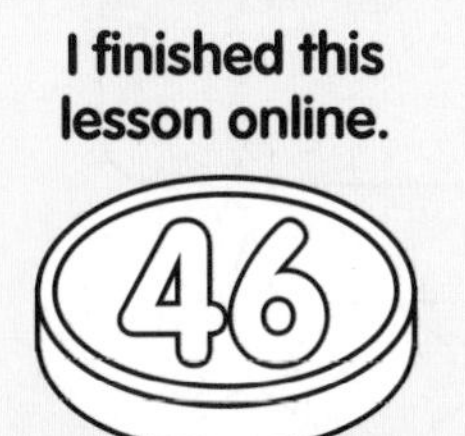			

this

1 Trace.

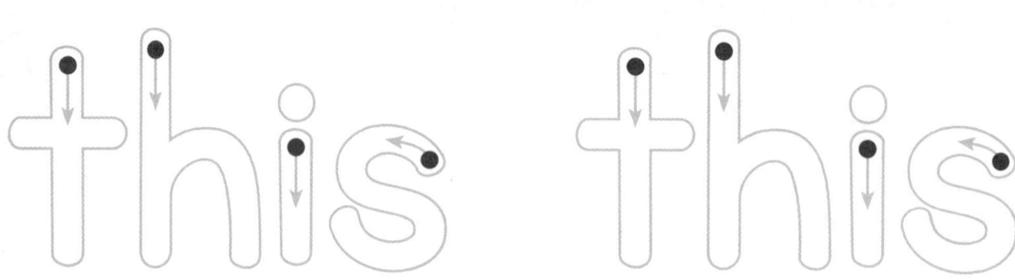

2 Help Scribble Stick find his way to his list.
Join up all the **this** words.

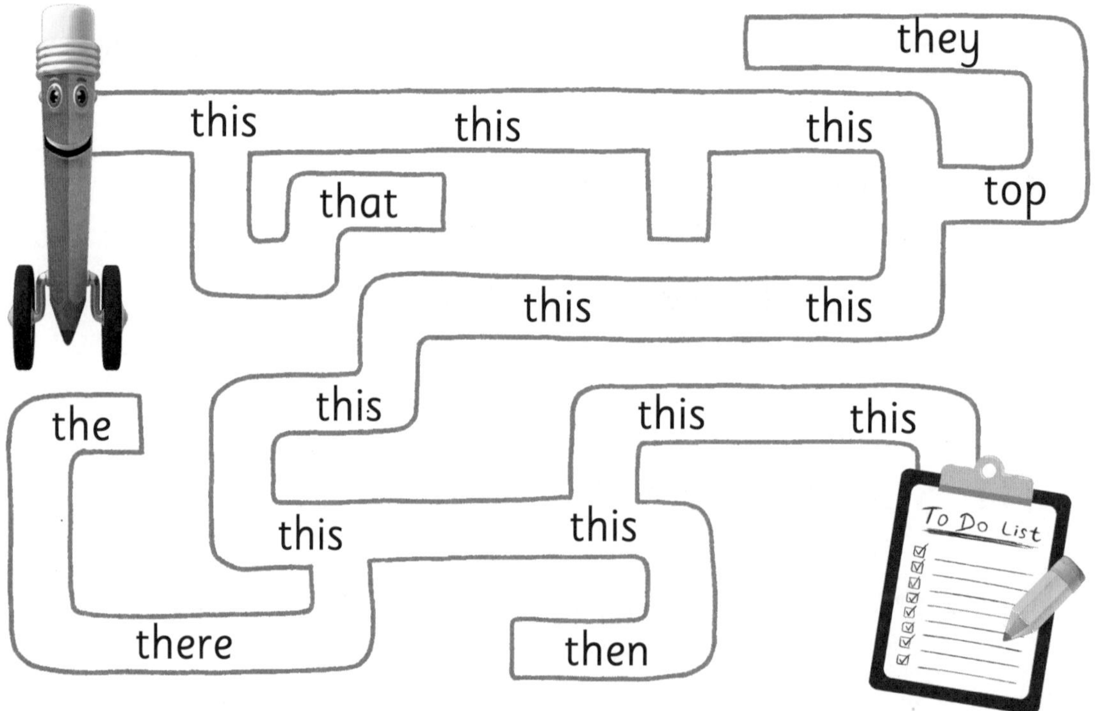

3 Circle the word **this**.

This is Sid the kid. This is the big pig. This is the big fish.

Color a star each time you find **this**.

1 Complete each sentence. Draw a picture.

This is Sid the kid.

This is a big fish.

2 Color the correct word.

This is the (six / big) pig.

(Can / This) the big pig wag it?

Yes! The big pig (the / can) wag it.

1 Write the words.

	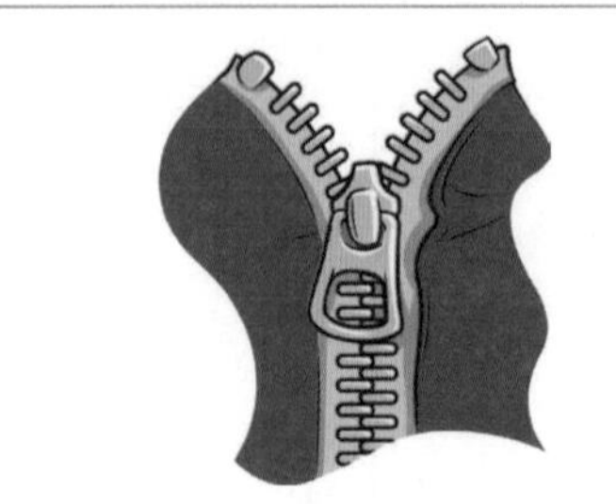	
fin		

	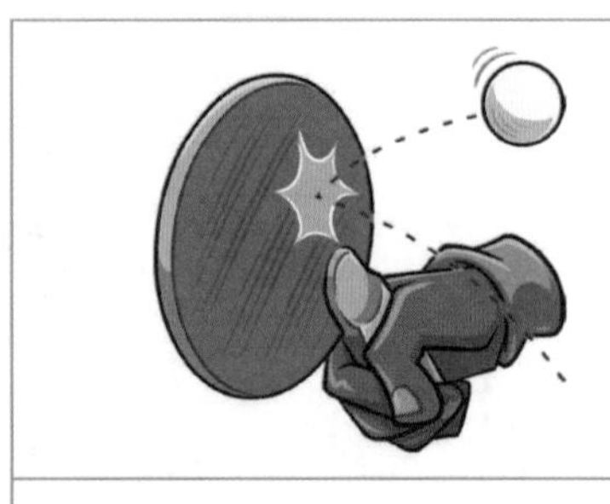	

WORD BANK

pig pin mix fig lid
six hit fin zip

this

1 In each group, color two pictures that rhyme.

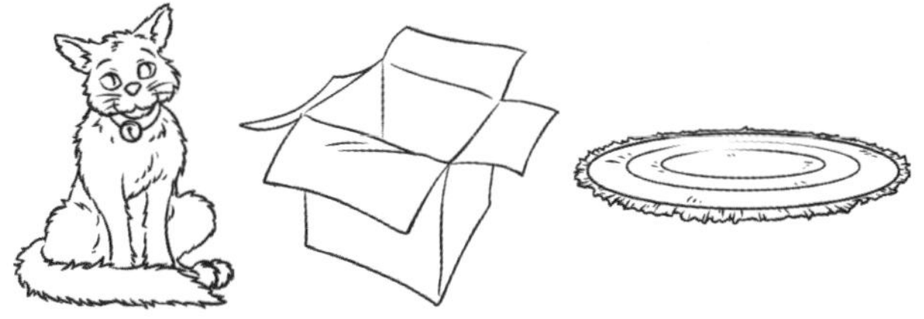

2 Color the **id** words blue, the **it** words yellow and the **ix** words red.

fix	hit	lid	sit	kid
fit	mix	hid	did	six

3 Complete the sentences.

This Can

_________ Sam see the big pig?

_________ is Sam the ant.

I finished this lesson online.	This egg hatched.	I know the word: this	I can read

1 Trace.

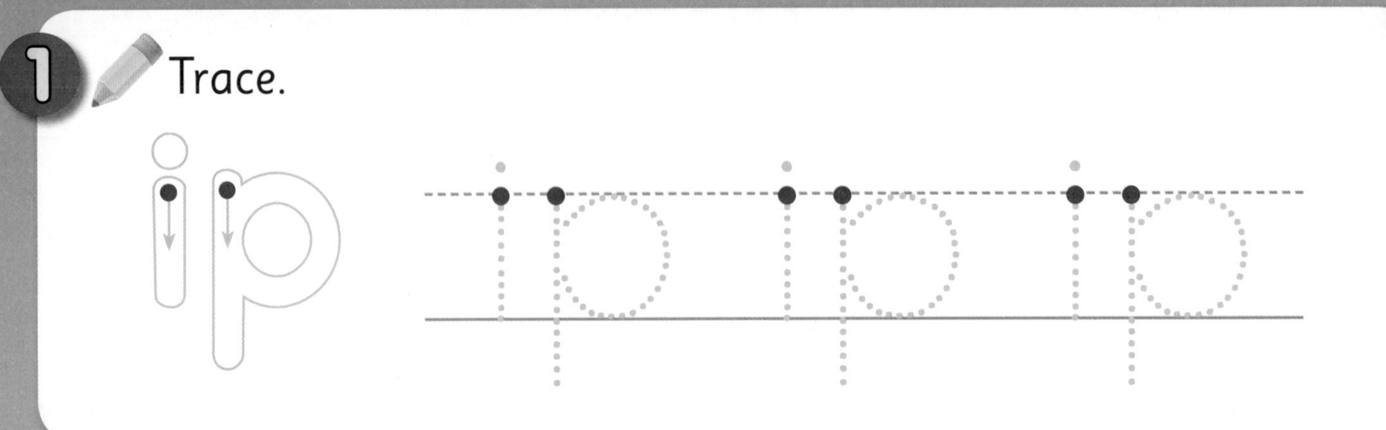

2 Color **ip** words.

pip	did	sit	hip	rip
fix	tip	sip	lip	dig

3 Match each picture to a word.

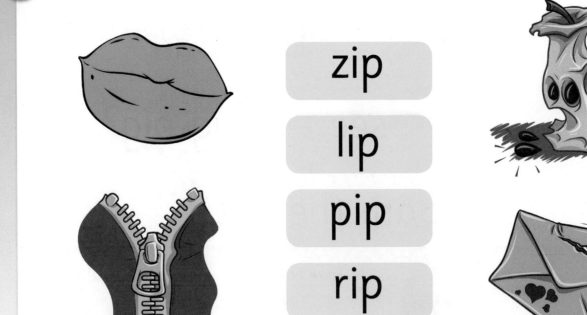

zip

lip

pip

rip

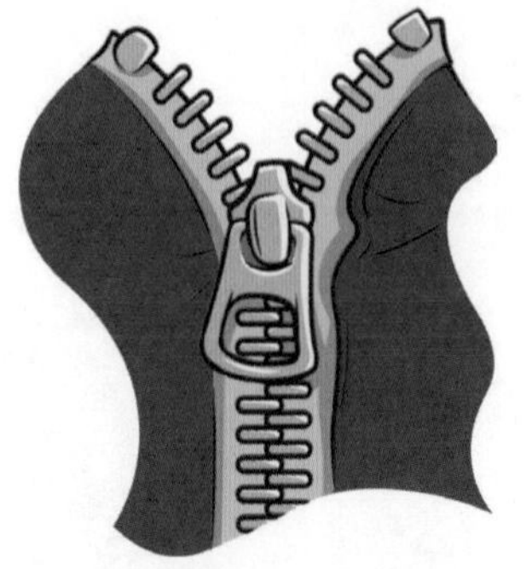

1 Complete.

Read	Write	Color
zip		
lip		
rip		
pip		

2 Draw a picture for this sentence.

I can see six pips.

1 Name each picture. Complete the sentence.

pig zip pip bin six

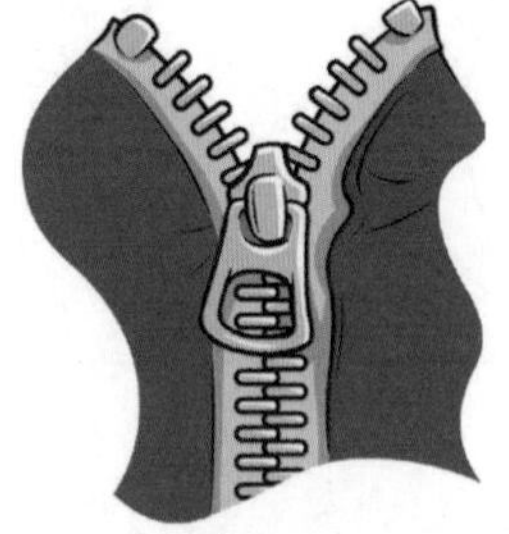

This is a ______________.

This is a ______________.

This is a ______________.

This is a ______________.

This is a ______________.

1 Trace.

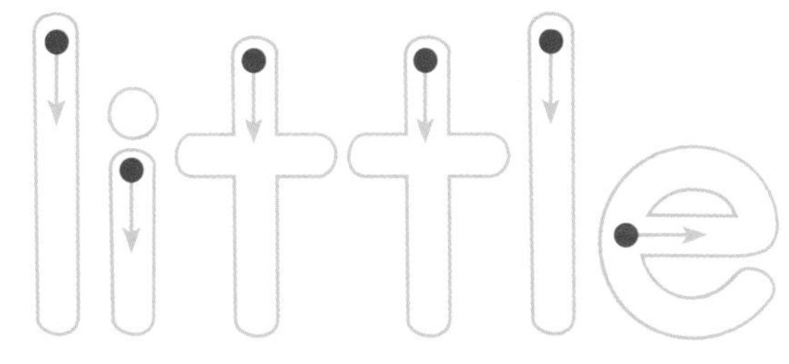
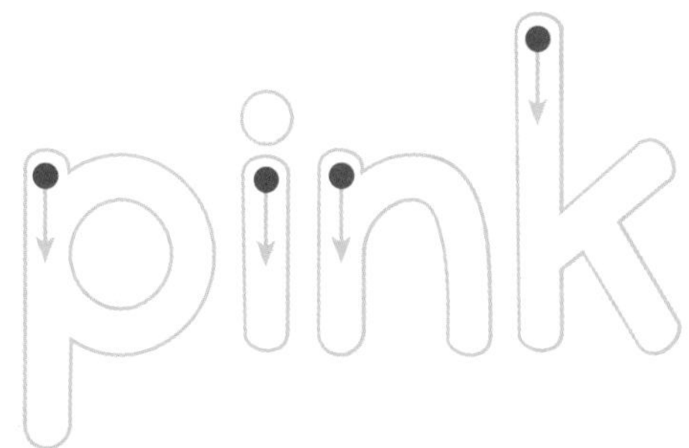

2 Help Thistle find his little cap. Color the path of **little** words.

little	yes	is	and	he
he	little	little	she	you
she	he	little	little	little
you	and	is	he	little

3 Write each word in its box.

little pink pig

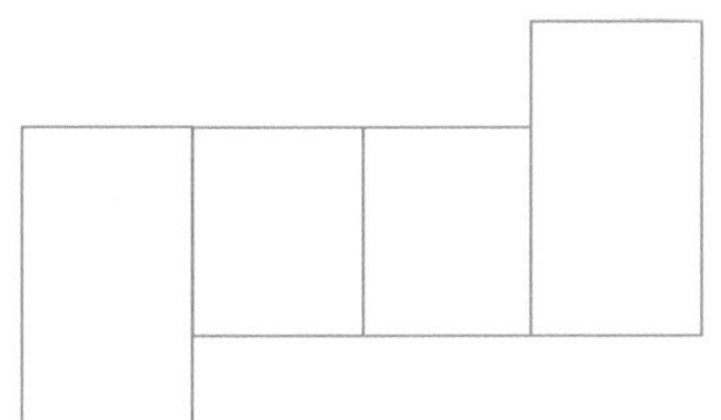
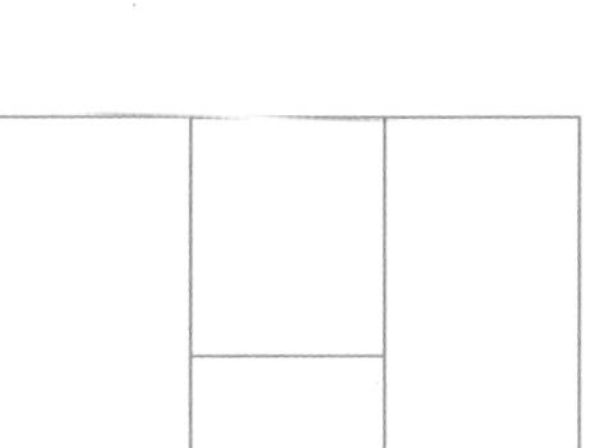
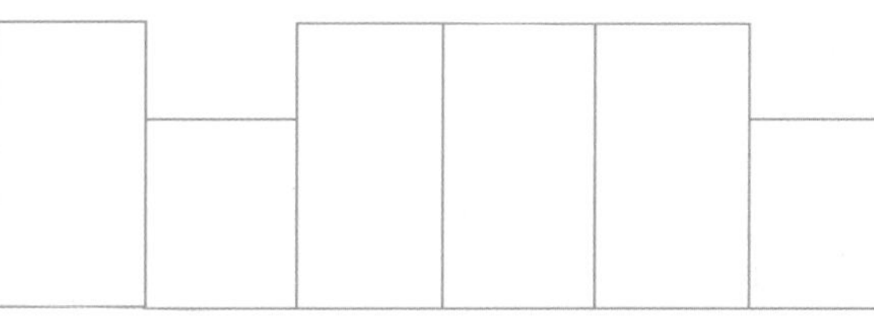

I finished this lesson online.	This egg hatched.	**I know** the **ip** word family: zip, pip, tip, lip	**I can read**

1 Trace.

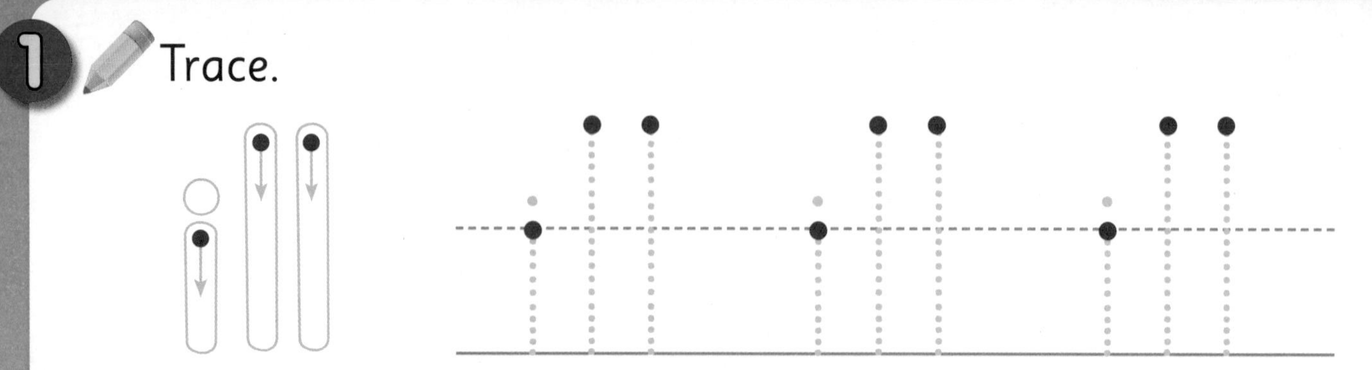

2 Complete.

Read	Write	Color
hill		
fill		
mill		
ill		

1 Complete the sentence.

The castle is on a

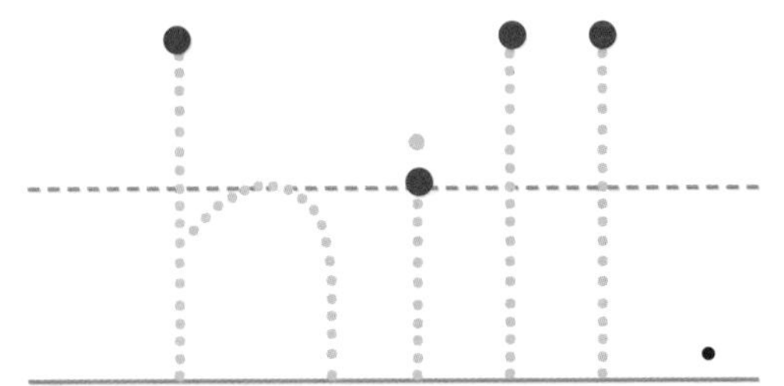

2 Color the correct word.

"I am il / ill," said Sam the ant.

Sid hid / hidd six pins.

This fish has bigg / big fins.

3 Color the **ill** words.

pill	hill	tin	bill	fill
fin	will	dig	into	mill

1 Match each word to a picture.

mix

hill

dig

Sid

mill

fill

sit

tin

2 Color the odd ones out.

hill	will	pill	sill	Jill
fin	mill	fill	bill	sit

Read, then answer the questions.

The hill

This is a hill.
The hill is little.
A tree is on the hill.

1. This is a ________.

   a fill   b hill   c mill

2. The hill is ________.

   a big   b long   c little

3. On the hill is a ________.

   a tree   b cat   c mill

I finished this lesson online.	This egg hatched.	I know the ill word family: hill, mill, will, fill	I can read

ing

1 Match each picture to a word.

king

ring

sing

wing

2 Color the rings that end in **ing**.

3 Color the correct word.

The little bird can (song / sing).

1 Complete.

Read	Write	Color
ring		
king		
sing		
wing		

2 Circle the word that matches the picture.

fin
fan

lip
leg

hit
mix

1 Complete the sentence.

The king can

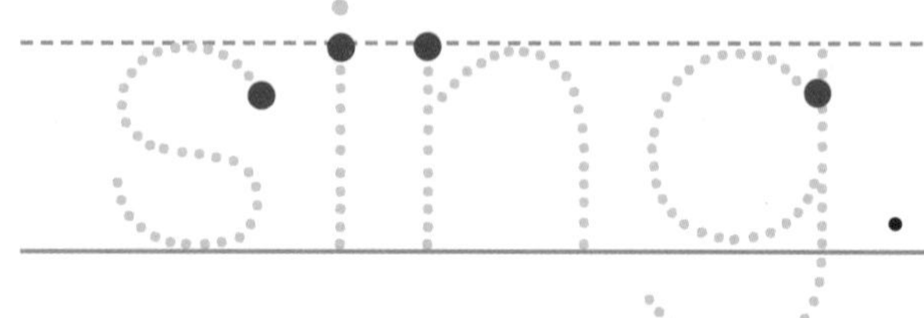

2 Complete the sentences.

wings ring sing

The king has a ______ .

The bird can ______ .

The bird has two ______ .

3 Circle the odd one out in each row.

sing wing ring bird king

dig fig win pig wig

Read, then answer the questions.

Blue bird

This is a bird.
A bird can sing.
A bird has two wings.

1 This is a __________ .

a bird b dog c bat

2 A bird can __________ .

a fill b ring c sing

3 A bird has two __________ .

a wet b wings c rings

I finished this lesson online.	This egg hatched.	I know the **ing** word family: wing, ring, king, sing	I can read

Quiz

1 Read the word. Color the pictures that match.

king		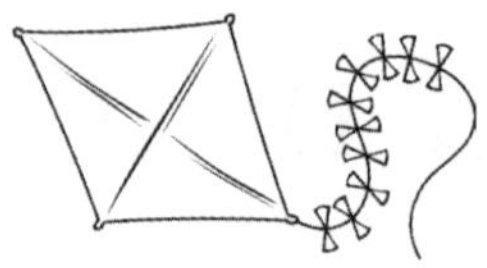	
horse			
zip	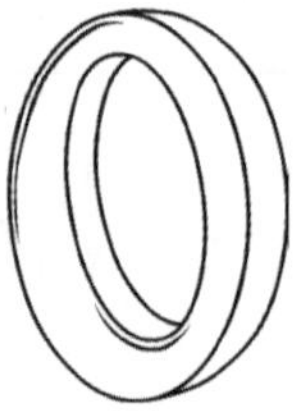		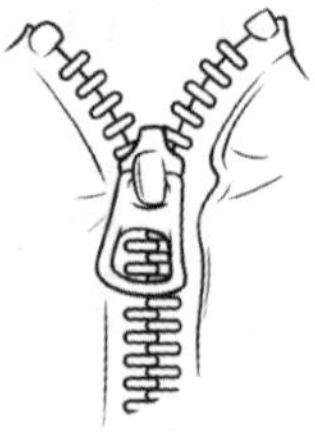
ring			

2 Color it **red** if it is little, color it **blue** if it is big.

Quiz

Read, then answer the questions.

The Queen's ring

The Queen has a ring.
It is little and red.
"I like my ring," she said.

3 The Queen has a ________ .

a ring b wing c red

4 The ring is ________ .

a blue b little c pink

5 The Queen said, "____________."

a I like my ring.

b I am the King.

c Like I am.

WOW!

YOU COMPLETED

MAP 5

YOU CAN:

- [ ] Write CVC words.
- [ ] Read these words: **little, sing, said, this**.
- [ ] Read lots of sentences, such as: **Can you see the little ring?**
- [ ] Read these books:

Fun Spot 5

1 Connect the dots from **n** to **z**.

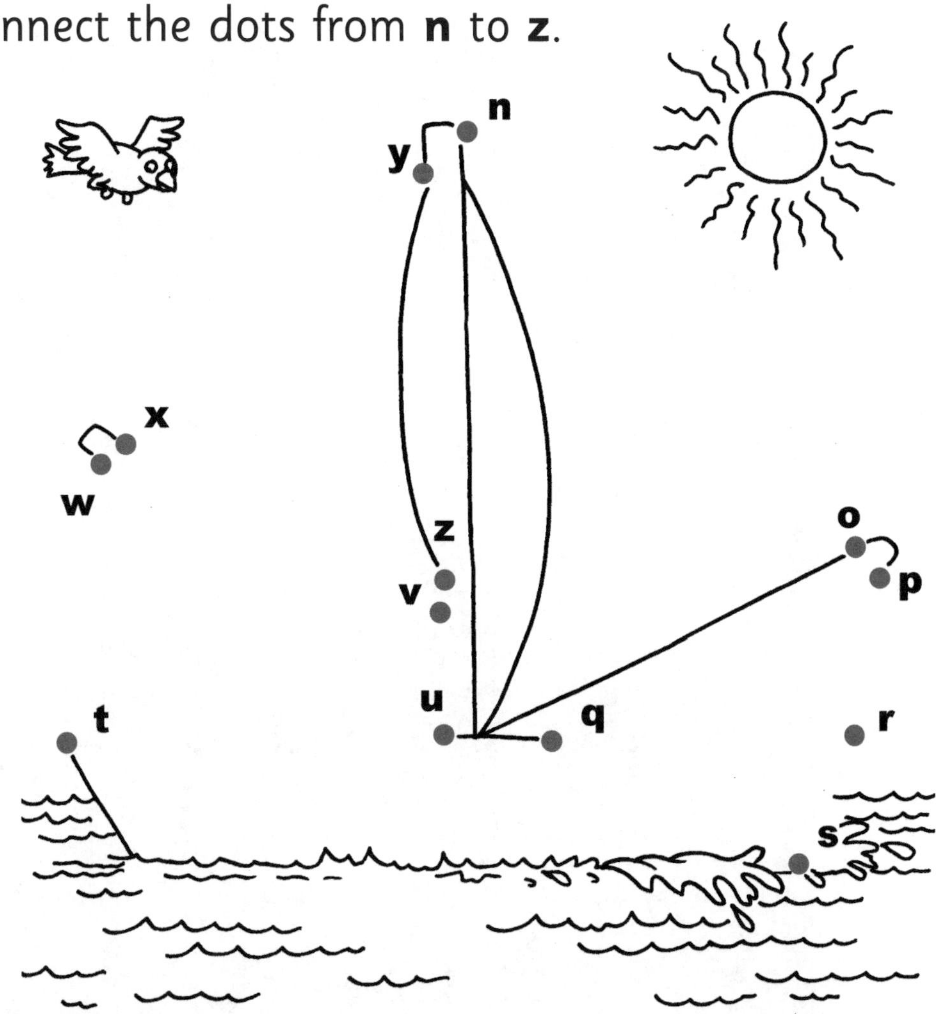

2 Match.

M	N	O	P	Q	R	S
n	p	m	o	r	s	q

T	U	V	W	X	Y	Z
v	w	t	u	y	z	x

Find the hidden pictures

Find each drawing in the picture.

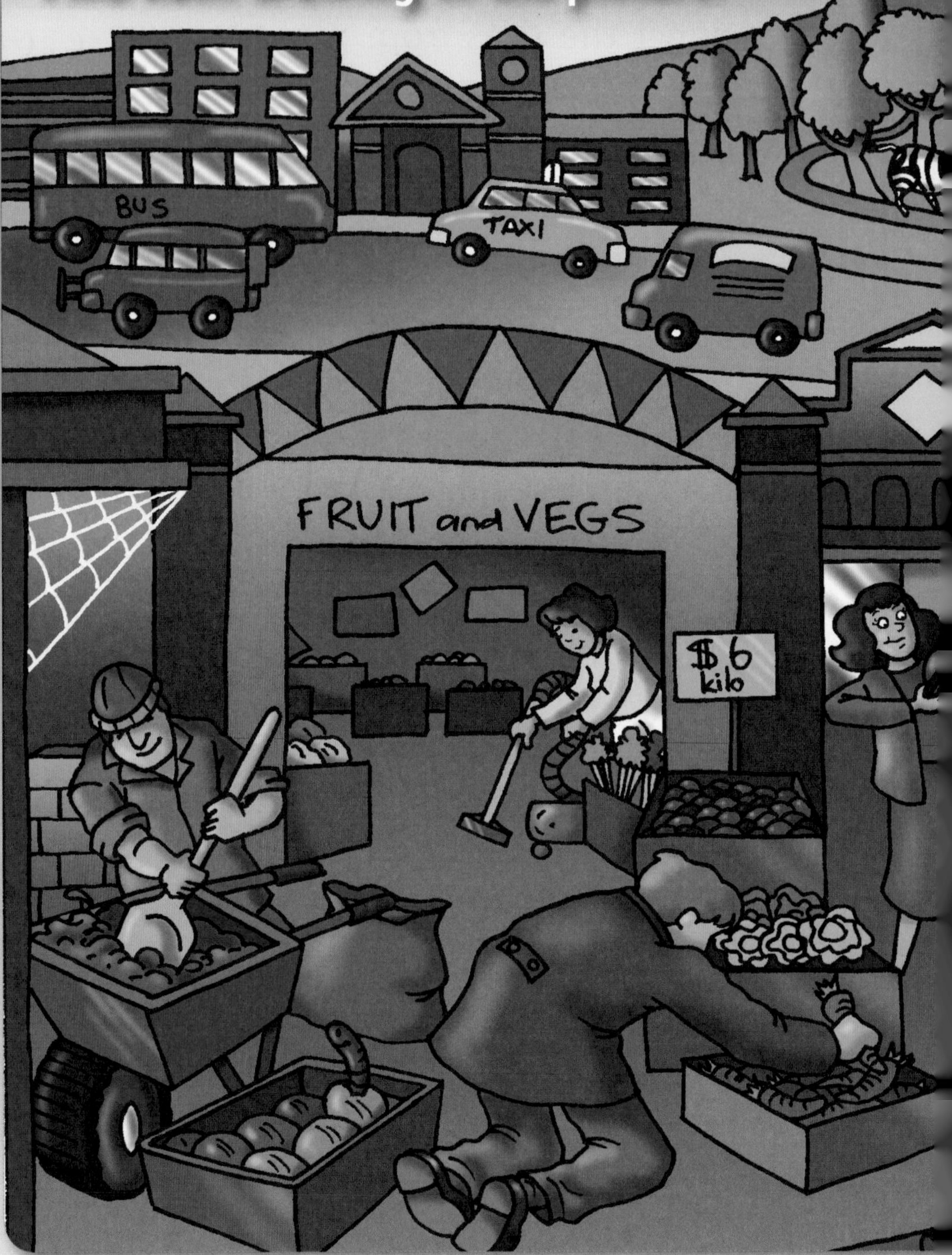

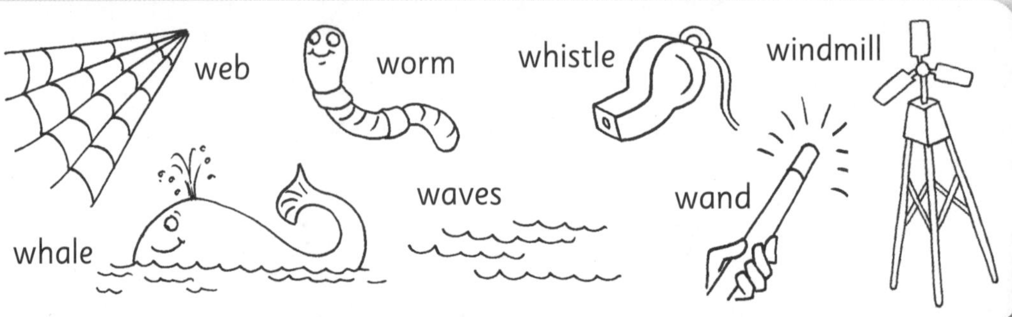

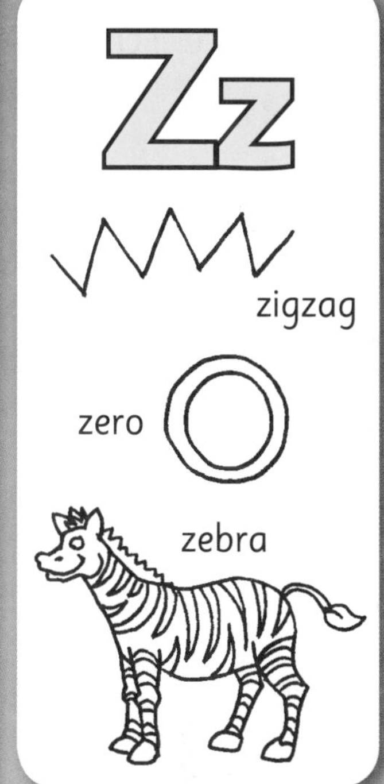
Zz
zigzag
zero
zebra

Yy
YOGURT
yogurt
yo-yo
yolk

Xx
x-ray
TAXI
TAXI
taxi
box
wax
six

1 Make rainbow words.

2 Color **go** in green and **by** in blue.

go	Ben	by	be	get
yet	bog	by	got	go
by	go	og	ug	go
go	by	go	by	get

3 Write **go** and **by**.

go go go go

by by by by

1 Complete each sentence.

Six big bees

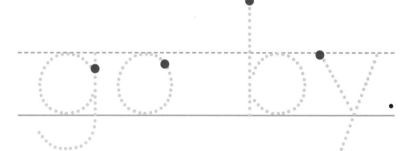

go by.

Six fat fish

go by.

Six black bats

_______________.

2 Draw six blue fish and three green fish.

1 Read the words. Color.

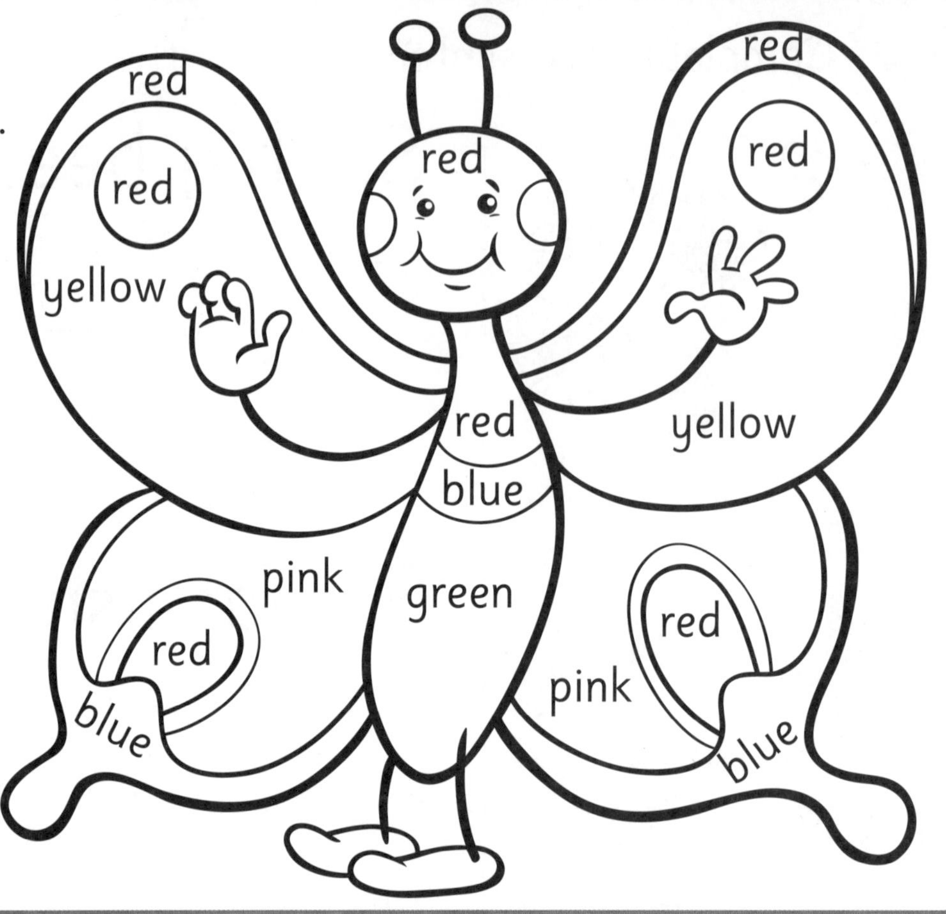

2 Get Go Go Gizmo to the rainbow.

Color the track to match the rainbow words.

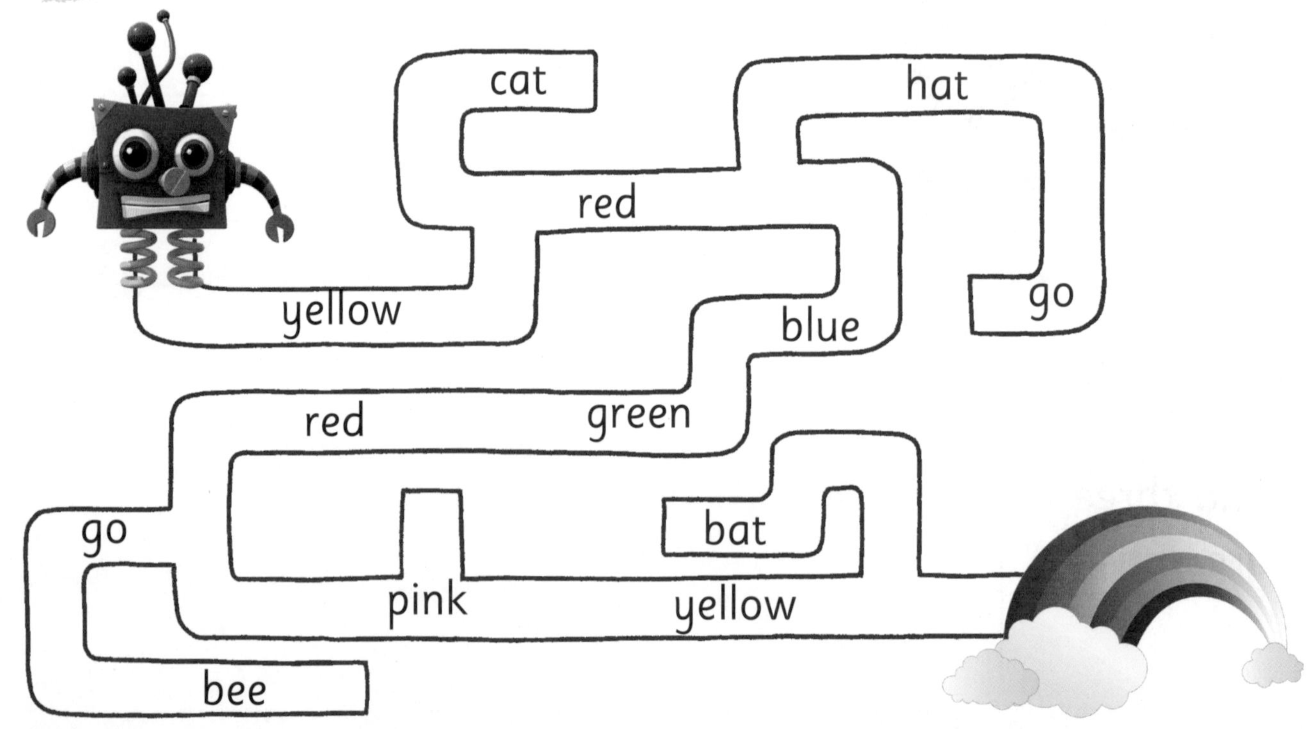

Read, then answer the questions.

Sam's three fish

Sam has three fat fish.
The big fish is yellow.
The green fish is little.

1. Sam has ________________ .

   a red fish b thin fish c fat fish

2. The big fish is ____________ .

   a red b yellow c green

3. The green fish is ____________ .

   a little b red c big

I finished this lesson online.	This egg hatched.	I know the words: go, by	I can read

look

1 Make a rainbow word.

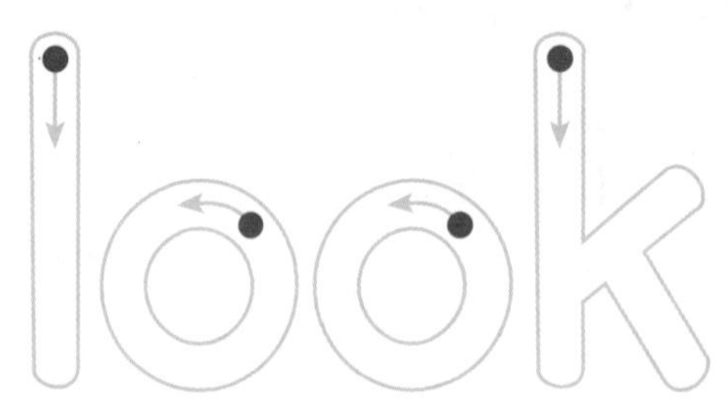

2 Read it 3 times.

Look at the ship.

3 Color **look**.

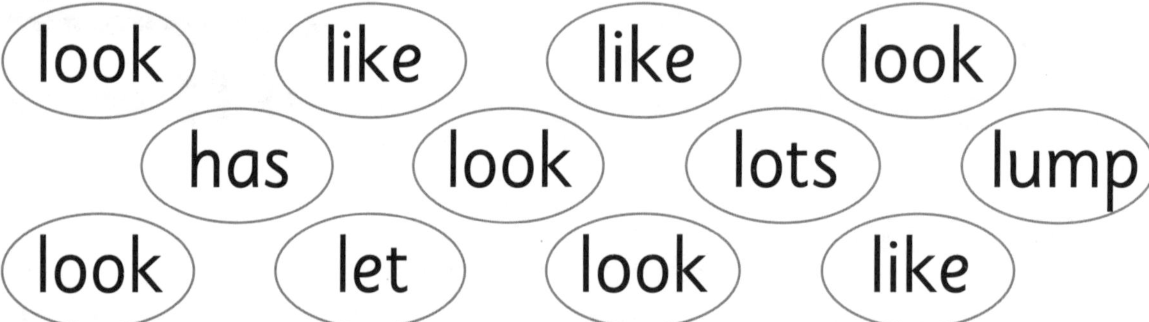

look like like look
has look lots lump
look let look like

4 Write **look**.

look look look

5 Circle the matching words in each row.

look can has look

got it got in

1 Match each word to a picture.

hot

dot

pot

cot

lots

2 Draw

dots on the dog.

a hot pot.

1 Match each word to a picture.

mermaid

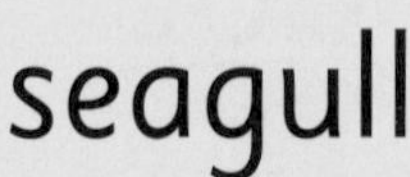

seagull

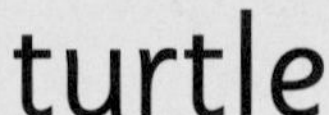

turtle

ship

dolphin

whale

2 Color the correct word. Cross out the wrong word.

This is a (whale) (mermaid) .

I can see a (seagull) (ship)

Can you see the (dolphin) (turtle)?

Read, then answer the questions.

Jazz

Jazz has a pot.
She got lots of dots.
The pot got hot.

1. Jazz has a ___________ .

   a pet b pot c pat

2. She got lots of ___________ .

   a dots b dogs c dolls

3. The pot got ___________ .

   a hit b hat c hot

I finished this lesson online.

This egg hatched.

I know the **ot** word family: hot, lot, pot, dot

I can read

1 Trace.

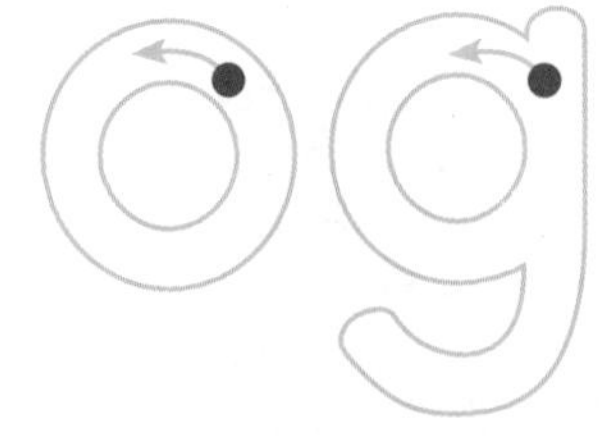

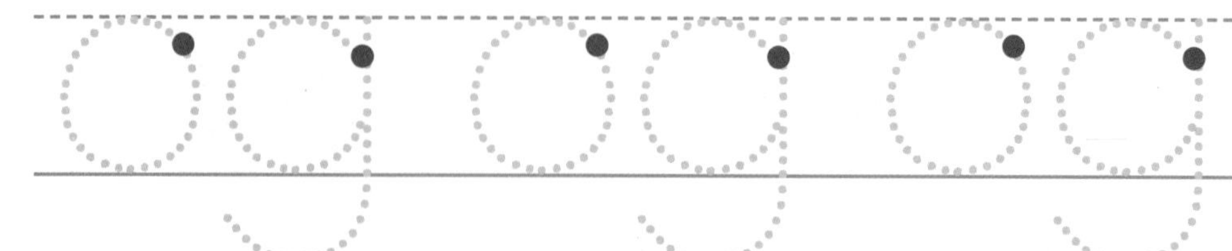

2 Complete the words.
Use Hedgehog dog's letters.

d l f
c j

____og
____og
____og
____og
____og

3 Color the correct word. Cross out the wrong word.

			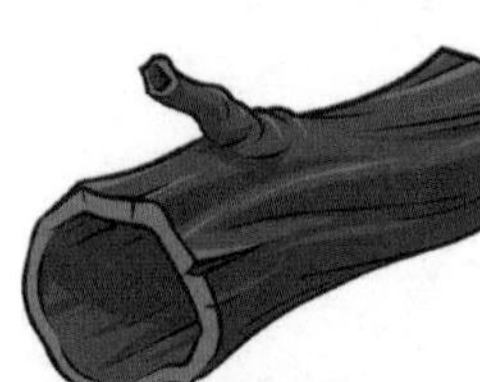
frog	log	dog	log
log	dog	cog	dog

1 Complete.

Read	Write	Color
dog		 
pot		 
log		 
fog		 
hot		 
cog		 

1 Complete each sentence.

socks mop rock

This pet got a

________________.

This pet got lots of

________________.

This pet got a

________________.

2 Draw a frog on a log.

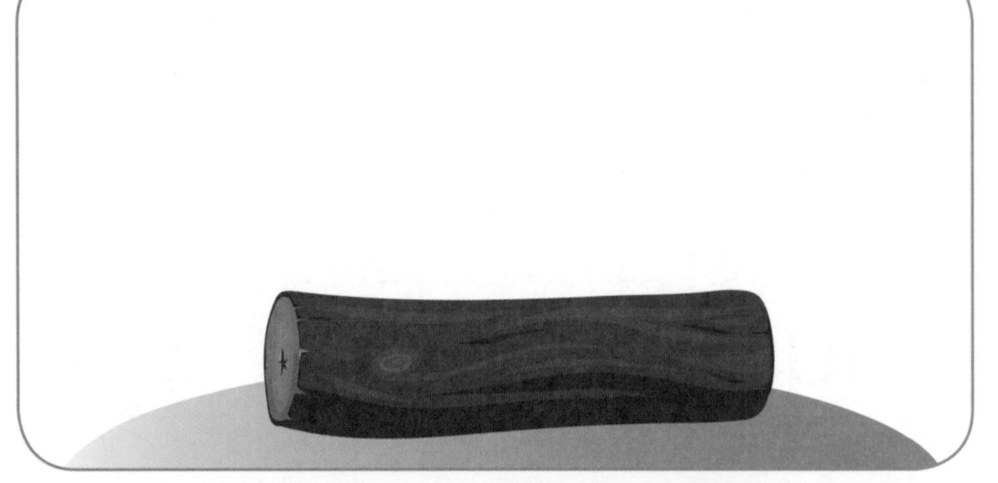

1 Read the word. Color the pictures that matches.

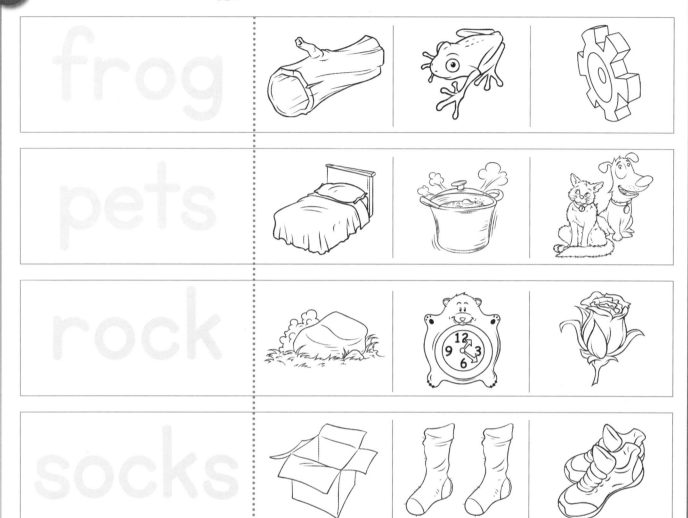

frog	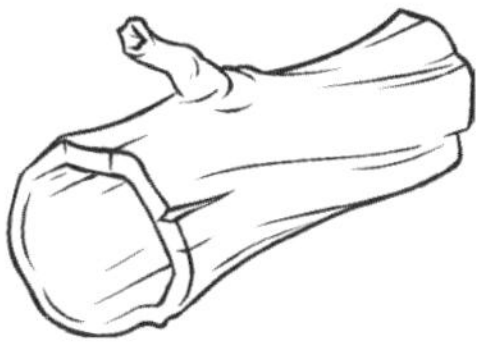		
pets			
rock			
socks		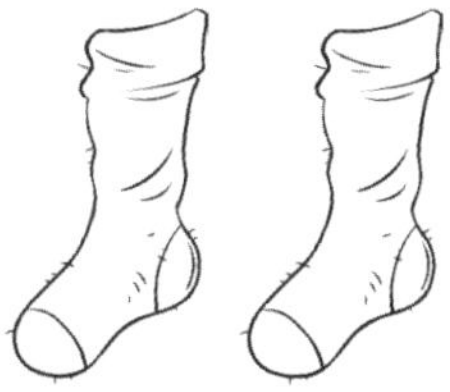	

2 Write the words.

____

____

I finished this lesson online.	This egg hatched.	I know the og and ock word families	I can read

1 Complete.

Read	Write	Color
top		 
hop		 
mop		 
pop		 
shop		 
stop		 

play

1 Make a rainbow word.

play

2 Read the sentence.

Sam and Jazz like to play.

3 Write **play**.

play play play

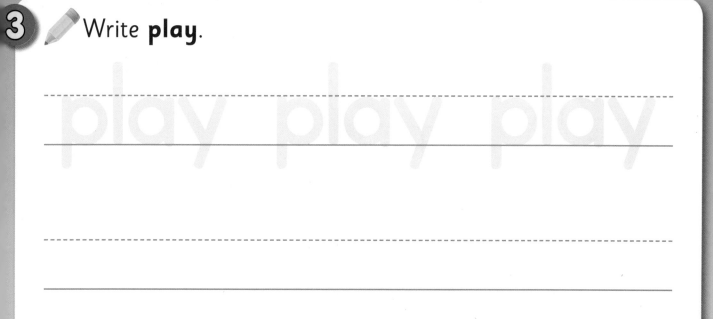

4 Write the sentence.

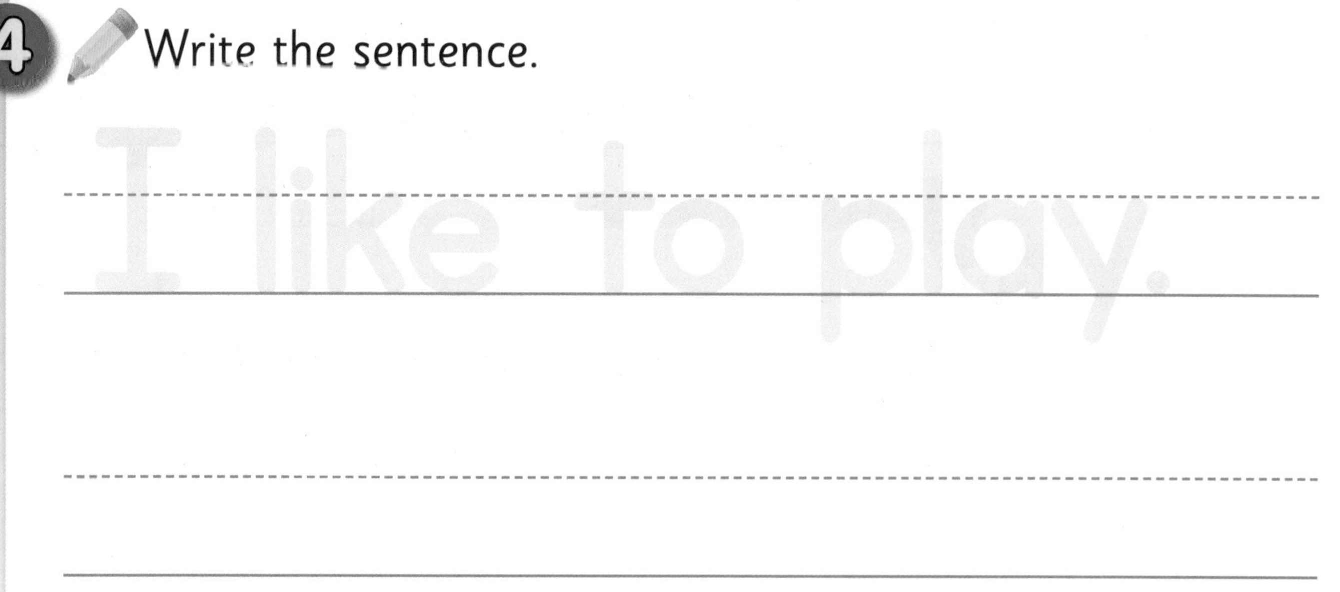

1 Color the **op** words. Write them.

cop

2 Write the words on the correct log.

hop
bog
dot
mop
cot
fog

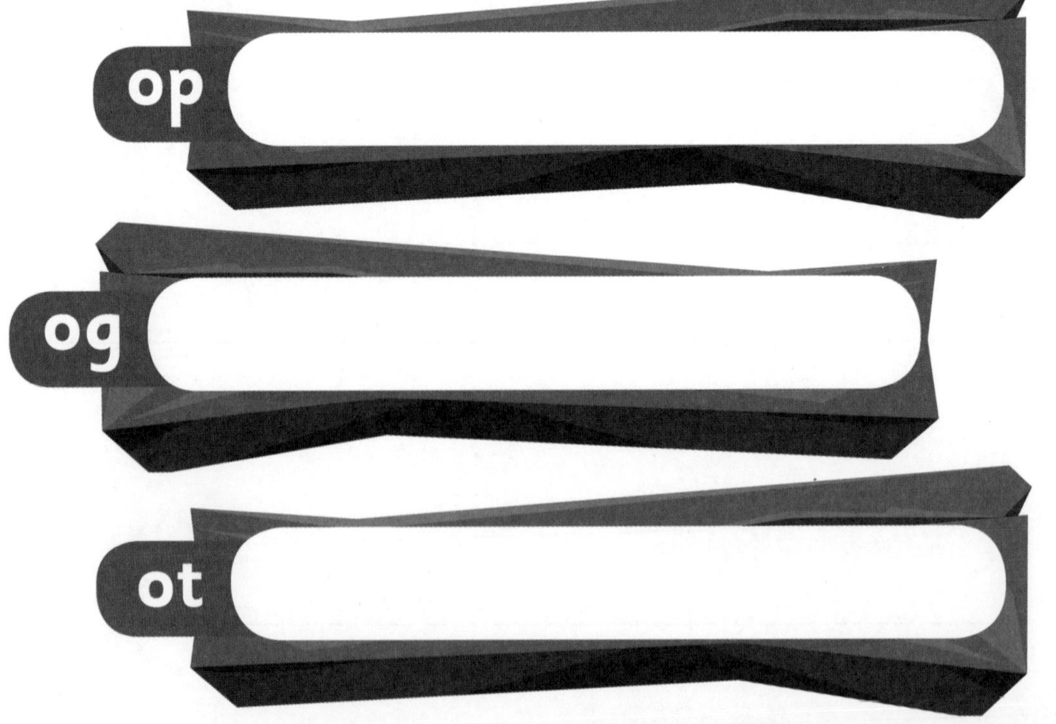

1 Complete each sentence with **play**.

Zee the bee can

________________________________.

Jazz the cat can

________________________________.

2 Use the word wheels to make words. Write the new words.

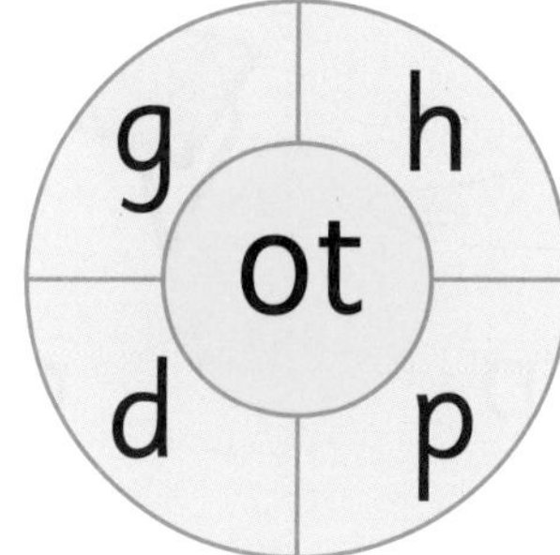

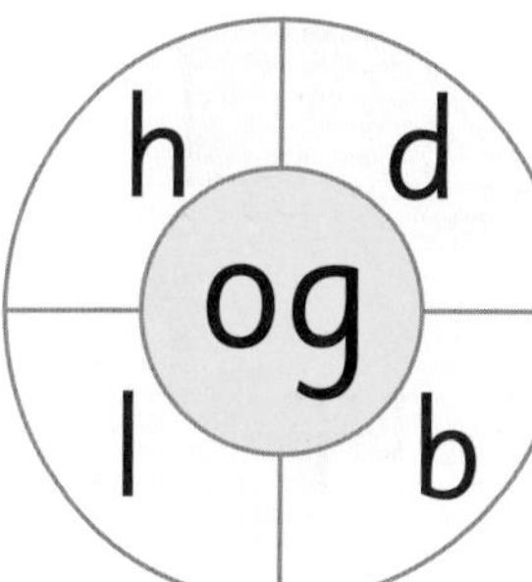

I finished this lesson online.	This egg hatched.	**I know** the word: play	**I can read**

1 Circle the correct word.

dig
dog

hot
hit

fun
fin

leg
log

tip
top

mop
met

cot
cat

ten
tan

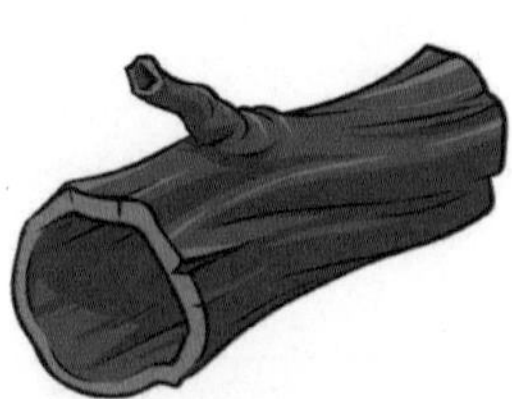

log
lot

stop
dots

frog
dog

shop
top

Complete each sentence.

pops   hot dog   pot   log

Top Dog got a

______________________.

The popcorn

______________________.

He hops onto a

______________________.

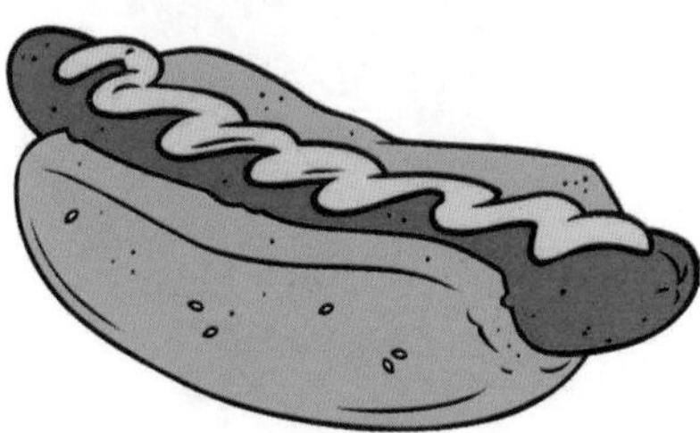
Top Dog got a

______________________.

1 Write the missing letter.

h___n

s___n

d___g

h___p

w___b

b___t

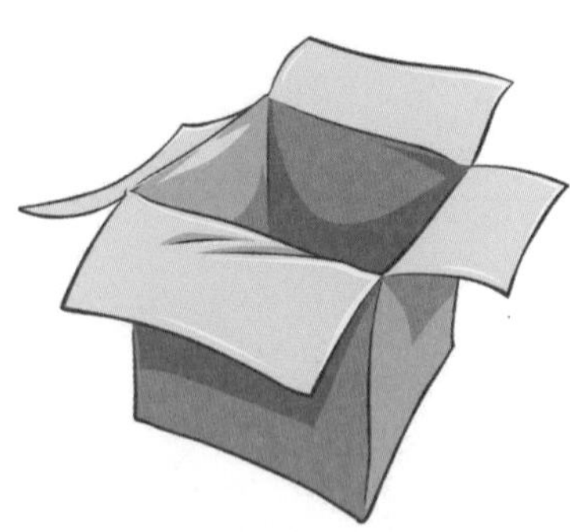

b___x

m___g

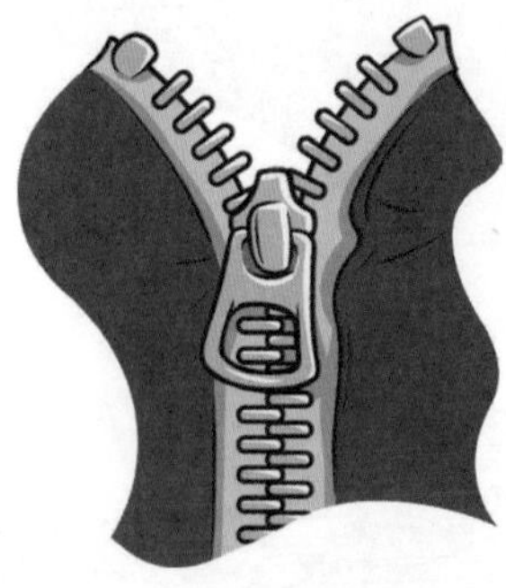

z___p

Read, then answer the questions.

The shop

Look at the shop.
The shop sells pots.
This pot has little red dots.

1. Look at the ________ .

   a ship   b shop   c shed

2. The shop sells ________ .

   a tots   b pots   c bots

3. The pot has little red ________ .

   a dots   b pots   c dogs

I finished this lesson online.	This egg hatched.	I know lots of short o words	I can read
55			

1 Make rainbow words.

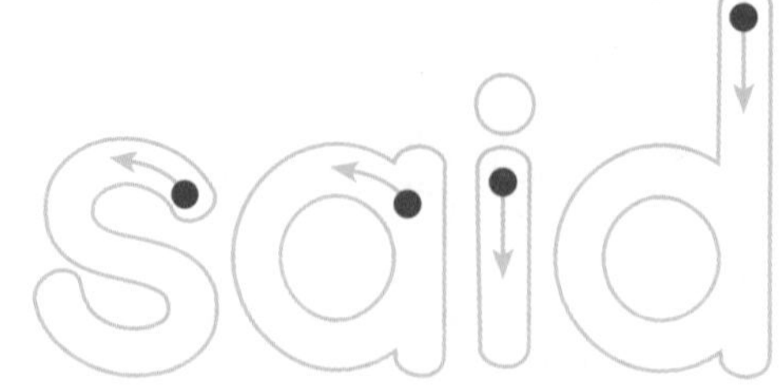

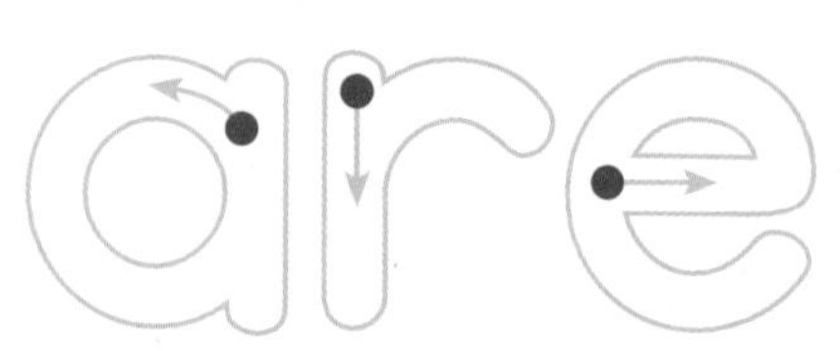

2 Color **said** in orange and **are** in blue.

said	sed	are	art
are	ant	are	sand
sad	are	said	are

3 Write **said** and **are**.

said said said

are are are

happy
sad

1 Match each word to a picture.

happy

sad

2 Color the flag.

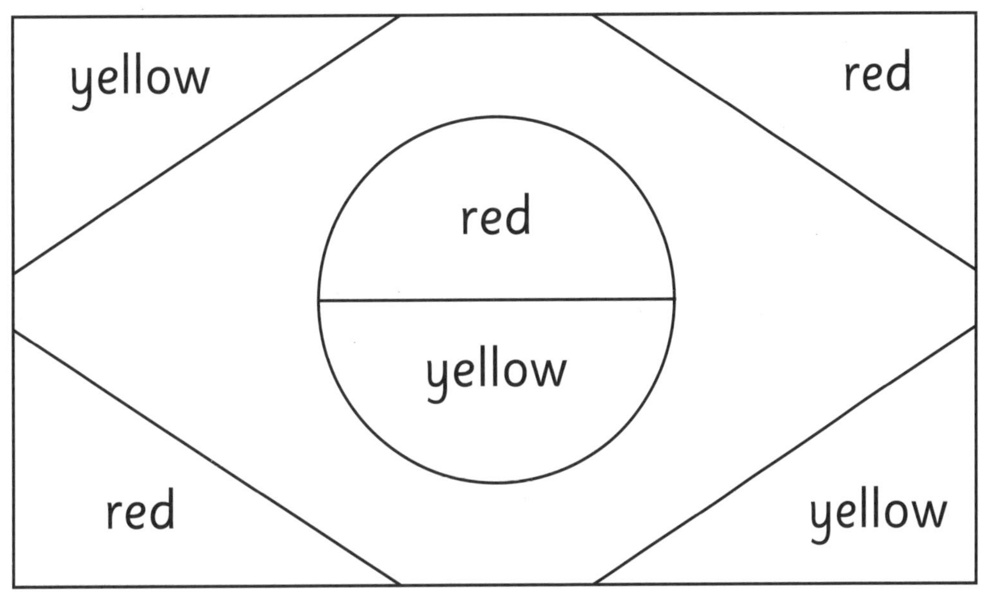

3 Join Grumble Goz to the **happy** words.

happy | not | happy

are | happy | are

said | happy

1 Read and trace.

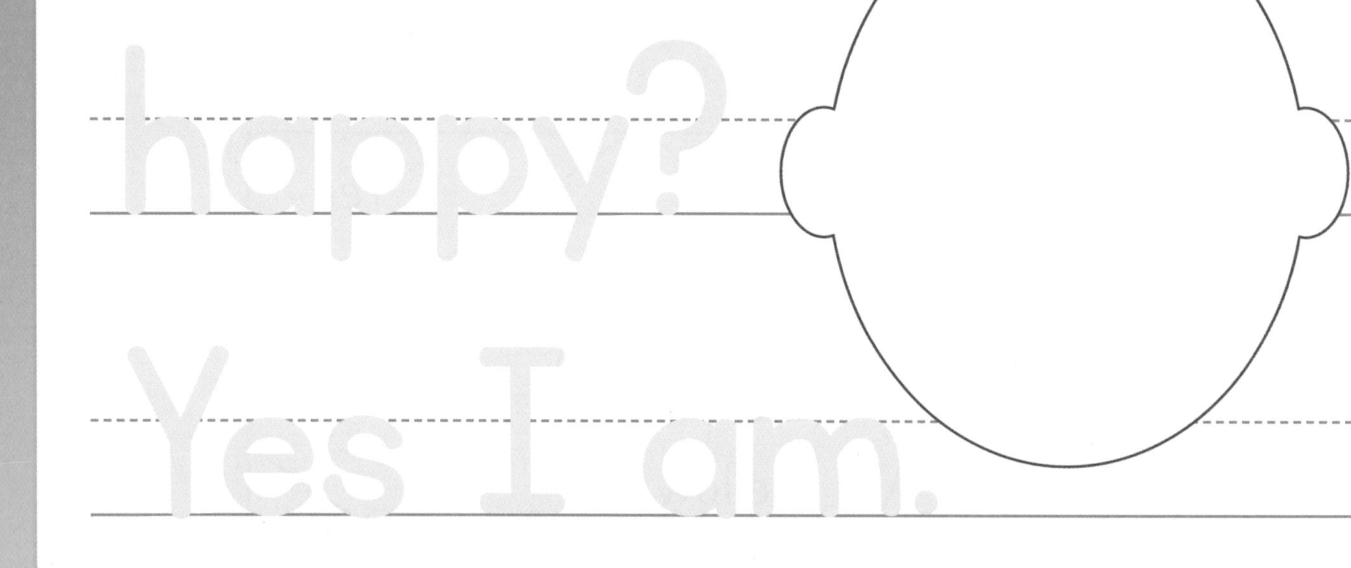
Draw yourself.
Are you happy?
Yes I am.

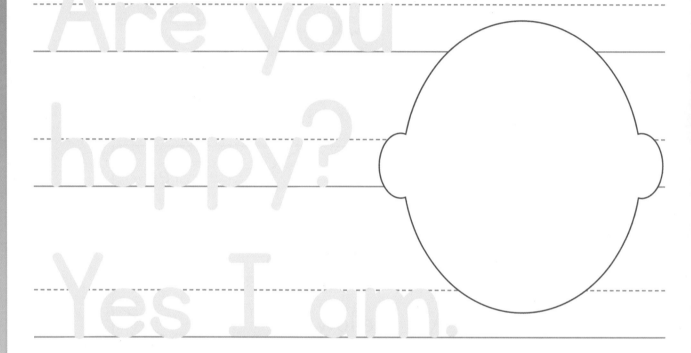

2 Color the correct word. Cross out the wrong word.

This The is Frogfish.

Is Are you happy, Frogfish?

"Yes, I am happy," he say said .

happy
sad

Read, then answer the questions.

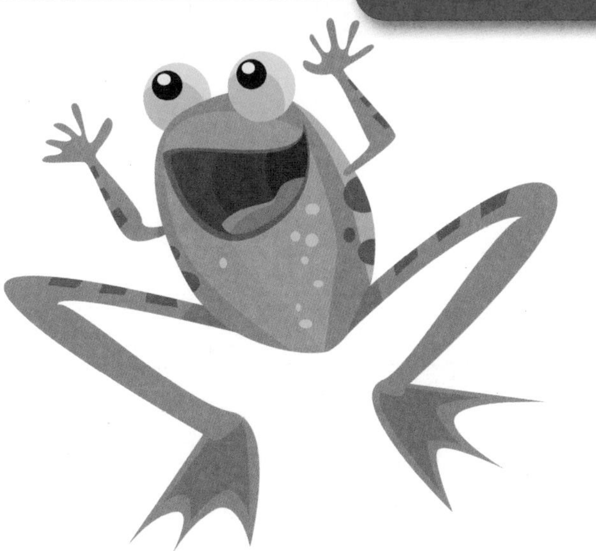

The frog

Look at the frog.
The frog can hop.
The frog is happy.

1 Look at the ________.

a fan b frog c happy

2 The frog can ________.

a hot b hip c hop

3 The frog is ________.

a sad b happy c hippy

I finished this lesson online.	This egg hatched.	I know the words: said, are happy	I can read
56			

his her

LESSON 57 SIGHT WORDS

1 Trace.

his her

2 Complete the labels.

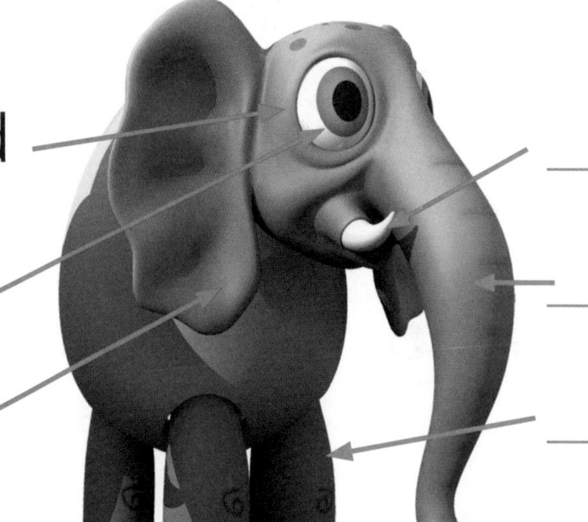

his	head		tusk
	eye		trunk
	ear		leg

3 Help Airy Fairy find her wand. Color the path of **her** words.

her	her	she	his	he
hen	her	her	hat	hop
and	has	her	has	hit
here	hip	her	her	her

his her

1 Match each word to a picture.

queen

prince

king

princess

knight

horse

2 Color the **royal** words. = red. Color the **sea** words. = blue.

queen

mermaid

turtle

ship

princess

knight

prince

whale

1 Complete the sentences.

her This his

_________ is the King.

He likes _________ castle.

_________ is the Queen.

She likes _________ crown.

_________ is the Princess.

She likes _________ horse.

_________ is the Prince.

He likes _________ game.

his her

Read, then answer the questions.

His or hers?

This is the Princess
and this is her horse.
This is the Prince
and this is his game.

1 The Princess has a ________ .

a game b horse c ring

2 The Prince has a ________ .

a game b horse c ring

3 He likes ________ game.

a her b its c his

I finished this lesson online.	This egg hatched.	I know the words: his, her, we	I can read

ock

1 Trace.

od ock od ock

2 Complete the words. Use Tick Tock Clock's letters.

d l
s r

_____ock
_____ock
_____ock
_____ock

3 Circle the matching word.

sock
socks

top
tops

clock
clocks

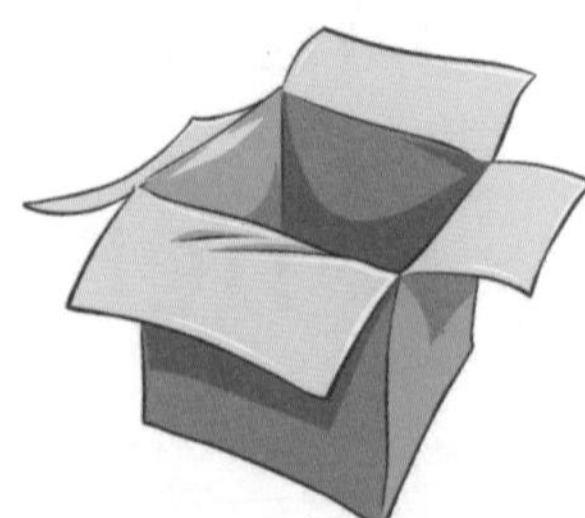

boxes
box

1 Complete each sentence.

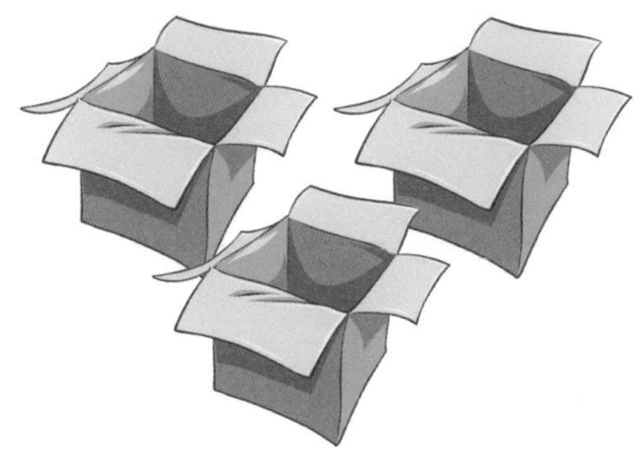

The fox got lots of

______________________________________.

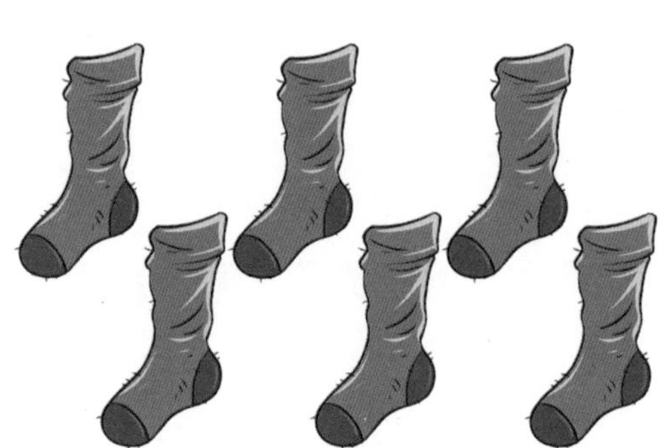

The fox got lots of

______________________________________.

2 Color the **ock** words = red, color the **od** words = green.

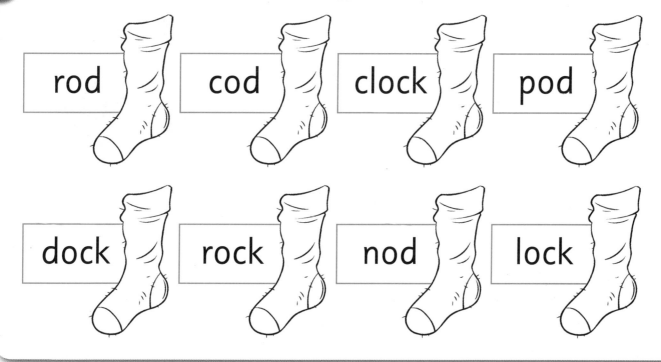

rod	cod	clock	pod
dock	rock	nod	lock

1 Join each sound to the word machine. Write each word.

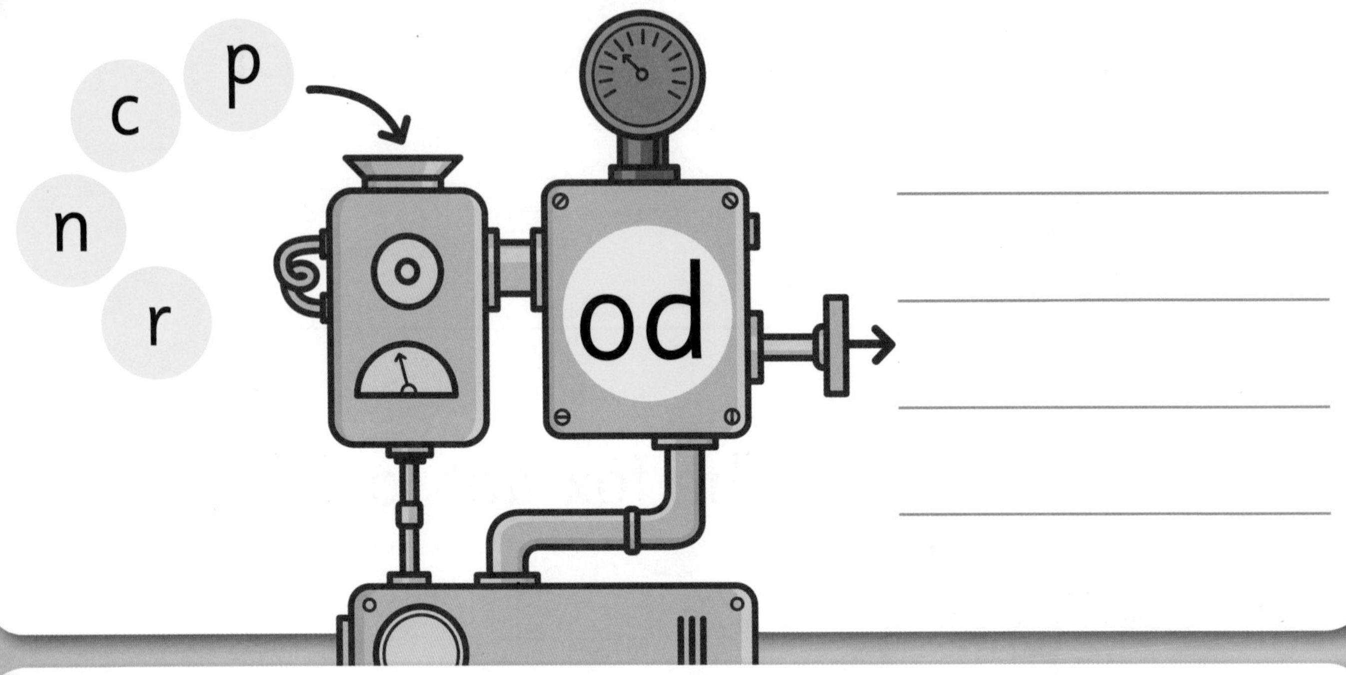

2 Match each word to a picture.

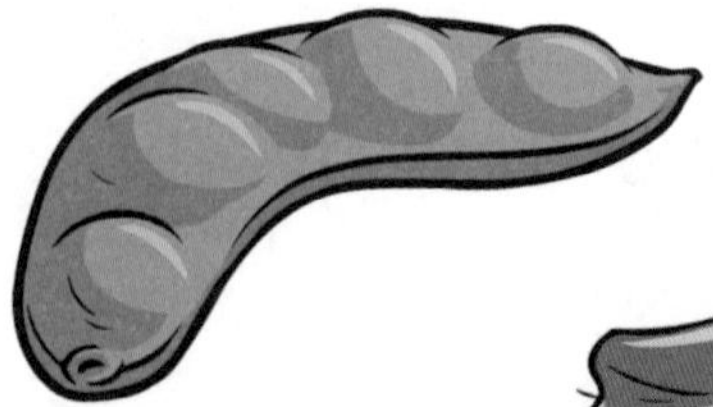

pod

rock

clock

rod

sock

lock

ock

Read, then answer the questions.

Pink rocks

I got a bag of rocks.
The rocks are for my fish.
The rocks are little and pink.

1. I got a bag of __________.
   a socks b rocks c fish

2. The rocks are for my __________.
   a rocks b pink c fish

3. The rocks are __________.
   a fish b little and pink c big

I finished this lesson online.

This egg hatched.

I know the ock word family: rocks, socks, clocks

I can read

1 Label each picture.

cod ______

p ______

h ______

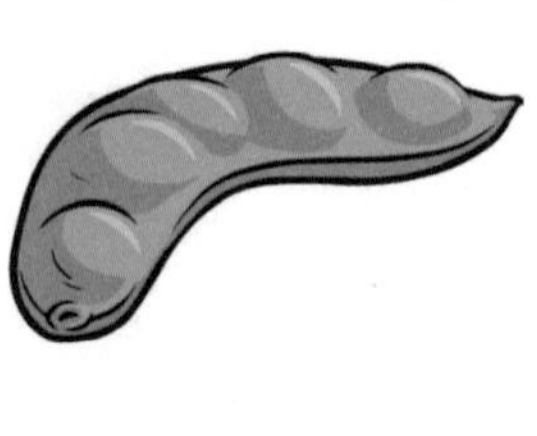

p ______

f ______

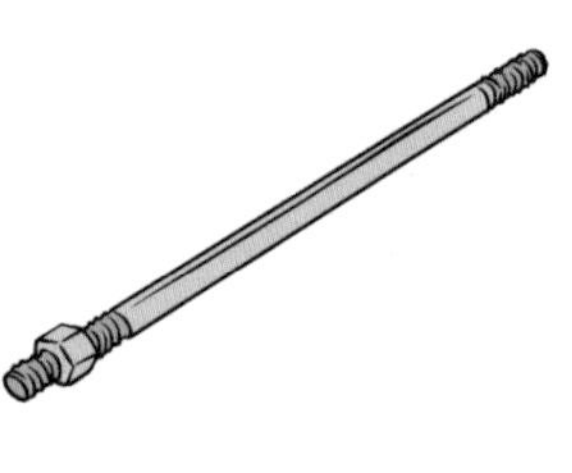

r ______

2 Color **od** words = blue, **ot** words = red.

nod	not	pot	pod	spot

3 Draw

a rod for this cod.

spots on this pot.

very

1 Make a rainbow word.

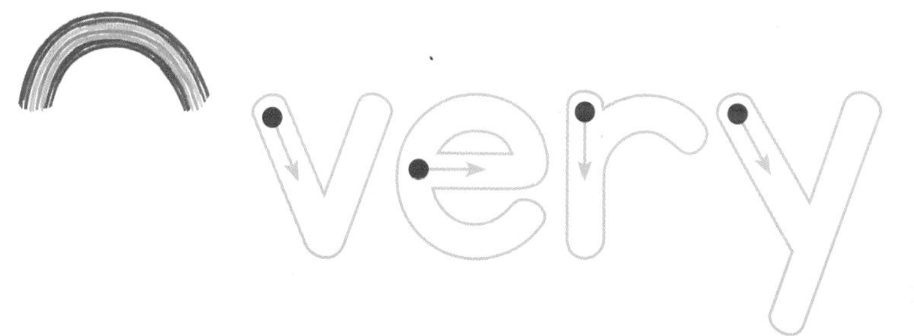

2 Read it 3 times.

Barry is very bossy.

3 Find **very**.

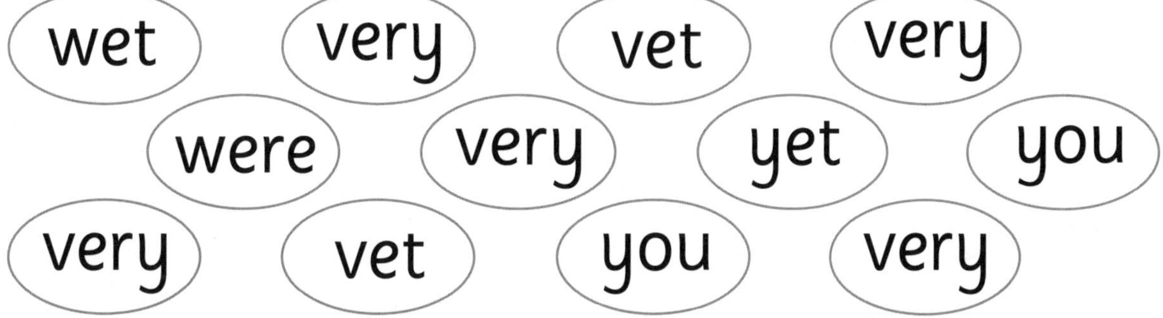

4 Write **very**.

very very very

5 Help Socky Fox find his sock. Follow the path of **very** words.

1 Match words to a picture.

bear

duck

horse

juggler

seagull

cat

fish

mouse

very

Read, then answer the questions.

Harry

Harry is a horse.
He can run and jump.
He is a very happy horse.

1 Harry is a __________ .

a bossy b jump c horse

2 Harry can run and __________ .

a swim b jump c very

3 He is very __________ .

a jolly b happy c hippy

I finished this lesson online.

This egg hatched.

I know the **od** word family and the word very.

I can read

Review

LESSON 60 WORD FAMILIES

1 Make word families.  Complete each word.

 r ot  ___ot

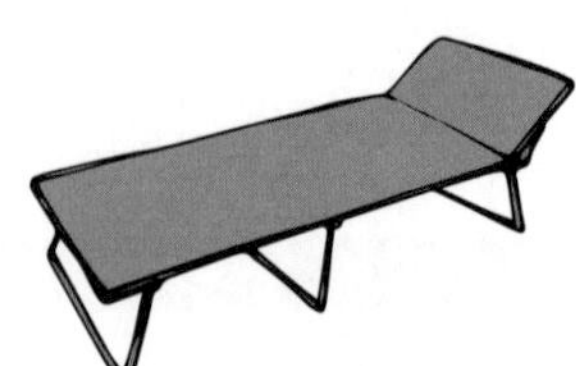 ___ot  ___ot

 ___ot  ___ot

 d og  ___og

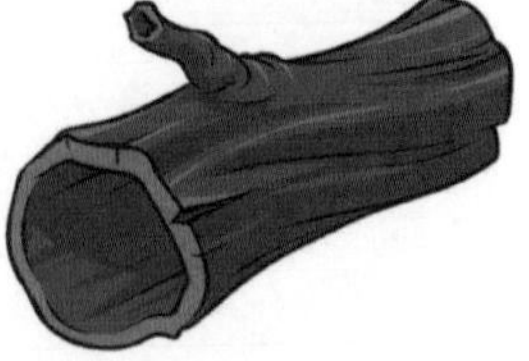 ___og  ___og

 ___og 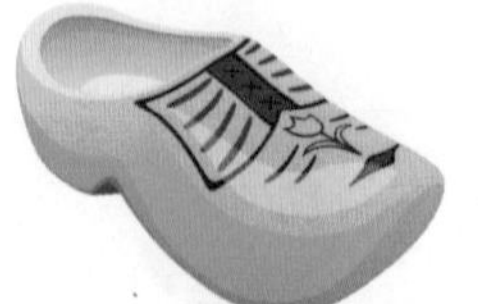 ___og

1 Make word families. Complete each word.

od words

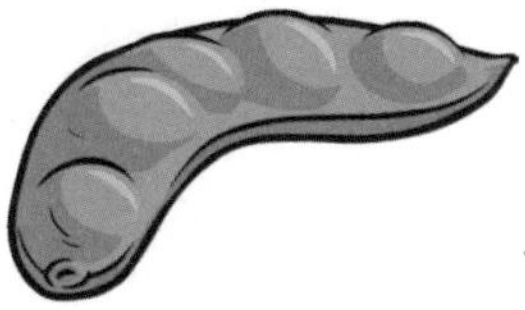

____od 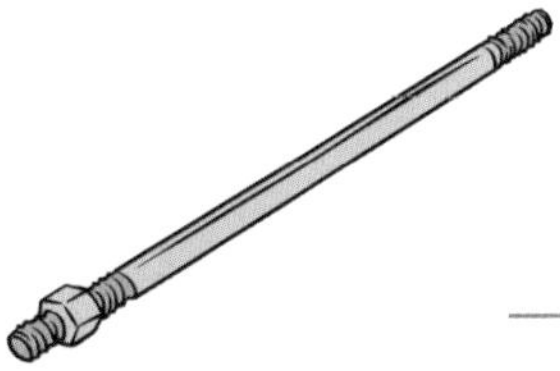 ____od

op words

____op  ____op

ock words

____ock 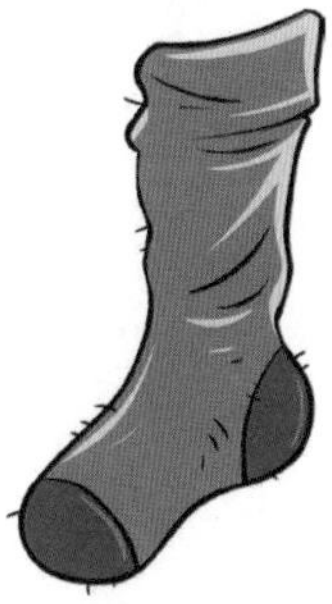 ____ock

2 Say the word for the picture. Find the word that rhymes.

hat mop rock mix

hop fog dot clock

1 Complete the crossword. Use the picture clues to help you.

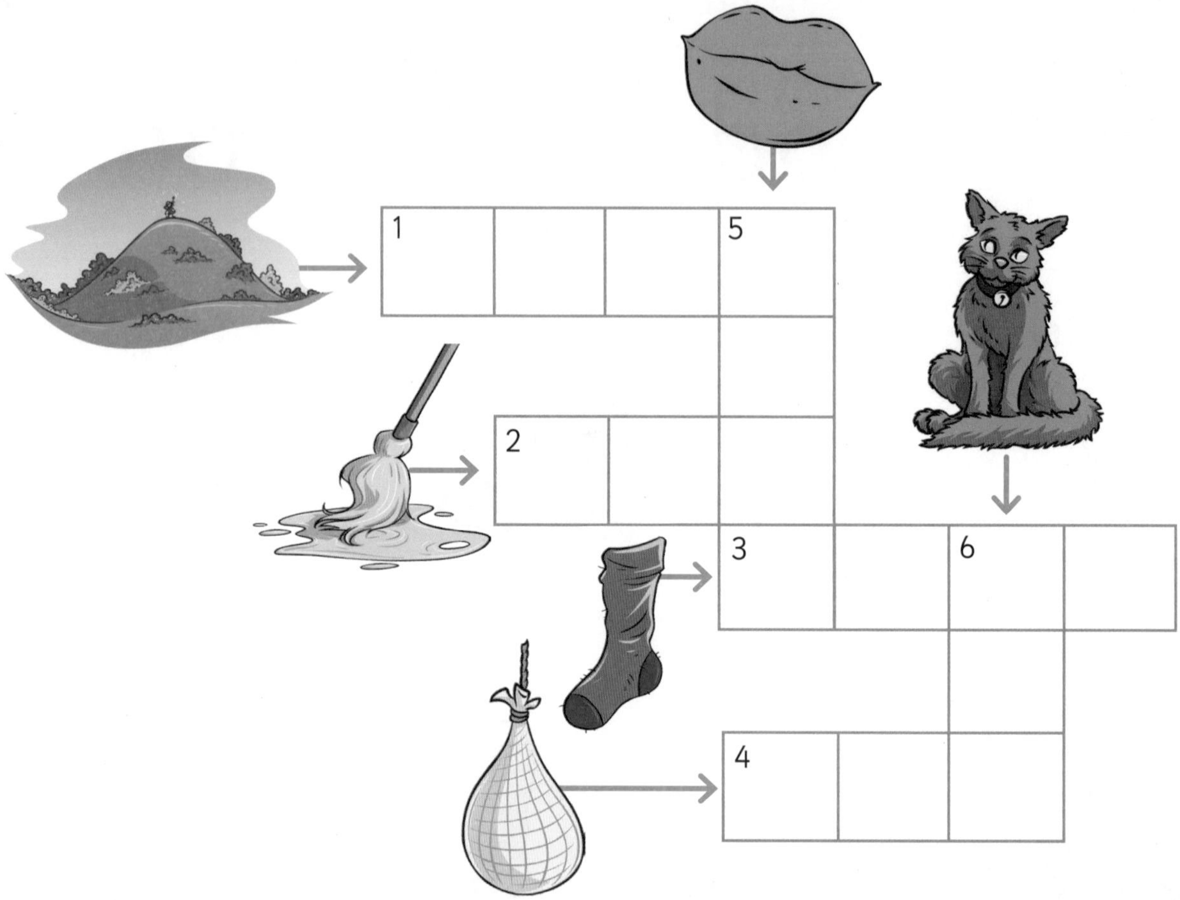

1			5		
	2				
			3		6
			4		

2 Say the word. Color the beginning, middle and end sound.

Write the word.

 s r  | i o  | t ck  ____________

 f p  | i a  | n f  ____________

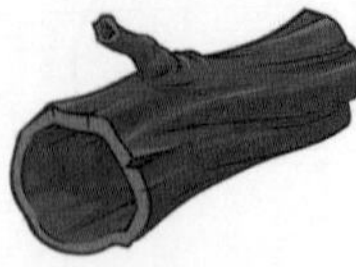 l m  | o u  | t g  ____________

Read, then answer the questions.

Frog and bird

The bird is blue and yellow.
The frog can hop and jump.
The bird likes the little green frog.

1 The bird likes the __________ .

a frog b dog c green

2 The frog can __________ .

a little b jump c fly

3 The frog is __________ .

a little and green b blue and yellow

I finished this lesson online.	This egg hatched.	I know the word families: ug, op, ock, ot	I can read

Quiz

1 Color the 2 pictures that rhyme.

2 Write the word in the box. Complete the sentence. Read it.

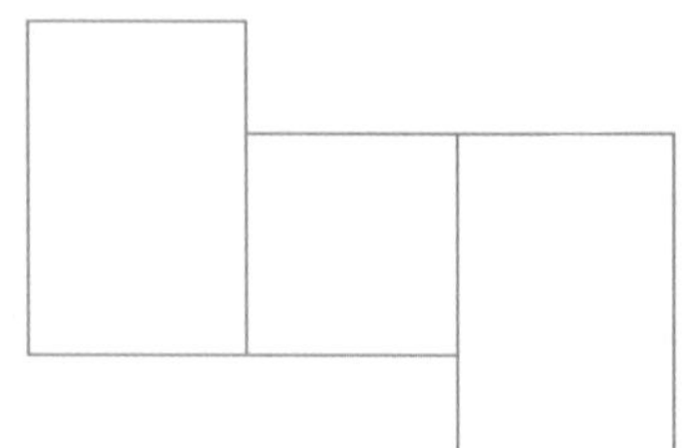

I play with my

________ .

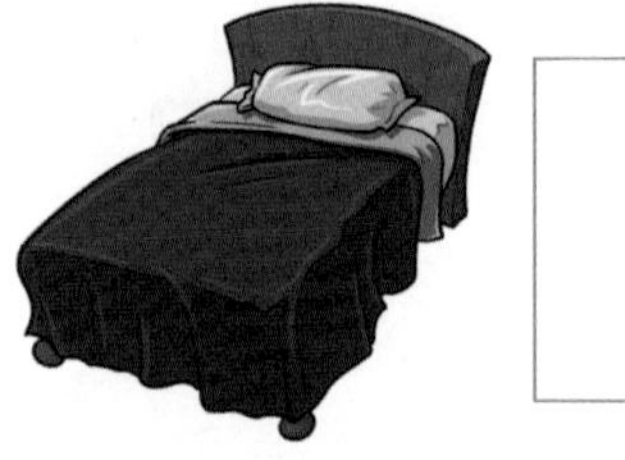

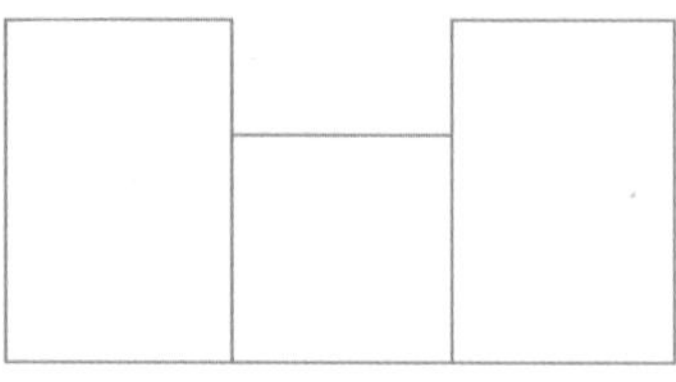

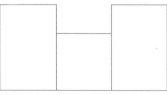

This is my

________ .

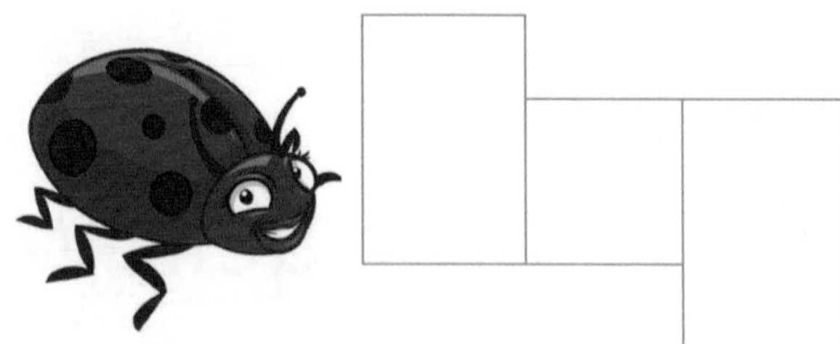

The ________ is little.

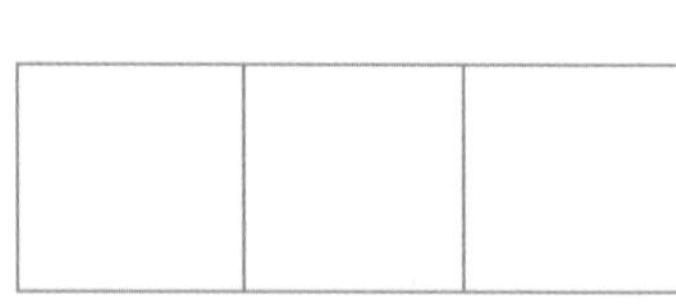

The ________ is hot.

Quiz

Read, then answer the questions.

Rat and duck

Look at the rat.
He can see the duck.
She has 2 legs and 2 wings.
She said Quack!

3 The rat can see the ________ .

a Quack b duck c rat

4 The duck has ________ .

a 4 legs b 2 wings c 2 beds

5 Who said Quack? ________

a the rat b the legs c the duck

AMAZING!

YOU COMPLETED

MAP 6

YOU CAN:

- [ ] Read and write **short vowel** word families.

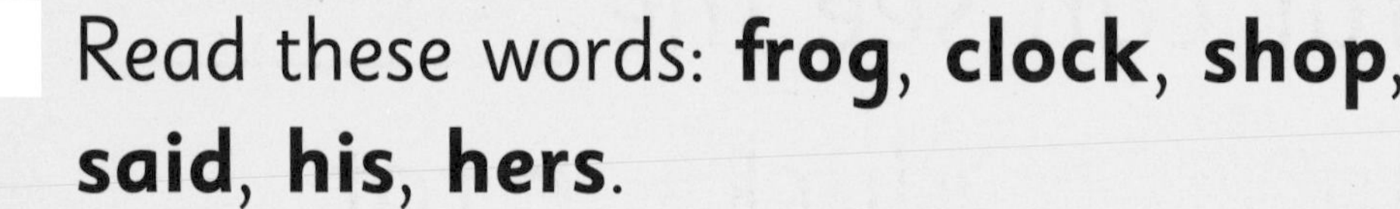
- [ ] Read these words: **frog**, **clock**, **shop**, **said**, **his**, **hers**.
- [ ] Read lots of sentences, such as: **Harry is a very happy horse.**
- [ ] Read these books:

Find your treasure.

Congratulations

This is to certify

---

has completed the

Reading Eggs Kindergarten

Program.

Date

Signature